SYNTHETIC FIBERS
IN PAPERMAKING

POLYMER ENGINEERING AND TECHNOLOGY

Editors: R. B. Akin, J. J. Scavuzzo, S. S. Stivala, L. J. Zukor

SYNTHETIC FIBERS IN PAPERMAKING

  edited by O. A. Battista

FILAMENT WINDING: its development, manufacture, applications, and design

  D._V. Rosato and C. S. Grove, Jr.

ADDITIONAL VOLUMES IN PREPARATION

SYNTHETIC FIBERS
IN PAPERMAKING

•

Edited by
O. A. BATTISTA

Manager of Interdisciplinary Research
Central Research Department
FMC Corporation
Princeton, New Jersey

•

INTERSCIENCE PUBLISHERS

a division of John Wiley & Sons, Inc.
New York · London · Sydney

AUTHORS

Hans F. Arledter, *Director, Hurlbut Research, Mead Central Research Laboratories, Chillicothe, Ohio*

Douglas G. Bannerman, *Market Development Manager, Textile Fibers Department, E. I. du Pont de Nemours & Co., Inc., Wilmington, Delaware*

O. A. Battista, *Manager of Interdisciplinary Research, Central Research Department, FMC Corporation, Princeton, New Jersey*

M. M. Cruz, Jr., *Leader, Special Products Section, Central Research Department, FMC Corporation, American Viscose Division, Marcus Hook, Pennsylvania*

Victor L. Erlich, *Vice-President in charge of Research and Development, Reeves Brothers, Inc., New York, New York*

Robert E. Foster, *Research Supervisor, Technical Division, Textile Fibers Department, E. I. du Pont de Nemours & Co., Inc., Wilmington, Delaware*

R. A. A. Hentschel, *Product Development Manager, E. I. du Pont de Nemours & Co., Inc., Wilmington, Delaware*

Stanley E. Knowles, *Associate Director, Hurlbut Research, Mead Central Research Laboratories, Chillicothe, Ohio*

William K. Saunders, *J. P. Stevens & Co., Inc., New York, New York*

Games Slayter, *Vice-President Research, Owens-Corning Fiberglas Corporation, Granville, Ohio*

Charles Houston Teague, *Manager, Fiber Research & Development, Reeves Brothers, Inc., New York, New York*

D. McLean Wyllie, *Chief Chemist, T. B. Ford Ltd., High Wycombe, England*

PREFACE

It is not often that one is afforded the opportunity of presenting a new book on a subject of wide and growing commercial importance. This is the first hard-cover book to combine the contributions of outstanding authorities on "Synthetic Fibers in Papermaking" into a single integrated volume.

The objective is to present in a manner as unified as possible the story of man's pioneering and now forthright efforts to extend a science, namely that of papermaking, far beyond any frontier envisioned over many past centuries. For this reason, it is hoped that this book will prove helpful to investigators who are interested in utilizing the economics of water as a vehicle for the fashioning of new and unique webs of fibrous materials to produce finished products of increasing utility, versatility, and value to mankind.

All of us who have worked in the preparation of this book will, I am sure, be very disappointed if a decade or so from now its contents do not require a complete revision and updating, perhaps even the expansion of each of its chapters into a separate hard-cover book. Certainly the prognosis for the growth of synthetic fibers in papermaking is most favorable.

The impact of the Space Age is clearly evident in the most recent developments in the manufacture of speciality papers requiring performance undreamed of even a few decades ago. As better, more versatile synthetic fibers are produced in the laboratory and brought to the market place, there seems little doubt that they will play an ever increasing role in blends with the more conventional papermaking fibers. One would expect that the market for both the natural and synthetic fibers in the appropriate combinations to give maximum price/performance ratios will result in increased demands for all such fibers. The information in this book should provide new horizons toward which the ingenuity and creativity of many disciplines may now be directed.

I am deeply grateful for the cooperation of my collaborators who have made this book possible, and I feel confident that those who will use this book will be equally appreciative of their contributions.

                                                        O. A. BATTISTA

FMC Corporation
Chemical Research and Development Center
Princeton, New Jersey
February 1964

ACKNOWLEDGMENTS

All the authors of this book acknowledge with appreciation the cooperation of the managements of their respective companies which has made this volume possible, including the use in some instances of previously unpublished data.

In addition, appreciation is expressed and acknowledged for the permission to use tables and figures which appear in this book and which have been selected from the following sources:

Alfred University (State University of New York, College of Ceramics), Department of Ceramic Research, Alfred, New York

The American Ceramic Society, Inc., Columbus, Ohio

American Society for Metals, Metals Park, Ohio

Astex Publishing Company, Guildford, England

The Boeing Company, Seattle, Washington

Ceramic Publications, Inc., Cleveland, Ohio

Chemical Engineering Progress, New York, New York

E. I. du Pont de Nemours & Company, Wilmington, Delaware

FMC Corporation, American Viscose Division, Marcus Hook, Pennsylvania

Industrial and Engineering Chemistry, Washington, D.C.

Johns-Manville, New York, New York

Lockwood Trade Journal Co., Inc., New York, New York

Materials in Design Engineering, New York, New York

SPE Journal, Stamford, Connecticut

TAPPI, and the Technical Association of the Pulp and Paper Industry, New York, New York

CONTENTS

INTRODUCTION

HANNS F. ARLEDTER

Director, Hurlbut Research
Mead Central Research Laboratories
Chillicothe, Ohio

Throughout history nonwoven fibrous materials have played an increasingly important role in aiding mankind to develop and advance living conditions. They are used in the clothing he wears, in the insulation that protects him and his equipment, in the base materials that record his ideas and his artistic ability, and in improving his surroundings.

The relatively short-fibered papers of the past which man has devised to fulfill his needs have served their purposes well. However, when the atomic and space age began, the shortcomings of conventional paper materials became apparent, and modern papermaking had to direct its resources and facilities toward the production of new specialty and technical papers in order to achieve the built-in characteristics required to meet new demands.

To date, an almost limitless number of paper grades fall into three broad classifications based on service requirements and inherent characteristics:

1. *Cultural papers.* These go back to the original purpose for which paper was made—writing and printing.

2. *Mechanical-technical papers.* The utility of these papers has grown as new uses for them have developed, such as wrapping, shipping cartons, liquid containers, and a host of others that reach into almost every human activity.

3. *Industrial papers.* This class is the newest. As the demand for higher performance, novel effects, and versatility has grown, the use of synthetic fibers has played a greater role in and added new dimen-

sions to the science of papermaking. With a heritage of fine crafts-manship and an increase in impulse, knowledge, and ingenuity, the paper industry is creating and producing new products in conjunc-tion with synthetic fibers in many applications which have raised safety standards, increased strength, improved production perform-ance, lowered cost, miniaturized instruments, and contributed other important advantages in numerous fields in a range of usefulness that is ever broadening. It is these "industrial papers," developed in recent decades with the help of new man-made fibers, binders, and tech-niques, that challenge the ingenuity of the end user.

During the last 20 years the rate of increase in the consumption of *cultural papers* has tended to decline, whereas the rate of consump-tion of the *mechanical-technical paper* group, which passed the cul-tural grades in tonnage in the 1920's, has been maintained. Now the *industrial paper* group is on the rise. It is this latter group and the new technology developed with it that should ultimately help to strengthen the position of the paper industry. The *mechanical-tech-nical paper* group will continue to play its important role in helping the industry to compete more effectively for markets now held by film, metal foil, foam, and felted or woven materials.

In speaking of modern industrial papers and their manufacture, the researcher in the paper industry no longer limits his art to conven-tional vegetable fibers. He thinks of a homogeneous or heterogeneous fibrous web held together with bonding media which impart to the composite structure the specific qualities desired for its use. This approach is not limited to kind, length, or diameter of fiber, whether it is wet or dry forming, has high or low density, directional or ran-dom fiber orientation, or two or three dimensions, bonded by like or unlike materials, or processed afterward by other means.

Today modern papermaking fibers are chosen from natural, vege-table, organic synthetic, ceramic, metal, glass, quartz, asbestos, mica, or any other fibrous material that nature or man has devised. The bonding media available to hold the fibrous structures together are of the same bewildering variety. Not only the organic chemist, physical chemist, or papermaker but the metallurgist, ceramic engi-neer, and glass technologist are joining their skills to contribute new binders and bonding techniques.

In this new age, papermaking and fiber technology have advanced swiftly, and scientific engineering talents have been blended with new skills. In every step of papermaking, from scientific forest farming to complex operations in papermaking, the emphasis is on new developments. The scientist and technologist envision hundreds of new services performed by paper. Its versatile and economical uses are geared to the needs of developing technical culture. In setting a prospective course into the orbit of tomorrow's markets, research proffers the creation of new paper products in wide areas of utility. A Surveyor rocket reaches the moon, a Marine probe passes Venus, a man-made star becomes the pivot of a whole new system of inter-global communications, a life-saving vaccine is discovered—something new happens every day. We read about these events; we marvel at them. Today the paper machine and the papermaking research laboratory—removed in the past from space-age developments—is playing perhaps an unpublicized but nevertheless an important part in many of these developments.

The sudden and rather rapid changes in this technology are opening up new environments and technological conditions which range from dense corrosive atmospheres to complete vacuums in which temperatures vary from −270 to 2000°C. and higher. New products must be able to retain useful strength and perform operational functions under conditions of high load, both static and shock, under electrical, chemical, and physical stress, and at the high speeds and friction of modern machinery. They must resist weather, bacteria, radioactivity, chemical deterioration, and other characteristics of the atmosphere and surroundings or other induced effects. Therefore in tomorrow's world opportunities will be found for the papermaker and nonwoven producer to provide new products with functions that will rapidly alter and increase the scope of the art.

The use of paper is so diverse, and all commercial, cultural, and social activities have become so dependent on it, that it is now an essential commodity. It ranks just below food and clothing in relation to the necessities of life. What is generally not realized is that paper and nonwovens today rank with iron in importance for technical activities. There is no other commodity that can even closely approach paper or iron. For example, the United States currently uses approximately 1000 lb. of iron and 500 lb. of paper per capita. If the specific gravity of paper versus iron is taken into account, it can be concluded that on a volume basis four times as much paper as iron is produced each year.

Paper shares the fate of iron in being more or less taken for granted. There were, for instance, 70 references to iron in the Old Testament, but only seven in the New Testament, which tends to indicate that after the birth of Christ iron had become common. *Plastics* are modern, and paper in combination with plastics loses its identity even if the composite consists of more than 60% paper and less than 40% resin, as in many common laminates.

Papermaking, of course, is an extremely old art and dates back many centuries, at least to the year A.D. 100 in China. Throughout this long period of time natural fibers, primarily of a cellulosic lineage, have almost completely occupied the attention of papermakers. For centuries expensive cotton, hemp, linen, and flax fibers, in the form of rags, were the predominant cellulosic papermaking materials. Documents that have weathered the ravages of time are good evidence that such fibers did and still do possess unusually serviceable properties in terms of strength and performance.

In more recent times, however, with the advent of papermaking from mechanical wood pulp in 1840 and chemical wood-pulp fibers as late as 1860, inexpensive paper products have become abundant. Such pulp fibers have many unique advantages from the point of view of being adaptable to the formation of a coherent wet web by means of conventional equipment. They are generally less expensive and their service requirements are usually less severe than those of textile products.

Throughout the history of papermaking, and up to the present time, man has attempted and continues to attempt to extract from natural fibers (wood-pulp fibers, in particular) every conceivable benefit in terms of useful service. There is evidence that a limit to what can be done with natural papermaking fibers in producing paper with substantial improvements in specific physical properties has almost been reached. Because of this seemingly static plateau, there is mounting justification for papermakers to be receptive to the utilization of premium synthetic fibers, particularly in blends with natural fibers, to achieve further advantages in new paper products that have never before been possible.

Organic synthetic fibers are relatively new. They have received wide acceptance in the textile industry only during the last 20 to 30 years and show every promise of expanding their usefulness for conventional textile applications as well as for nonwoven textile products in the years that lie immediately ahead. The versatility of the organic chemist in producing synthetic polymers in fiber form for a host of service requirements has been capitalized on so that their performance/price ratio has come within the reach of consumers of textiles.

Equal strides have been made in the last decades by the glass and ceramic industry in the development of versatile and less expensive glass and ceramic fibers useful for textile and industrial applications.

Metal fibers for textiles are still extremely expensive; therefore new techniques are being considered for their production at lower cost, and considerable effort will be needed to fulfill the requirements.

The synthetic fibers in the textile industry have managed to contribute, particularly in blends with natural fibers, outstanding physical properties which in terms of the service performed and the life of the fabric have overcome the seemingly insurmountable obstacle of cost. The mushrooming multi-billion-dollar synthetic-fiber industry, dependent as it has been almost exclusively on the textile trade, stands as proof that tailor-making fibers to meet certain rigorous performance functions can offset an otherwise seemingly hopeless basic-cost picture.

Already it is quite commonplace to read in the literature about the manufacture of paper on a papermaking machine with almost every known synthetic fiber—rayon, nylon, Dacron®, Acrilan®, Dynel®, glass, silica, ceramic, metal, and a host of others. Yet only a few years ago descriptions of such noncellulosic materials for the preparation of paper not only were lacking in the literature, but the manufacture of such papers by conventional methods would have been considered utterly impractical by the majority of the workers specifically concerned with the papermaking industry. It was not until 1936 that Eloed received a German patent describing a 100% man-made regenerated cellulosic fiber paper (viscose rayon) and not until September 1950 that the first 100% submicron glass-fiber paper was produced by Callinan et al., on a pilot paper machine at the Bureau of Standards. It was as late as 1953 and 1954 that Arledter produced for the first time 100% true organic synthetic-fiber papers made from Dacron, nylon, Orlon, and Dynel and reported the first metal-fiber paper produced on a pilot-plant paper machine.

Commercial production of viscose rayon paper and papers containing Vinyon® fibers started about 1945, and glass- and ceramic-fiber papers were produced on production paper machines in 1951 and 1952. It might be said that the growing literature describing this use of synthetic fibers is tangible evidence that man-made fibers are about to make aggressive inroads into the fields of papermaking, inroads that will parallel the extensive advances that these very same fibers have already made in the textile fields. We can even expect that keen competition will develop between the paper, airlay-nonwoven, and textile industries in the future.

For centuries one of the basic differences between paper and textiles has been that papers are produced from short fibers of only 1 to 4 mm., giving essentially a two-dimensional dense product. Textiles and airlaid nonwovens, on the other hand, are made from much longer fibers, which are open and three-dimensional.

Great strides have been taken in the last few years by a number of companies in the development of nonwoven fabriclike structures made on paper-machine equipment. No longer are these products merely papers from synthetic fibers; now they approach nonwoven textile structures. The papermaker has learned, in a technical breakthrough, to use fibers with a length of 6 to 30 mm. with the conventional wet papermaking system, facing and surmounting the problems of dispersion and web uniformity which increase with the length of the fiber. The possibilitiy of increasing the maximum fiber length still further, at even lower denier and with still softer fibers, is not an improbability.

The rapid progress that man has made in his ability to produce paper materials from longer fibers with new ranges of properties has been stimulated by previously unknown devices, techniques, and manufacturing methods which should prove to be of great practical value for general papermaking. It might well be that techniques now in development for the production of synthetic-fiber paper will revolutionize conventional methods of vegetable-fiber paper manufacture. Paper and boards made of standard wood fibers should reach new heights in physical performance when the papermaker takes advantage of all the knowledge that is available now and expected in the future.

Another problem concerns the necessity of providing new materials and methods to bond the fibers of which the paper is composed. The type of bonding in ordinary paper is that which develops between cellulosic fibers dried in contact with one another. This natural bond does not occur in most synthetic fibers. The work necessary to add to the knowledge of bonding techniques of fibers and webs by planned synthesis of polymers and fibers and the modification of natural products has led to new bonding systems and methods which are made to fit the rheology of a given system. Moreover, the necessary evil of bonding the fibrous web both cohesively and adhesively has already been made to contribute more than just bonding. It can be made to carry its share of the load and to provide additional physical properties.

Active and close cooperation between the papermaker, the nonwoven technologist, the synthetic-fiber producer, the resin industry, and the machine builder has been beneficial to the art of web bonding and has resulted in advancements. It is believed that this cooperative trend and ingenious engineering of the resin, fiber molecules, and binder-application methods will continue, leading ultimately to new standard papers and webs of even greater utility than those available now.

Synthetic-fiber bonding, furthermore, will help to establish a background of understanding of natural cellulosic as well as of synthetic-fiber bonding. There should develop a tendency in the paper industry to modify or supplement the natural bonding by the use of the new additives.

Modern research programs are aimed at achieving new fibers and nonwoven paper materials made from them to satisfy a multitude of performance requirements. Reports dealing with novel products—comparing them with standard paper products—show with truly astonishing results how far the scope of papermaking has widened. The following short review outlines the basic progress of synthetic-fiber development which has been reported in the technical journals of the paper, textile, metal, chemical, and electrical industries of the last 10 years:

1. The fold test of papers can be increased from 10,000 to 2,000,000 by use of synthetic fibers.

2. The tensile strength can be doubled and improvements up to 10 times are within the realm of possibility.

3. The paper tear test can be increased three to five times.

4. The theoretical life expectancy of a given paper can be raised 100 to 1000 times.

5. The wet strength of paper was traditionally poor in the early recorded history of papermaking; with the advent of wet-strength resins it improved to 20 to 50% of dry strength of the paper. Today synthetic-fiber papers of 85 to 100% wet strengths are feasible.

6. Today synthetic-fiber paper which retains useful performance characteristics at temperatures as low as $-270°C$. and as high as $1700°C$. can be produced.

7. Synthetic-fiber webs can be produced with an electrical resistance as low as 10^{-4} ohm/cm. and as high as 10^{-16} ohm/cm; this increases the range of regular paper which is normally only $10^{10} - 10^{15}$ ohm/cm.

8. Filter paper of vastly improved retentivity, with pore sizes of 0.3 to 100 μ combined with filter-speed improvements of ten to 1000-fold are now standard production items.

9. Synthetic-fiber paper-reinforced plastic laminates with a flexural strength of 100,000 p.s.i. (threefold increase) and an impact strength 20 to 30 times higher than is possible for regular cellulosic absorbent papers are a reality in the laboratory.

10. Paper of lower basis weight (down to 5 gm/m².) can now be made with the help of thinner and longer synthetic fibers.

11. Synthetic-fiber paper (made of Teflon® fibers) that is not attacked by acid or alkali or nearly any chemical known to man can be produced. On the other hand, paper that dissolves readily in water can be manufactured.

In recent years papermaking has been widened in scope to cover a whole spectrum of technical possibilities. The new synthetic-fiber technology applied to papermaking presents new concepts, systems, engineering practices, fabrication techniques, and material developments. Advanced papermaking, an art that nobody in the industry can afford to be without, has become a tool in today's rapidly advancing sciences.

The theoretical papermaker setting out to formulate a specialty paper or a working model to prove his theories can be compared with an architect designing a building. He can choose from a multitude of building blocks—fibers of controlled dimensions (thickness and length) and a vast range of predetermined physical properties—and, with the help of a wide selection of well-defined binders, sizes, and fillers tailored to fit functional properties, his task is to arrange them into a structure that will serve a particular purpose. Furthermore, he now has mechanical and papermaking devices to form the composite web in a number of novel ways that differ from those of the conventional fourdrinier or cylinder machine.

Considering these tools, one is tempted to speculate that a new papermaking science, previously defined by no one, can now develop and flourish on experiments unhampered by speculation and misconceptions. This science will no longer be papermaking alone because it will require changes in physical and chemical concepts and techniques. The researcher in the industrial paper area must develop a new outlook—and he must possess a certain degree of austerity in his discipline as befits the science of physics.

The development of a more theoretical papermaking science has been handicapped by tradition and by a selection of fiber systems and observations too narrow to permit a mathematical approach to many phenomena. At this time old concepts must be supplemented by more recent results, and old theories have to be revised.

It is because of the growing impact which synthetic fibers of all types are unquestionably going to have on the papermaking industry that this book has been written. It is offered by way of introducing an era in which man-made fibers will become a vital part of the art of papermaking. It presents large amounts of interesting data concerning the methods and results of technical applications of synthetic fibers in papermaking, emphasizes the present state of the art, and enumerates those materials that have recently come into prominence as original technical tools for various materials.

Synthetic fibers will give rise to an almost endless series of paper formulations in which the natural and man-made fibers will, for each end use, become united in the manufacture of products of greater durability and improved serviceability for mankind. Composites of different fibers and binders may permit the creation of materials that will take advantage of the desirable properties of the constituents while minimizing the undesirable properties. The utilization of 100% synthetic-fiber papers will be dependent on their physical and chemical properties which make them far superior for certain end uses than papers made from vegetable fibers.

So far, the price/performance ratio of true synthetic-fiber papers has not permitted them to make commercial inroads except as specialty products. Large-scale paper-machine production of these expensive papers has not been realized because of the lack of markets. The cost of paper-machine-made nonwoven synthetic-fiber products is still high. Unlike conventional paper, which is usually sold by the ton, the more expensive industrial papers made of or containing the synthetic fibers are sold today in much smaller units. Some of them cost $3 to $6/lb., others as much as $60/lb. Some specialties are sold for $1/sq. ft. or more. Such papers usually are produced on small and narrow slow-running pilot-plant paper machines. Remarkable progress has been made, however, in the utilization of some specific papers (ceramic, glass, and viscose rayon) in the last few years, and they are now manufactured in substantial commercial amounts on production paper machines.

Although there has been no major breakthrough to electrify the industry or materially increase the amount of paper being produced, a feeling of satisfaction and optimism seems to prevail among the nonwoven paper producers in regard to the future of this business.

The manufacture of synthetic-fiber papers and webs is a long-range endeavor that will materialize only if these products find acceptance and if new markets guarantee a production volume of interest for the large-volume paper-machine operations. The prognosis for their future is, nevertheless, highly favorable, and the information in this book is the first major attempt toward bringing all facets of this industry into current focus.

It may take only 60 to 70 seconds to produce a sheet of paper on a given paper machine, from the headbox, where the fibers of pulp float in an ocean of water, to the reel, where the unending sheet of paper, now formed and dried, is wound on a giant spool. In these 70 seconds the paper machine can produce a ribbon of paper 18 to 25 ft. wide and more than a quarter of a mile long. It is capable of producing webs at speeds of 1 to 2500 ft./minute or more, and it can, therefore, produce as many as 50,000 to 2,000,000 lb. of a given web in 24 hours. The full impact of the work done in the research laboratories in the new technology and the developments for using synthetic fibers will be felt only after the full potential of papermaking is realized by demands for large volumes of synthetic fiber papers and further reductions in unit cost. When these barriers are bridged, the paper machine will be the tool to bring new and vibrant life to this important segment of the traditional and dignified papermaking industry.

1

RAYONS

M. M. CRUZ, JR.

Leader, Special Products Section
Central Research Department
FMC Corporation American Viscose Division
Marcus Hook, Pennsylvania

Of all the man-made fibers that are candidates for papermaking, the rayons are among the first, if not the first, from which paperlike structures were produced on papermaking equipment. They stand out as one of the more promising of the synthetic papermaking fibers for the following reasons:

1. They possess a distinct price advantage over most of the organic or inorganic synthetic fibers.
2. They are cellulosic and quite compatible with water slurries of other cellulose fibers so that they can be handled by conventional papermaking techniques and equipment.
3. They posses most of the inherent advantages of any synthetic fiber, such as control of denier, length, strength, elongation, cleanliness, and optical uniformity. It would seem, then, that the cellulosic rayons proffer a strong potential for continuing commercial development in blends with natural vegetable fibers, in blends with other synthetic fibers, or in 100% formulations by themselves.

The great compatibility of rayon fibers with cheap wood-pulp furnishes and the ease with which their diameter can be controlled make them advantageous for the bulking of papers when an improvement in porosity is desired. Their cleanliness, strength, and bulking properties also make them valuable components in saturated papers in which they are blended with wood pulp fibers. Conventional rayons are finding increasing favor in various nonwoven products, for which they are made into a wet web and subsequently

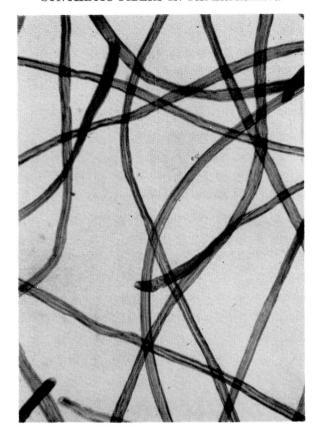

Figure 1.1.   Regular rayon staple brushed three hours in a paper beater (175×).

treated with various coating materials to give them wet strength and other desirable properties. For many years, of course, rayon fibers have been an integral component of the tea-bag type papers in which a high level of porosity is so important.

Conventional viscose rayon fibers, it should be pointed out, do not, when beaten exhibit the fibrillatable properties of natural cellulosic fibers (see Figure 1.1). Furthermore, despite the inherent presence of numerous potential hydroxyl groups, typical rayon fibers do not engage hydrogen bonding forces when dried down from a water-laid web, even with the application of pressure, to the same extent as beaten and fibrillated natural vegetable fibers. Nevertheless, there is every reason to believe that the use of available as well as appropriately tailored rayon fibers will continue to expand within the paper industry wherein advantages can be gained from such controllable and critical papermaking variables as denier (or fiber diameter) and length.

Typical physical properties of a regular-strength rayon fiber and a high-strength rayon staple fiber are shown in Figure 1.2. Here we see Instron curves which demonstrate the tensile strength versus elongation properties of these rayon fibers. The high-strength XL fiber is characterized by its toughness and better moisture resistance.

Figure 1.3 shows handsheet data for tensile, tear, and burst properties for a glassine type furnish with time of beating. These curves are basic to the papermaking industry, and they demonstrate conclusively that, with natural wood-pulp fibers, it is a general papermaking rule that beating increases the tensile strength of papers while it correspondingly results in a decrease in the tear properties.

The addition of three types of commercial rayon fibers to an overbeaten glassine furnish stock is shown to have a most pronounced

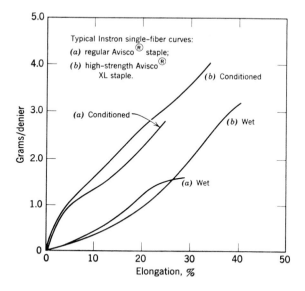

Figure 1.2. Typical Instron single-fiber curves: (a) regular Avisco® staple; (b) high-strength Avisco® XL staple.

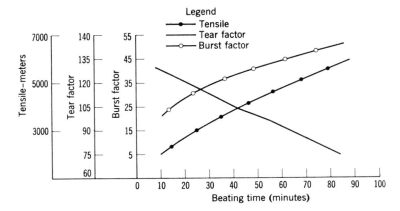

Figure 1.3. Effect of beating time on properties of glassine pulp (handsheet data).

effect on the tear factor in Figure 1.4. The contribution of small amounts of 1.5 denier, $\frac{1}{4}$-in. rayons to improvements in the tear properties of a blend of over-beaten glassine pulp furnish and rayon fibers is directly related to the tensile strength of the individual blending fibers. As seen in this diagram, XL fiber makes a

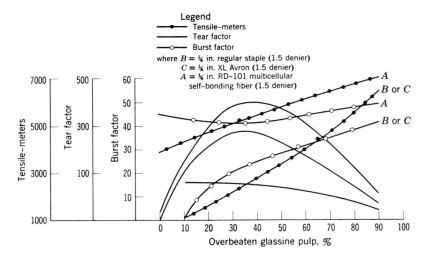

Figure 1.4. Blends of paper-grade rayons and glassine pulp (Canadian standard freeness = 52).

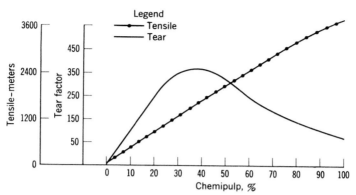

Figure 1.5. Blends of regular ¼-in rayon staple with beaten chemipulp (Canadian standard freeness = 90).

much greater contribution to tear improvement in the blends than, for example, a regular rayon fiber with a lower tensile strength.

Figure 1.5 shows the effect of ¼-in. regular rayon staple fiber in blends with chemipulp, beaten to a relatively low Canadian Standard Freeness, on both tensile and tear properties. An optimum improvement in tear factor is achieved with the addition of 70 to 80% rayon staple. A parallel effect is observed in the next diagram (Figure 1.6), wherein handsheet data are shown for a similar blend,

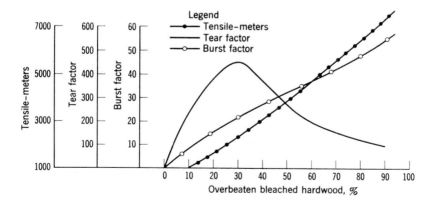

Figure 1.6. Blends of Avisco® regular ¼-in. staple with bleached hardwood furnish (Canadian standard freeness of pulp = 145) (handsheet data).

except that this time it is between regular ¼-in. rayon and overbeaten bleached hardwood furnish.

It might reasonably be expected, however, that the long-range growth of rayon fibers in the paper industry will come about as a result of the development of greatly improved types of rayon fibers, fibers that are engineered to contribute important performance properties in paper and paper products that cannot be achieved more economically.

The incorporation of 50 to 75% 1.5 denier, ¼-in. cut-rayon staple in a sulfite-rayon furnish and the subsequent addition of a given amount of short-cut Vinyon staple resulted in marked improvements in the tear properties. The results are shown in Table 1.1 (1)

TABLE 1.1

Physical Properties of Papers Made from Sulfite Pulp and
Regular Rayon Staple and Vinyon (18-lb. handsheet) (1)

Furnish (%)		Vinyon (%) Dry Basis	Tensiles/ (lb./in.)	MIT Double Fold	Mullen Burst/ (lb./in.)	Elmendorf Tear (gm.)
Sulfite	Rayon					
100	0	0	4.4	6	16	28
100	0	5	9.6	710	22	24
75	25	5	7.7	650	20	29
50	50	5	6.0	525	21	61
25	75	5	3.5	15	17	54

In addition to the foregoing conventional types of rayon, three novel man-made cellulosic papermaking fibers may be mentioned at this time.

SELF-BONDING RAYON FIBERS

Fiber RD-101 is the American Viscose Division's self-bonding rayon fiber, specifically designed for the preparation of papers and other wet-formed nonwoven materials. By the use of RD-101, paper can be made for the first time from 100% man-made fiber without the necessity of working the fiber or adding pulps, fillers, or bonding agents other than water to form a paper sheet. With RD-101 the

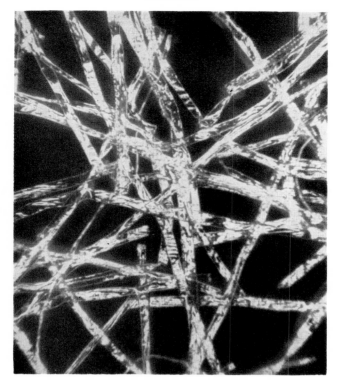

Figure 1.7. RD-101 1-lb. sheet (175×).

processing performance of other papermaking fibers can be improved, as can the quality of papers made from them.

The self-bonding character of this new fiber makes possible a wide range of wet-formed nonwovens of various textures and physical properties, either with or without the addition of other bonding agents. These properties may now be controlled almost at will with the different varieties of viscose rayon being produced in lengths suitable for processing on papermaking equipment.

Figure 1.7 is a photograph of a 1-lb.-basis weight sheet of RD-101 (1.5 denier, ¼-in). Note the manner in which the multicellular fibers cross over one another and bond at large areas of contact to produce strong, low-basis weight, open webs.

A cross section of a 20-lb.-basis weight RD-101 sheet is shown in Figure 1.8.

The degree of bonding of RD-101 multicellular papermaking fiber

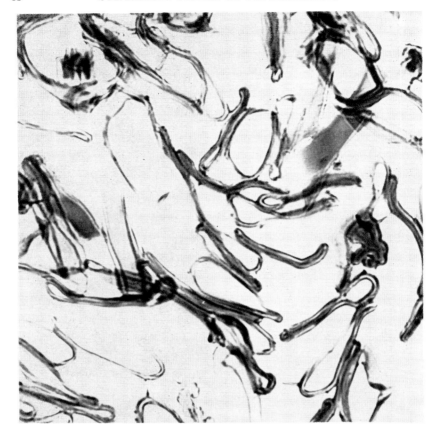

Figure 1.8. Cross-sectional view of RD-101 multicellular fibers. T. M. FMC Corporation, American Viscose Division.

is controlled by the size, number, and wall thickness of the multi-cellular compartments in the individual filaments. Figure 1.9*a,b* shows the manner in which the "bubbles" appear in a low-bonding and a high-bonding RD-101 multicellular fiber, respectively. Cross-sectional and lateral views of a sheet of RD-101 paper are compared in Figure 1.10*a,b*.

In the next series of diagrams several variables are illustrated for a specific rayon fiber, namely RD-101. In Figure 1.11 the effect of fiber length on physical properties is clear. The tensile strength is quite constant over a range of lengths from $\frac{3}{16}$ in. up to about $\frac{1}{2}$-in., falling off on either side of these limits. The tear factor, on the

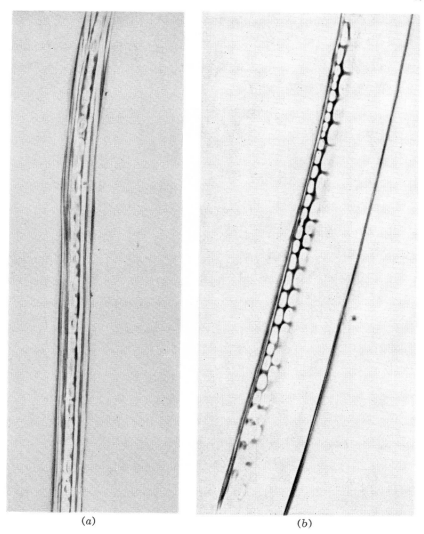

Figure 1.9. (a) Low-bonding RD-101 filament (375×); (b) high-bonding RD-101 filament (750×). (Note surface air pockets.)

other hand, appears to increase in direct proportion to the length of the fiber, whereas burst follows a pattern similar to tensile strength.

Denier/filament is developed as an extremely important variable in Figure 1.12, with an optimum physical property across the board

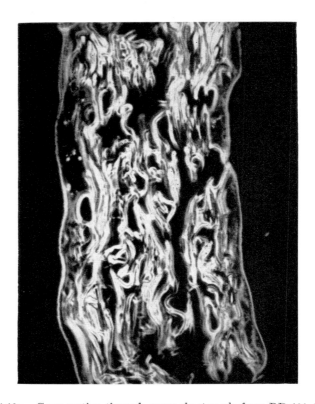

Figure 1.10a. Cross section through paper sheet made from RD-101 (175×).

appearing between 3 and 5 denier/filament. The effect of basis weight is shown in Figure 1.13, and apparently all handsheets bear a constant relationship to basis weight above a minimum of about 10 lb.

RD-101 fiber possesses unusually good wet-strength resin receptivity, especially for the urea-formaldehyde type wet-strength resins, as given in Table 1.2. The receptivity of RD-101 for wet-strength resins is similar to that for unbleached kraft.

Paper sheets can be made readily from blends of RD-101 and short-cut rayon fibers. When such webs are given an aftertreatment with a 60% ZnCl$_2$ solution, high tensile and tear properties, both dry and wet, can be obtained (see Table 1.3) (2).

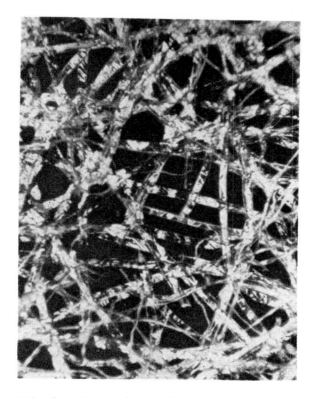

Figure 1.10b.   Lateral view of paper sheet made from RD-101 (175✕).

In addition, RD-101 blends with natural cellulose fibers contribute to some improvement in both tensile and tear properties, as the data show in Table 1.4 (2).

FIBRILLATABLE RAYON FIBERS

May, Isenberg, and McLeod (3) reported that regenerated cellulose fibers do not develop fiber-to-fiber bonding by mechanical beating.

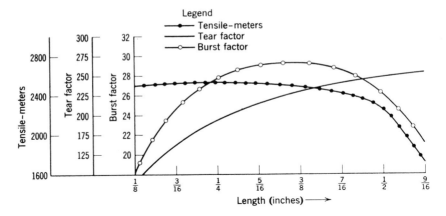

Figure 1.11.　Effect of fiber length on the physical properties of RD-101, multicellular self-bonding fiber.

Unlike the natural cellulose fibers, the regenerated cellulose lacks a fibrillated structure.

Shearer (4) developed a rayon staple that would fibrillate to a certain degree by mechanical beating. This was brought about by the modification of the rayon fine structure during the spinning step.

At a later date two types of experimental fibrillatable rayon fibers were developed in the Research Laboratories of The American Viscose Division of FMC Corporation.

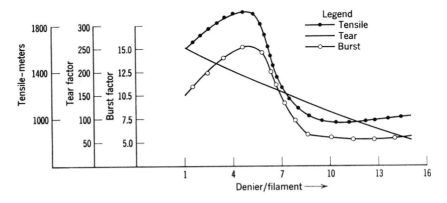

Figure 1.12.　Effect of denier on physical properties of RD-101 multicellular self-bonding fiber (40% stretch).

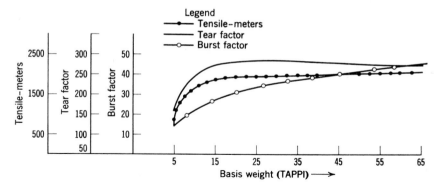

Figure 1.13. Effect of basis weight on physical properties of RD-101 multicellular self-bonding fibers.

1. One type is obtained by treating conventional rayons chemically so that they will fibrillate readily by subsequent beating in water (5). Fibrillation is brought about by a controlled prehydrolysis treatment of the rayon. The relationship between the degree of polymerization and fibrillation characteristics is given in Table 1.5.

TABLE 1.2
Wet-Strength Resin Receptivity of RD-101
(1.5 denier, $\frac{1}{4}''$ cut)

Paper Properties

Type of RD-101	Chemical, % b.o.f.[1] Resin	$Al_2(SO_4)_3$		TAPPI Ream Weight	Breaking Length (m.)	Tear Factor	Elongation (%)	Wet Strength (%)
High	—	—	D	43.9	2778	193	4.7	
bonding	Kymene 234	1.7	D	44.8	3470	163	7.3	20
	3.0		W		655	200	19.4	
	Uformite 700	2.0	D	46.7	3958	184	8.4	30
	3.0		W		1184	238	28.1	
	Kymene 234	1.7	D	42.9	3440	232	6.2	20
	6.0		W		670	207	19.6	
Low	—	—	D	45.3	1844	—	1.5	
bonding	Kymene 234	1.7	D	47.6	2731	—	4.2	13
	3.0		W		354		9.7	

Note. pH @ 0.3% consistency—4.6.
[1] Based on fiber.

Figure 1.14 shows a filament of this kind of fiber undergoing progressive fibrillation. The individual fibrils formed in this way are still quite thick (approximately 7500 Å) and therefore are more hydrophobic than the fibrils in ordinary beaten natural fibers. A single fibril at $25,000\times$ is shown in the micrograph of Figure 1.15.

TABLE 1.3

Physical Properties of Rayon Handsheets after Zinc
Chloride Treatment (2)

Composition of Sheets

	95% XL Rayon 5% RD-101	75% XL Rayon 25% RD-101	40% XL Rayon 60% RD-101	50% Regular Rayon 50% RD-101
Treatment time, sec.	30.0	120	10	30
Ream weight, lb.	52.3	46.7	51.3	48.4
Gauge, mils	8.9	6.2	5.1	4.0
Breaking length, m.				
dry	1820	3380	4508	3754
wet	439	1029	1664	1493
Mullen burst, p.s.i.				
dry	46	52	52	46
wet	17	31	31	28
Elongation, %				
dry	5.3	11.6	13.9	7.4
wet	15.6	21.6	24.6	—
Elmendorf tear, gm.				
dry	647	737	342	219
wet	222	344	379	302

Note. All fibers used were unbeaten 1.5 denier $\frac{1}{4}$ in. No other materials were present: bonding of the untreated sheets due to the RD-101 fiber present. All samples were immersed in 60% $ZnCl_2$ at room temperature for the time indicated.

The fibrillatable regenerated cellulose fibers illustrated in Figure 1.15 produce high bulk, for porous papers have relatively low tensile strength unless they are aftertreated with resinous binders. They do not benefit from normal papermaking hydrogen bonding forces between fibrils because the diameters of the fibrils are still too great to allow significant hydration. In essence, therefore, the base paper

TABLE 1.4
Physical Properties of Papers Containing RD-101 (2)

Composition of Sheets

% RD-101	100	100	100	100	5	10	—
			(no additives or binders)				
% Bleached kraft	—	—	—	—	95	90	100 (control)

Basis weight[1]							
(TAPPI)	7.4	18.0	42.5	50.0	104	108	107
Caliper (mils)	1.3	2.0	4.5	4.9	9.9	10.1	10.0
Breaking length[2]							
(meters)	2811	3724	3558	3300	4749	4470	4389
Burst factor[3]							
(Mullen)	29	28	46	42	43	43	40
Tear factor[4]							
(Elmendorf)	207	185	179	142	209	196	192

Notes. Values are based on TAPPI test standards.

[1] TAPPI basis weight is weight in pounds of 500 sheets each 25 x 40 in.

[2] Breaking length is the length in meters of a strip of paper, the weight of which equals the breaking load. Pounds per inch break = (breaking length) $\times$ (ream weight) $\times 7.9 \times 10^{-1}$.

[3] Burst factor = $(50 \times$ Mullen burst) $\div$ (TAPPI ream weight) in p.s.i.

[4] Tear factor = $(71.1 \times$ Elmendorf tear) $\div$ (TAPPI ream weight) in grams.

TABLE 1.5
The Relation of the Average Basic Degree of Polymerization
and Fibrillation of Rayon (5)

Sample	Hydrolysis Treatment, 10% H_2SO_4	Average (4,5) Basic D.P.	Fibrillation after Beating
Control	None	370	None
I	12 min. at 65°C.	290	Very few fibrils
II	20 min. at 65°C.	220	Good
III	10 min. at 80°C.	160	Excellent
IV	10 min. at 85°C.	135	Excellent
V	20 min. at 75°C.	50	Powdered, no fibrils

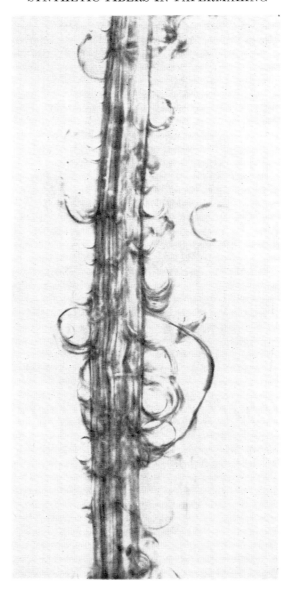

Figure 1.14.   Fibrillatable viscose rayon fiber showing fibril formation on brushing (750×).

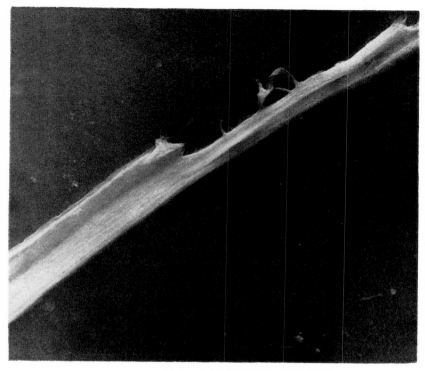

Figure 1.15. Electron micrograph of an FPSP fibril (25,000×).

sheet develops the strength it does because of the physical inter-
tangling of the constituent thick fibrils; the large fibrils are stiff and
do not engage many hydrogen bonds upon being dried in the form of
a web. Gaseous and liquid filtration uses would appear to be most
suitable for this class of fiber.

2. A most unusual class of fibrillatable fiber has been developed
on an experimental basis, also by American Viscose Division.
Called "hybrid" fibers (8), this class will fibrillate on relatively mild
mechanical beating to give unique fibrils with diameter as low as
150 Å or less. Such regenerated cellulose fibrils are unique because
they are in the same dimensional range as those in the beaten natural
fibers and they exhibit true hydrogen-bonding properties. An electron
micrograph of an experimental man-made hybrid fiber showing long
fibrils with diameters of less than 150 Å is illustrated in Figure 1.16.
These fibrils were produced by chemically treating a hybrid fiber

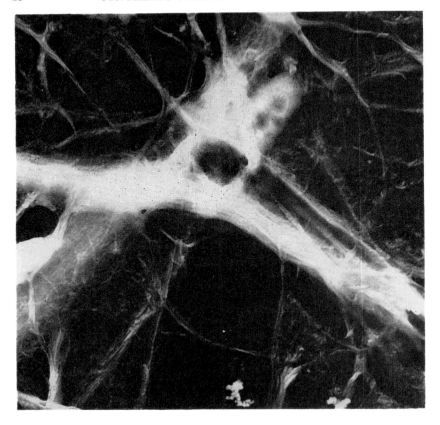

Figure 1.16.   Hybrid fibrils (150 Å:25,000×).

comprising 50% viscose rayon and 50% hydroxyethyl cellulose and subsequently beating the fibers to produce the fibrils. A patent is pending on the production of such fine fibrils from hybrid fibers by this process (8).

Physical properties of a few fibrillatable hybrid-fiber compositions have been assembled in Table 1.6. The physical properties of such hybrid-fiber papers will, of course, be determined by several variables —degree of fibrillation, diameter of fibrils, and the hydrophilic nature of the groups on the surfaces of the fibrils.

In Table 1.7 the marked effects on physical properties to be obtained by fibrillating a hybrid fiber comprising varying amounts of regenerated cellulose and polyacrylate are given.

TABLE 1.6
Fibrillatable Hybrid Fibers

Dry Paper Properties

Sample	TAPPI Ream Weight	Breaking Length (m.)	Tear Factor	Burst Factor
D	42.6	2346	93	13
E*	39.3	2858	98	14
E**	36.6	2939	126	12
G	—	1043	126	18
H	37	2630	51.5	31

D   = 50% regenerated cellulose, 50% hydroxyethyl cellulose, D.S. = 0.2.
E* = brushing in Waring Blendor, 30 minutes.
E** = brushing in Waring Blendor, 40 minutes.
G   = 50% regenerated cellulose, 50% amylopectin.
H   = 52% regenerated cellulose, 48% alkali soluble methyl cellulose.

TABLE 1.7
Properties of Regenerated Cellulose-Polyacrylate Hybrid Fibers

Composition of Hybrid Fiber			Dry Paper Properties						
Regenerated Cellulose (%)	Poly-acrylate (%)	Treatment	TAPPI Ream Weight	Breaking Length (m.)	Tear Factor	Burst Factor	Elonga-tion (%)	Caliper (mils)	Specific Volume
95	5	Not fibrillated	44.3	88	85	7	1.7	9.9	4.04
85	15	Not fibrillated	43.4	169	97	7	1.0	9.8	4.08
75	25	Not fibrillated	43.4	675	139	8	0.9	9.0	3.75
95	5	Fibrillated	46.7	132	73	6	2.1	10.3	3.98
85	15	Fibrillated	45.3	373	151	9	1.4	9.6	3.83
75	25	Fibrillated	45.7	2006	303	14	1.8	8.2	3.24

3. A third type, which has not yet been evaluated in the trade, is a self-bonding hydrophilic fiber known experimentally as Avisco's Fiber 776, which serves to glue together conventional rayon fibers into nonwoven products of clothlike texture.

Fiber 776 is a hydrophilic fibrous cellulose-ether binder. The physical properties of sheets made from it are related to the degree of substitution (D.S.). The influence of D.S. on paper sheets made with 100% Fiber 776 fibers is shown by the data in Table 1.8. As

TABLE 1.8

Influence of Degree of Substitution on Properties of Paper
Made from 100% Fiber 776

					Dry Physical Properties		
Type	Hydroxy-ethyl (%)	Degree of Substitu-tion	Fiber Diameter (microns)	TAPPI Ream	Breaking Length (m.)	Burst Factor	Elonga-tion (%)
Fiber A	4.3	0.17	22–23	49.4	2015	20	2.0
Fiber A	4.3	0.17	12–13	42.9	3183	31	3.7
Fiber B	8.2	0.32	16–17	45.7	3732	33	4.7

noted, the self-bonding forces that are engaged for this fibrous binder increase as the D.S. or hydrophilic nature of the fibrils increases.   Figure 1.17 further illustrates the role of increasing D.S. on a 25/75 blend hydrophilic fibrous binder (Fiber 776) and ¼ in. XL.

An interesting comparison of the physical properties of two hydrophilic man-made paper fibers is made in Table 1.9: carboxyethyl fiber versus hydroxypropyl fiber. Of special interest is the high tear factor obtainable with the hydroxypropyl fiber as compared with the carboxyethyl fiber.

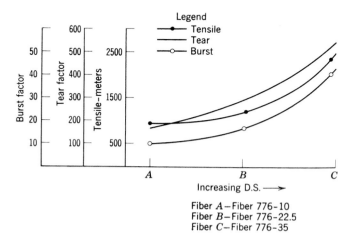

Figure 1.17.   Effect of D.S. of fiber 776 on bonding strength with ¼-in. XL fiber.

TABLE 1.9

Paper Properties of Carboxyethyl and Hydroxypropyl
Cellulose Fibrous Binders

| Fibrous Binder | Composition | | Dry Paper Properties | | | | | | |
	XL Rayon (%)	Fibrous Binder (%)	TAPPI Ream Weight	Breaking Length (m.)	Tear Factor	Burst Factor	Elonga- tion (%)	Thick- ness (mils)	Spe- cific Vol- ume
I	90	10	40.5	3119	219	33	3.6	6.2	2.76
I	75	25	43.4	2598	290	26	3.2	7.0	2.91
J	85	15	41.5	2387	617	52	7.3	8.0	3.48

I = carboxyethyl cellulose fiber binder.
J = hydroxypropyl cellulose fibrous binder.

Carboxyethyl cellulose also makes a good hydrophilic fibrous binder, which is prepared by adding acrylonitrile to viscose before spinning. It is particularly sensitive to pH during sheet formation but under proper conditions gives good physical properties (see Table 1.10).

TABLE 1.10

Effect of pH on Carboxyethyl Cellulose Binder

Dry Paper Properties

pH	TAPPI Ream Weight	Breaking Length (m.)	Tear Factor	Burst Factor	Elonga- tion (%)	Thick- ness (mils)	Specific Volume
4.4 (H$_2$SO$_4$)	44.3	2929	201	20	3.1	6.3	2.6
6.4	43.4	3626	165	32	4.0	6.2	2.6
8.2 (Ca(OH)$_2$)	43.4	3626	101	30	3.5	5.8	2.4
8.7 (NaOH)	43.3	3626	88	30	3.6	5.7	2.4

Carboxyethyl cellulose fibrous binder prepared by addition of 6% $CH_2=CHCN$ based on viscose.

A patent is pending on the preparation of these types of hydrophilic fibrous binders (9).

BONDED RAYON STRUCTURES

Synthetic thermoplastic fibers were used to produce commercially waterlaid heat-sealing paper as early as 1944 (10). This heat-sealing paper consists of short-cut rayon and Vinyon staple.

In 1960 a program was undertaken by Dr. James Russell in the Research Laboratories of the American Viscose Division to study the preparation of wet-formed nonwoven "fabrics" from blends of short-cut rayons with polyolefin fibers followed by subsequent heat-sealing of these structures (11).

High tear strength and high burst strengths were found to be related to the elastic properties of the binder-rayon system. These elastic properties are manifested by the incorporation of binders having second-order transition temperatures (brittle temperature) well below room temperature. This is true for emulsion-type binders. Such nonbrittle fibrous binders should be partly crystalline; otherwise they will be tacky. Examples of suitable materials are branched and linear polyethylenes, isotactic polypropylene and low melting polyamide, and polyester resins. Vinyon and cellulose acetate do not satisfy these requirements. Vinyon has a brittle temperature of 90°C., and cellulose acetate has an even higher second-order transition temperature. (See Tables 1.11 and 1.12).

TABLE 1.11

Polyethylene versus Vinyon as Fibrous Binder for Rayon

A

% Vinyon	% Rayon[1]	Tensile (lb.)	Measured Tear (gm.)
0	100	0	4
10	90	2.1	104
20	80	5.0	136
30	70	8.5	64

B[2]

% Polyethylene	% Rayon	Tensile (lb.)	Measured Tear (gm.)
0	100	0	4
10	90	3.0	224
20	80	6.3	168
30	70	5.3	88

[1] Rayon used: 1.5 denier $\frac{1}{4}$-in. XL staple.

[2] Note the superior tear properties of polyethylene over Vinyon acrylic fiber.

TABLE 1.12

Comparison of Different Fibrous Polyolefins as Binders

Type of Fibrous Polyolefin

Binder %	High-Density, High-Orientation Polyethylene (Marlex 50[1])		Low-Density, High-Orientation Polyethylene (Alathon 14)[1]		High-Density, High-Orientation Polypropylene (Profax[2])	
	Measured tear (gm.)	Tensile (lb.)	Measured tear (gm.)	Tensile (lb.)	Measured tear (gm.)	Tensile (lb.)
5	77	1.2	—	—	—	—
10	109	3.7	64	5.5	240	2.7
20	206	5.2	280	4.0	341	9.0
30	—	—	269	6.7	240	11.0

[1] Marlex 50 and Alathon 14 resins were pressed at 260°F., 300 p.s.i. for 30 sec.

[2] Profax-bonded sheets were pressed at 320°F., 300 p.s.i. for 30 sec. Rayon used was 1.5-denier, $\frac{1}{4}$-in. XL staple.

It is, of course, desirable for the tear, tensile, and impact burst strengths of bonded sheets to be high, and it is known that these properties are interdependent on each other. The end use of the "nonwoven bonded" structures will necessarily determine the physical properties that are of prime importance, which must be built into the paper.

COMPARISON OF FIBROUS AND POWDERED POLYOLEFINS

A powdered binder such as Alathon 14, 20% resin, based on the weight of the sheet, was used to obtain the data in Table 1.13, 1.14, and 1.15 using 1.5-denier, $\frac{1}{4}$-in. staple (XL) as the base fiber.

TABLE 1.13

Fibrous versus Powdered Binder (Alathon 14) (20% Binder)

Property	Fibrous	Powdered	
		20 Mesh	40 Mesh
Measured tear (gm.)	280	160	344
Tensile (lb.)	4.0	2.2	3.9

TABLE 1.14
Effect of Sieve Size of Powdered Alathon 14

Size	Measured Tear (gm.)	Tensile (lb.)
Through 20 mesh	160	2.2
Through 40 mesh	344	3.9
Through 60 mesh	Similar to 40 mesh	

TABLE 1.15
Influence of Anchoring Agents for the Polyolefin-Powdered Binder

Alathon 14	Without Accobond 3900		With Accobond 3900	
	Tear (gm.)	Tensile (lb.)	Tear (gm.)	Tensile (lb.)
15	80	1.9	373	5.9
20	184	2.5	344	7.5
25	293	4.2	357	9.8
30	280	3.9	289	9.6
35	224	6.3	277	9.9

The rayon and binder were dispersed in water containing 0.7% Accobond 3900 (melamine formaldehyde resin). From this stock furnish handsheets were prepared. The pressing temperature seems to have a definite effect on tear and tensiles, with high strengths obtained at lower pressing temperature. The pressing time showed slight decrease in strength because of a slight degradation of rayon. The optimum conditions found were 375°F. for 30 seconds at 300 p.s.i.

Russell (11) undertook two statistically designed experiments to study the several process variables. Summaries of his findings are provided in Tables 1.16 to 1.19.

TABLE 1.16
Effect of Amount of Binder and Type of Binder (average values for anchoring agents) On Tear Strength (expressed in grams)

	10	20	30
Alathon	406	432	310
Marlex	576	443	330
Profax	475	448	322

TABLE 1.17
Effect of Various Anchoring Agents (average values of all binders)
On Tear Strength (expressed in grams)

	Amount of Binder		
	10%	20%	30%
Accobond 3900	480	457	294
Accobond 3907	572	437	338
(melamine formaldehyde resin)			
PEI	565	448	330
(polyethyleneimine)			

TABLE 1.18
Effect of Anchoring Agent (average for all samples studied)
On Tear Strength (expressed in grams)

	Amount of Anchoring Agent		
	0%	1%	2%
Accobond 3900	490	395	394

TABLE 1.19
Effect of State of Subdivision of Binder (average of all samples)
On Tear Strength (expressed in grams)

	Mesh Size		
	40	60	100
Experiment A	426	416	438
	40	5 denier	30 denier
Experiment B	401	355	415

An increase in binder content showed a decrease in tear strength. No difference was apparent in types of binder studied at the 20 and 30% levels except Marlex 50, which seemed superior at the 10% level. The tear strength was not dependent on the state of subdivision of the binder material.

The addition of anchoring agent again showed a slight but definite tear improvement.

Table 1.20 summarizes the effects of binder content, particle size of binder, and amount and type of anchoring agent on the sheet tensile properties.

TABLE 1.20

Factors Affecting Tensile Strength

A. Effect of Amount and Type of Binder (average of all anchoring agents)

	% Binder		
	10	20	30
Alathon	6.8	10.2	15.0
Marlex	6.3	11.0	13.8
Profax	6.1	10.6	12.9

B. Effect of Various Anchoring Agents (average values for all binders)

	% Binder		
	10	20	30
Accobond 3900	6.4	12.1	13.3
Accobond 3907	5.5	9.3	13.1
(melamine formaldehyde resin)			
PEI	7.9	10.5	15.3
(polyethyleneimine)			

C. Effect of State of Subdivision of Binder

	40 mesh	60 mesh	100 mesh
Experiment A	9.3	11.5	10.3
	40 mesh	5 denier	30 denier
Experiment B	5.7	5.9	8.1

To achieve optimum handsheet properties, an intermediate amount of binder must be incorporated, since high tear strength and burst strength are obtained at low binder content, whereas high tensiles are obtained with high binder content. The particle size of binder has no definite effect on either tensile- or tear-strength properties.

FIBROUS POLYOLEFIN BINDERS

Polyolefin fibers can be dispersed more uniformly with rayon than the powdered polyolefins. A laboratory-size Valley beater was used to disperse the rayon-polyolefin fiber blend.

Two statistically designed experiments based on five variables with three levels of each variable were studied. The results are given in Table 1.21 and Figures 1.18 through 1.29.

TABLE 1.21
Statistically Designed Experiments for Fibrous Polyolefin Binders

Variable	Levels		
Type of Binder	Polyethylene A	Polyethylene B	Polypropylene
Amount of binder	15%	25%	35%
Type of rayon[1]	RXL	HEXL	LEXL
Type of anchoring agent	Accobond 3810	Accobond 3907	Polyethyleneimine
Amount of anchoring agent (2% solution)	0	40 ml.	80 ml.

[1] R = regular elongation type XL staple (Avisco)
H = high elongation type XL staple (Avisco)
L = low elongation type XL staple (Avisco)

EFFECT OF BINDER

Polyethylene is superior to polypropylene except in tear strength. This may be attributed to better adhesion properties of polyethylene with cellulose and the high modulus of polypropylene.

The physical fiber form of the polyolefin fiber is destroyed by heat sealing, and, similarly, the denier of the filament should have no effect.

The carbonyl content of the binder appears to have no effect on binding ability. This conclusion is supported by a comparison of polyethylene A (low carbonyl) and polyethylene B (high carbonyl) polyolefin fibers.

EFFECT OF AMOUNT OF BINDER

Tear strength decreases with increasing binder content, whereas the burst and tensile strengths increase.

EFFECT OF ANCHORING AGENT

Anchoring agents have favorable effects on the physical properties. Accobond 3907, a melamine formaldehyde resin and polyethylenei-

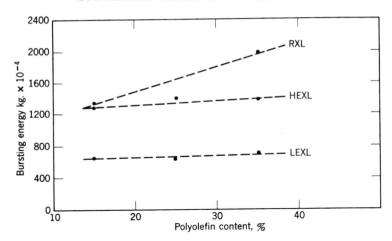

Figure 1.18.   Bursting energy—average for all polyolefins.

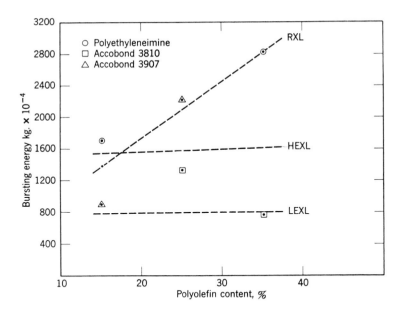

Figure 1.19.   Bursting energy—polyethylene A.

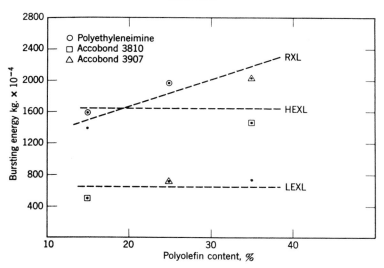

Figure 1.20.   Bursting energy—polyethylene B.

mine qualify in this regard.   Accobond 3810, a urea formaldehyde resin, is pH-sensitive.   The concentration of anchoring agents such as wet-strength resins reaches an optimum level in effectivity.   Higher concentrations were used in this study and more work is needed to determine the minimum amount needed.

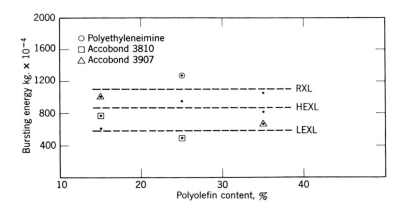

Figure 1.21.   Bursting energy—polypropylene.

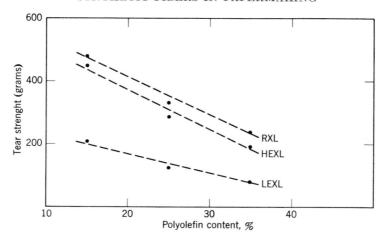

Figure 1.22.   Tear strength—average of all polyolefins.

INFLUENCE OF PHYSICAL PROPERTIES OF RAYONS

Qualitatively, it was shown that the tensile and elongation prop-erties of the rayon-polyolefin handsheets are directly proportional to the tensiles and elongation of the rayon used.   The bursting energies and tear strengths obtained by using regular XL rayon staple and high elongation XL rayon are superior to low elongation XL rayons,

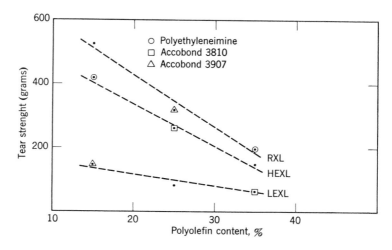

Figure 1.23.   Tear strength—polyethylene A.

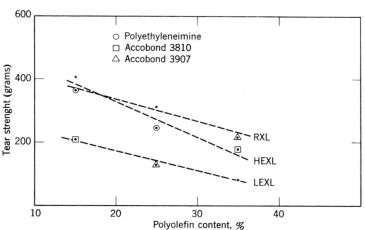

Figure 1.24. Tear strength—polyethylene B.

whereas tensile strengths of bonded sheets are better for regular XL and lower elongation rayon handsheets. Of the three rayons examined, regular XL staple gave the best over-all physical properties.

Figure 1.30 shows predicted sheet properties at variable binder contents employing the best binder (polyethylene), the best anchoring agent (Accobond 3907), and regular XL staple.

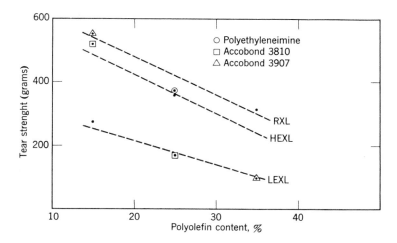

Figure 1.25. Tear strength—polypropylene.

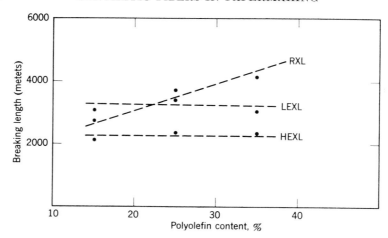

Figure 1.26. Breaking length—average of all polyolefins.

Handsheets with optimum physical properties consist of 75% regular XL staple and 25% polyethylene staple with Accobond 3907 as the anchoring agent. Heat sealing is made at 375°F. Handsheet properties have a breaking length of 4000 m., tear strength of 325 gm., and a bursting energy of 2200 kg. × 10⁻⁴. These properties are similar to the best emulsion bonded sheets obtained. A quantitative treatment of these physical data can be made by comparison of the

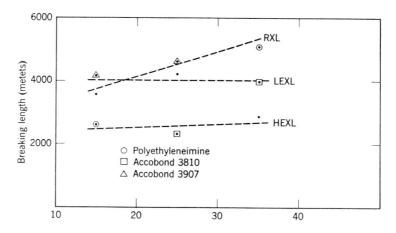

Figure 1.27. Breaking length—polyethylene A.

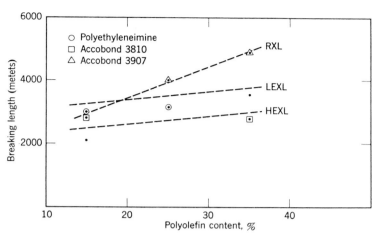

Figure 1.28. Breaking length—polyethylene B.

tensiles and elongation of the rayon staple and average tensiles and elongation of handsheets. These data are given in Table 1.22.

The sheet-to-yarn elongation ratio showed that the elongation of the average sheet is half the elongation of the staple used. The ratio of the average sheet strength to the rayon yarn strength is constant.

In an ideally bonded sheet the sheet properties will remain un-

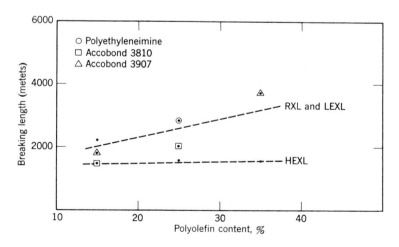

Figure 1.29. Breaking length—polypropylene.

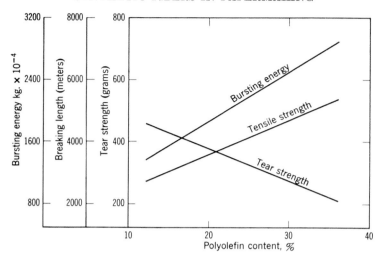

Figure 1.30. Predicted sheet properties using regular XL, polyethylene and anchoring agent.

TABLE 1.22
Relationship of Yarn to Handsheet Physical Properties

Rayon	Elongation (%)		Sheet/Yarn Yarn Elonga-	Tensiles (grams/denier)		Sheet Strength/
	Yarn	Sheet (av.)	tion (av.)	Yarn	Sheet	Yarn Strength
LEXL	10	4.4	0.44	3.0	0.4	0.13
RXL	26	11.6	0.45	3.5	0.39	0.11
HEXL	32	16.4	0.51	2.5	0.25	0.10

changed no matter what improvements are made in the binder.   This is because the fiber or the fiber-to-binder bond will be breaking.   The physical properties of an ideally bonded sheet were approximated by using the highest sheet physical properties obtained in this study and the ratio of high sheet properties to yarn properties was determined. The data are given in Table 1.23.

The results indicated that the maximum possible sheet tensile is about 15% of the incorporated fiber and the maximum possible elongation is about 55% of the fiber elongation.

The data assembled in this chapter on rayons in papermaking illustrate that the role of synthetic fibers in the manufacture of new

TABLE 1.23
Maximum Values of Yarn to Handsheet Physical Properties

Rayon	Ratio of Highest Sheet Tensile to Fiber Tensile	Ratio of Highest Sheet Elongation to Fiber Elongation
LEXL	0.16	0.54
RXL	0.16	0.53
HEXL	0.14	0.59

types of paper products will probably develop by combining synthetic fibers and natural fibers in optimum proportions to achieve the most economical price/performance properties in a product tailored to meet specific applications. In addition, there appear to be opportunities for lower priced synthetic fibers, at least, to be engineered and fashioned into papers comprising substantially 100% of such synthetic fibers. A few of the potentialities have been pointed out, although at the same time we wish to emphasize that many of these applications are in the very early stages of commercial development, especially in the case of the experimental types of the *new* rayon fibers described in this chapter.

REFERENCES

1. Technical Service Bulletin S-13, Technical Service Department, Product Information Department, American Viscose Division, FMC Corporation. Marcus Hook, Pennsylvania, U.S.A.
2. Technical Service Bulletin S-12, Ibid.
3. *Paper Trade J.* **142**, 36–42 (January 6, 1958).
4. H. E. Shearer, British Patent **687,041** (February 4, 1953).
5. O. A. Battista, U. S. Patent 3,052,593.
6. O. A. Battista, *Ind. Eng. Chem., Anal. Ed.,* **16**, 351–354 (1944).
7. O. A. Battista, "Hydrolysis and Crystallization of Cellulose," *Ind. Eng. Chem.,* **42**, 502–507 (1950).
8. O. A. Battista, M. M. Cruz, Jr., and F. H. Reichel, Jr., patent pending.
9. M. M. Cruz, Jr., and R. L. McDowell, patent pending.
10. F. H. Osborne, U. S. Patent 2,414,833 (January 28, 1947).
11. J. Russell, unpublished work.

2

THE ACRYLICS

ROBERT E. FOSTER

Research Supervisor, Technical Division
Textile Fibers Department
E. I. du Pont de Nemours & Co., Inc.
Wilmington, Delaware

Acrylic fibers are based on polymers and copolymers of acrylonitrile, $CH_2{=}CHCN$, formed by addition, or free-radical, polymerization. The polymerization reaction is regarded as typical of vinyl-type monomers and can be written as follows: In. represents the free-radical fragment arising from the initiator, which is usually an organic peroxide or unstable nitrogen compound.

Initiation

$$\text{In.} + CH_2{=}CHCN \rightarrow \text{In. } CH_2CH\cdot \atop | \atop CN$$

Chain propagation

$$\text{In. } CH_2CH\cdot + (n+1)CH_2{=}CHCN \rightarrow$$

$$\text{In. } CH_2CH \left(CH_2CH \atop | \atop CN \right)_n CH_2CH\cdot$$

The growing polymer chain may be terminated by any of several mechanisms, all of which may occur during the course of the polymerization: (1) chain transfer with solvent; (2) chain transfer with preformed polymer; (3) disproportionation; (4) reaction with an initiator fragment; (5) combination with a second growing polymer chain.

Termination

1. Chain transfer with solvent or modifying agent:

$$\text{In.} \left(\begin{array}{c} CH_2CN \\ | \\ CN \end{array}\right)_{n+1} \begin{array}{c} CH_2CH\cdot \\ | \\ CN \end{array} + MH \rightarrow \text{In.} \left(\begin{array}{c} CH_2CH \\ | \\ CN \end{array}\right)_{n+1} \begin{array}{c} CH_2CH_2 \\ | \\ CN \end{array} + M\cdot$$

The modifier or solvent radical M can start another polymerization chain by a mechanism similar to the original initiation.

2. Chain transfer with preformed polymer proceeds in an analogous manner but generates a new polymer radical that will give rise to chain branching:

$$\text{In.} \left(\begin{array}{c} CH_2CH \\ | \\ CN \end{array}\right)_{n+1} \begin{array}{c} CH_2CH\cdot \\ | \\ CN \end{array} + \begin{array}{ccc} -CH_2CHCH_2CHCH_2CH- \\ | \quad\quad | \quad\quad | \\ CN \quad CN \quad CN \end{array}$$

$$\text{In.} \left(\begin{array}{c} CH_2CH \\ | \\ CN \end{array}\right)_{n+1} \begin{array}{c} CH_2CH_2 \\ | \\ CN \end{array} + \begin{array}{ccc} \overset{\cdot}{-CH_2CHCH_2CCH_2CH-} \\ | \quad\quad | \quad\quad | \\ CH \quad CN \quad CN \end{array}$$

The new radical will initiate a new polymer chain that will result in a long "branch" on the preformed polymer chain:

$$\left(\begin{array}{c} CH_2CH \\ | \\ | \quad CN \end{array}\right)_n \begin{array}{c} CH_2CH\cdot \\ | \\ CN \end{array}$$

$$\begin{array}{ccc} -CH_2CHCH_2CCH_2CH- \\ | \quad\quad | \quad\quad | \\ CN \quad CN \quad CN \end{array}$$

3. Two growing polymer chains may interact by disproportionation, involving, at least formally, a hydrogen transfer:

$$\text{In.} \left(\begin{array}{c} CH_2CH \\ | \\ CN \end{array}\right)_x \begin{array}{c} CH_2CH\cdot \\ | \\ CN \end{array} + \text{In.} \left(\begin{array}{c} CH_2CH \\ | \\ CN \end{array}\right)_y \begin{array}{c} CH_2CH\cdot \\ | \\ CN \end{array} \rightarrow$$

$$\text{In.} \left(\begin{array}{c} CH_2CH \\ | \\ CN \end{array}\right)_x \begin{array}{c} CH_2CH_2 \\ | \\ CN \end{array} + \text{In.} \left(\begin{array}{c} CH_2CH \\ | \\ CN \end{array}\right)_y \begin{array}{c} CH\!=\!CH \\ | \\ CN \end{array}$$

A saturated polymer molecule may be formed by the combination of two radical species:

4. Reaction with initiator fragment:

$$\text{In.} \left(\begin{array}{c} CH_3CH \\ | \\ CN \end{array}\right)_{n+1} \begin{array}{c} CH_2CH\cdot \\ | \\ CN \end{array} + \text{In.} \rightarrow \text{In.} \left(\begin{array}{c} CH_2CH \\ | \\ CN \end{array}\right)_{n+1} \begin{array}{c} CH_2CH \text{ In.} \\ | \\ CN \end{array}$$

5. Combination with a growing polymer chain:

$$\text{In.} \left(\begin{array}{c} CH_2CH \\ | \\ CN \end{array}\right)_{n+1} \begin{array}{c} CH_2CH\cdot \\ | \\ CN \end{array} + \begin{array}{c} \cdot CHCH_2 \\ | \\ CN \end{array} \left(\begin{array}{c} CHCH_2 \\ | \\ CN \end{array}\right)_z \text{In.} \rightarrow$$

$$\text{In.} \left(\begin{array}{c} CH_2CH \\ | \\ CN \end{array}\right)_{n+1} \begin{array}{c} CH_2CH \\ | \\ CN \end{array} - \begin{array}{c} CHCH_2 \\ | \\ CN \end{array} \left(\begin{array}{c} CHCH_2 \\ | \\ CN \end{array}\right)_z \text{In.}$$

These termination reactions do not occur with equal probability; chain transfer (1) appears to be the most important. Thus control over the extent of the polymerization can be provided by capitalizing on the efficacy of various chain transfer agents, their concentration, and the kinetics of transfer versus polymerization steps.

Another important parameter subject to control is the kind of monomer molecules present during the polymerization. If a second polymerizable vinyl compound is available for reaction, the growing acrylonitrile polymer chain may add to the acrylonitrile or to the second monomer:

$$\text{In.} \left(\begin{array}{c} CH_2CH \\ | \\ CN \end{array}\right)_n \begin{array}{c} CH_2CH\cdot \\ | \\ CN \end{array} + \begin{array}{c} CH_2 = CH \\ | \\ X \end{array} \rightarrow \text{In.} \left(\begin{array}{c} CH_2CH \\ | \\ CN \end{array}\right)_n \begin{array}{c} CH_2CH\cdot \\ | \\ X \end{array}$$

etc.

The properties of the final polymer are governed to a considerable degree by the molecular weight (degree of polymerization) and by the amount and type of comonomer present.*

To form fibers, a viscous solution of the acrylonitrile polymer is extruded ("spun") through small holes in a spinneret and the solvent is evaporated to yield the solid polymer in filaments. These filaments must be stretched, or "oriented," to develop strength inherent in the polymer and then cut to the desired staple length. As described in Chapter 10, "Structure-Property Relationships," this ori-

* Vinyl polymerization is a large and complex subject, which has been extensively studied. For a more comprehensive treatment, the reader is referred to C. E. Schildknecht, *Vinyl and Related Polymers,* John Wiley and Sons, New York, 1952.

entation increases the number of interchain bonds, which are the nitrile-nitrile dipolar bonds in acrylonitrile polymers.

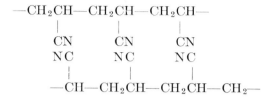

It can be seen that the interchain binding forces will be altered by the presence of a second monomer in the polymer chain.

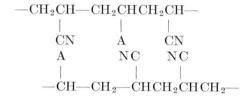

In practice, acrylic fibers are spun from copolymers of acrylonitrile in order to modify the processability, dyeability, flammability, etc., of the fiber. Comonomers which can be used include most polymerizable vinyl compounds. The U. S. Government has established labeling standards, defining acrylic fibers as those prepared from fiber-forming polymers containing at least 85% by weight of acrylonitrile units and modacrylic fibers as those prepared from fiber-forming polymers containing less than 85% and more than 35% of acrylonitrile units. Table 2.1 lists producers of acrylic and modacrylic fibers with their trade names, if any.

Acrylic fibers are recognized as outstanding in resistance to chemicals, heat, and light, and these attributes can be capitalized on in sheet structures containing these fibers. Table 2.2 summarizes physical and chemical properties of use in papermaking.

As described in Chapter 9, "Web Formation and Bonding," the filaments are cut to the desired staple length, and after treatment with a suitable finish to provide water dispersibility are in proper condition for processing by papermaking techniques in typical fashion for synthetic hydrophobic fibers.

In contrast to most synthetic fibers, however, properly processed acrylic fibers can be made self-bonding by beating in water which forms a fibrillated fiber structure. The preparation of these fibers has been described by Brown (1), Wooding and Woodberry (2), and

TABLE 2.1
World Fiber Producers[1]

Country and Producer	Trade Name
United States	
American Cyanamid Co.	Creslan
Chemstrand Company	Acrilan
Dow Chemical Company	Zefran
E. I. du Pont de Nemours & Co.	Orlon
Eastman Chemical Products, Inc.	Verel (modacrylic)
Union Carbide Chemicals Co.	Dynel (modacrylic)
Belgium	
Union Chemique	Acribel
Canada	
Du Pont of Canada	Orlon
France	
Courtaulds	Courtelle
Crylon	Crylon
West Germany	
Bayer	Dralon
Phrix	Redon
Chemifaser	Dolan
Israel	
Israeli Chemical	No name
Italy	
Asca	Leacril
Japan	
Asahi	Cashmilon
Mitsubishi	Vonnel
Nippon Exlan	Exlan
Toho Rayon	Baslon
Nitto Boseki	Nitlon
Netherlands	
Du Pont	Orlon
Nyma	Nymcrylon
Spain	
Fibracril	No name
Sweden	
Superfosfat	Tacryl
United Kingdom	
Courtaulds	Courtelle
Chemstrand	Acrilan

[1] Free world only.

Holmes and Anderson (3). The fibrils provide mechanical entanglement during wet laydown and strength to the web to permit further processing. This property was employed by Arledter (4) in his early work with synthetic-fiber papers. Because the interfiber bonds are mechanical in nature, and the acrylic fiber is insensitive to water, wet sheet strength is about 50% of the dry sheet strength of these webs. The effect of fibrillation on sheet strength is shown in Table 2.3.

TABLE 2.2

Properties of Fibers[1]

Property	Orlon	Acrilan	Zefran	Creslan	Dynel	Verel
Breaking tenacity, grams/denier						
standard	2.3–2.6	2.0–2.7	3.3–3.7	2.4–2.9	3.0	2.5–2.8
wet	1.8–2.1	1.6–2.2	2.9–3.3	3.3	3.0	2.4–2.7
Tensile strength, p.s.i.	32–39,000	30–40,000	53,000	40–43,000	50,000	42–47,000
Elongation at break						
standard	20–28	36–40	30–35	42–56	39	33–35
%—wet	26–34	44–49	30–35	32	39	32–34
Specific gravity	1.16	1.17	1.18	1.18	1.30	1.37
Water absorbency:						
70°F., 65 % R.H.	1.5	1.5	2.5	1.1–2.2	0.4	3
70°F., 95 % R.H.	4	5	5	2.6	1	
Effects of acids and alkalis	Generally good to excellent resistance to acids Fair to good resistance to alkalis				Little effect	Alkali causes some discoloration
Effects of solvents and bleaches	Good resistance to common solvents and bleaches				Softened or warm acetone. fected by solvents	dissolved in Not afdry cleaning
Resistance to sunlight, mildew, aging, abrasion	Excellent resistance		Excellent resistance			Not attacked by mildew

[1] Textile World Man-Made Fiber Chart, 1962.

TABLE 2.3

Properties of Nonfibrillated and Fibrillated Acrylic Fiber Papers (4)

Degree of fibrillation	None	Well fibrillated
Basis weight (24 × 36–500), lb.	82	84
Thickness, mil	35	14
Tensile strength, gm./in.	None	10,500
Wet tensile strength, gm./in.	—	4000
Bursting strength, lb.	None	28

Arledter has shown that the strength of fibrillated acrylic fiber papers may be greatly increased by hot calendering or by impregnation with binder resins. These improvements are tabulated in Tables 2.4 and 2.5.

TABLE 2.4
Effect of Hot Calendering on Properties (5)

Temperature	72°F.	200°F.	220°F.	240°F.
Basis weight (24 × 36–500), lb.	83	83	83	83
Thickness in mils	7.5	6.5	6	6
Tensile strength, gm./in.	7800	10,300	14,500	18,800
Mullen burst, lb.	21	40	48	59

The resin binders have not been disclosed, but presumably the acrylic sheet was saturated in a suitable emulsion or solution, dried, and cured.

TABLE 2.5
Properties of Acrylic Sheets Containing Binder (4)

Binder	A	B	A
Binder, %	2	6	2
Basis weight, (24 × 36–500), lb.	80	85	30
Thickness, mil	15	16	7
Tensile strength, gm./in.	13,500	16,000	2900
Tensile strength, lb./in.	30	35.5	6.5
Wet tensile, gm./in.	7000	8000	1700
Bursting strength, lb.	30	40	8

A third method which involves a technique known as "salt bonding" can be used for bonding the acrylic fiber webs. This process, described in Chapter 9, involves treating the web with an aqueous solution of salts such as zinc chloride or calcium thiocyanate. These so-called hydrotropic salt solutions are swelling agents or solvents for the polymer at certain concentrations. Thus, at fiber crossover points, the swollen fibers fuse together, and when the salt is leached out by water the polymer precipitates and an interfiber bond is formed (6,7,8).

The formation of acrylic webs from nonfibrillated acrylic fibers requires special processing steps to facilitate handling of the un-bonded sheet. These steps are discussed more fully in Chapter 9. Low percentages of wood pulp (2), hydroxyethyl cellulose (9), natural gums, or synthetic binders have been employed. The synthetic binders that have been described include Du Pont Company's fibrid (10) system,* low-melting fibrillated binder polymers (11), and the use of nonfusible fiber, such as glass or cellulose coated with a thermoplastic exhibiting wet tack (12). The advantages in these binder systems lie in their ability to hold the nonself-bonded fibers together by mechanical means, thus permitting subsequent heat bonding by oven fusing or calendering. It is thus possible to capitalize on the physical properties of the oriented fiber. For example, with the use of Du Pont Fibrid 201 tensile strengths of the bonded sheet approaching the theoretical maximum are possible (Table 2.6).

TABLE 2.6

Properties of Sheets of Orlon[1]/201 Fibrid (13)

Fiber: 3 denier, $\frac{1}{4}$ in.
Fibrid content: 30%
Heat bonded at: 190°C.

	Pressed (600 lb./in.^{2})	Fused, No Pressure
Basis weight (24 × 36–500), lb.	60	60
Tensile strength, gm./in.	11,000–13,000	6000–7000
Elongation, %	13	5
Tear (Elmendorf, gm.)	450	450

[1] Registered Du Pont trademark for its acrylic fiber.

Handling of the synthetic fiber and binder stocks is well discussed in Chapter 9. The principles described there apply directly to acrylic fibers, that is, the use of low consistencies in the furnish, about 0.1% or less, adequate agitation, and the proper ratio of length to diameter of the fiber. Orlon, for example, can be obtained in 2 denier, $\frac{1}{4}$ in., 3 denier, $\frac{1}{4}$ in., 6 denier, and 10 denier cut to appropriate lengths for operability.

Brissette and Eldred (14) have found analogous performance with Dynel, a modacrylic fiber. In handsheet preparation with fibers of 2 to 24 denier these workers observed good dispersions in the deckle box and good sheet formation when fiber lengths of $\frac{1}{8}$ to $\frac{1}{2}$ in. were used. The wet-web strength of the hydrophobic fiber mat is low, and, therefore, the use of a binder is required to permit removal of the web from the wire. Brissette and Eldred employed 5 to 25% cellulose pulp or a resin emulsion binder for this purpose. Ultimate sheet strength was developed by calendering with the aid of a solvent

* Fibrids have been produced experimentally by Du Pont, but have not been commercialized.

at about 140°C. These heat-bonded webs displayed high bursting strength, as shown in Table 2.7 (14).

TABLE 2.7

Bonded Sheets of Dynel

Furnish: 60% $\frac{1}{4}$ in., 20% $\frac{1}{2}$ in., 20% $\frac{1}{8}$ in., 2-denier Dynel

Equipment: Three-roll positive pressure calender set for 100 lb./in. of nip.

	I	II
Additive for wet-web strength	5% polyvinyl, acetate	5% cellulose
Solvent	5% propylene carbonate	5% propylene carbonate
Temperature, °C.	140	140
Speed, f.p.m.	25	25
Bursting strength (points/100 lb.)	110.5 (59 p.s.i.)	187 (100 p.s.i.)

SPECIAL ATTRIBUTES AND USES OF ACRYLIC-FIBER PAPERS

Properties of the acrylic fibers, as shown in Table 2.2, can be capitalized on in sheet structures made from these fibers. Particularly outstanding is the durability of acrylic-fiber sheets to outdoor exposure, action of chemicals, molds, and ultraviolet light. Arledter has reported (4), for example, that a paper of 100% fibrillated acrylic fiber could be buried in the ground for months without significant loss of strength. Exposure to 50% aqua regia at 120°F. for three weeks caused little deterioration. The retention of tensile strength of sheets of Orlon after exposure to various agents is shown in Table 2.8 (13).

TABLE 2.8

Per Cent Retention of Tensile Strength After One Week at 122°F.

Reagent	% Retention
H_2O	90
NaOH (10%)	87
NaCl (10%)	89
H_2SO_4 (30%)	87
HCl (10%)	95
HNO_3 (10%)	83
H_2O_2 (3%)	73

The low water sensitivity of the acrylic fibers is manifested in high wet tensile strength and dimensional stability at varying humidities of the corresponding sheet structures. Arledter (4) has reported that this stabilizing effect is shown also with blend structures of cellulose pulp and the acrylic fiber. With only 5% of fibrillated acrylic fiber present with cellulose fibers, the mixture showed an improvement of 20 to 25% in dimensional stability.

Of specialty interest, some counts of Orlon are available without the usual pigment or delusterant present, a so-called "bright" fiber. In this form the fiber possesses a refractive index close to that of acrylic and polyester resins. Thus, if the sheet containing Orlon is saturated with one of these resins and cured, the fiber becomes invisible; the result is a clear, transparent plastic laminate. This processing has been employed for the manufacture of decorative panels, surfacings for plywood, and the like.

Acrylic papers have been employed also as reinforcements for phenolic laminates for electrical uses. Arledter (5) has evaluated such structures, employing not only fibrillated acrylic fibers but straight synthetic fibers as well. Properties of these laminates are shown in Table 2.9.

TABLE 2.9
Properties of Phenolic Laminates

Laminate Thickness: 62–67 mil.   Phenolic Resin Content: 47–50%

	A	B	C
Fibers employed	100% fibrillating acrylic fibers	60% fibrillating acrylic fibers + 40% precut long acrylic fibers	60% fibrillating acrylic fibers + 40% precut long nylon fibers
% Moisture absorption	0.15	0.25	0.11
Flexural strength, p.s.i. lengthwise	23,100	16,800	24,600
Crosswise	15,200	12,100	18,900
Izod impact strength, ft./lb.			
Lengthwise	1.07	1.10	2.7
Crosswise	0.81	0.9	2.0
Insulation resistance, megohms C/96/90/40	10,000,000	10,000,000	10,000,000
Loss factor A	0.048	0.047	0.043
Loss factor D/48/50	0.065	0.065	0.083

The chemical, thermal, and sunlight resistance of acrylic-fiber papers suggests their use in applications in which cellulosic papers are unsatisfactory: for example, filter media for corrosive liquids or vapors, plastic laminates for high temperature or outdoor service, and substrates for electrical insulation for service up to 130°C. (15).

REFERENCES

1. B. J. Brown, *Proc. J. Text. Inst.*, **53**, 682 (October 1962).
2. W. M. Wooding and N. T. Woodbury, U. S. Patent 2,810,646 (October 22, 1957).
3. R. R. Holmes and N. T. Anderson, U. S. Patent 3,047,422 (July 31, 1962).
4. H. F. Arledter, *TAPPI*, **42**, 177A (February 1959).
5. H. F. Arledter, Annual Meeting of New England *TAPPI*, June 6, 1959.
6. J. K. Hubbard, F. H. Koontz, J. R. McCartney, and R. A. A. Hentschel, *TAPPI*, **38**, 257 (May 1955). J. K. Hubbard, U. S. Patent 2,920,992 (January 12, 1960).
7. J. T. Taylor and P. J. McLaughlin, ASTM Special Publication No. 241, 26.
8. K. Klein, SVF Fachorgan Textilveredlung, **13**, 61 (1958); C. A., **52**, 14166 (1958).
9. H. E. Shearer, U. S. Patent 2,810,644 (October 22, 1957).
10. R. A. A. Hentschel, *TAPPI*, **44**, 22 (January 1961).
11. W. A. Miller and C. N. Merriam, Jr., British Patent 836,328 (June 1, 1960).
12. J. H. Mathews, U. S. Patent 3,035,965 (May 22, 1962).
13. Adapted from Du Pont Textile Fibers Technical Bulletin NP-19, 1960.
14. R. S. Brissette and N. R. Eldred, *TAPPI*, **42**, 136 (January 1959).
15. R. C. Berry, G. R. Traut, and N. L. Greenman, Materials in Design Engineering, **52**, No. 7, 10 (December 1960).

3

THE POLYAMIDES

DOUGLAS G. BANNERMAN

Market Development Manager
Textile Fibers Department
E. I. du Pont de Nemours & Co., Inc.
Wilmington, Delaware

Nylon, the generic term coined for polyamides, is probably the best known of all synthetic fibers. This first truly synthetic fiber was created in the late 1930's by a team of research men under the leadership of Dr. Wallace H. Carothers in the laboratories of the Du Pont Company. The first commercial plant began operation in the United States in December 1939, and the fiber met with instant success. Rapid expansion in this country followed during the war years, for nylon had important military applications in parachute cloth and airplane tire cord.

Nylon fiber was also being developed and commercialized in Germany at about the same time. During the war years (1939–1945)

TABLE 3.1
1961 World Production of Certain Fibers[1]

Fiber	Billion Pounds	% of Total
Cotton	22.3	67
Rayon	5.3	16
Wool	3.3	10
Nylon	1.0	3
Acetate	0.6	1+
Polyester	0.3	1−
Polyacrylic	0.3	1−
Others	0.3	1−
Total	33.4	100

[1] *Textile Organon*, June 1962.

the Germans brought nylon to a high state of development for the same military uses. The German nylon, a different species from the early domestic nylon, is discussed later in this chapter.

The importance of nylon fiber is best illustrated by examination of its place in the world production of fibers given in Table 3.1.

In 1961, less than 25 years after its introduction, one billion pounds of nylon, representing 3% of the total production of fibers in the world and 13% of all man-made fibers, were produced. One reason for its success is the tremendous versatility of the fiber. Its properties can be varied through process and product modifications so that it has become the preferred fiber for delicate textile uses such as lingerie and for tough industrial uses such as shoe sewing thread, ropes, and tire cord.

PRODUCERS OF NYLON

A summary of world producers of polyamide fibers as of January 1964, is given in Table 3.2.

MANUFACTURING METHODS

A brief consideration of the chemical nature of nylon is in order so that its processability in papermaking operations and its performance in the final product can be better understood (1). Nylon is the generic term given to a synthetic linear polyamide which has recurring amide groups:

$$
\begin{array}{c}
-\text{C}-\text{N}- \\
\parallel \quad | \\
\text{O} \quad \text{H}
\end{array}
$$

Two methods of manufacture are used commercially which lead to two different nylons.

The first method is the reaction of a dibasic acid with a diamine, as illustrated in the following equation:

$$
\text{HOOC}-\text{R}-\text{COOH} + \text{H}_2\text{N}-\text{R}'-\text{NH}_2 \rightleftharpoons
$$

$$
\text{HOOC}\left[\begin{array}{c} -\text{R}-\text{C}-\text{N}-\text{R}'- \\ \parallel \quad | \\ \text{O} \quad \text{H} \end{array}\right]_x \text{NH}_2 + \text{H}_2\text{O}
$$

The principal nylon manufactured in the United States is prepared from adipic acid (R is $-\text{CH}_2\text{CH}_2\text{CH}_2\text{CH}_2-$) and hexamethylenediamine (R' is $-\text{CH}_2\text{CH}_2\text{CH}_2\text{CH}_2\text{CH}_2\text{CH}_2-$) and is designated 66 nylon because of the six carbon atoms in each reactant. The

TABLE 3.2
World Producers of Nylon Fibers[1]

Country and Producer	Type	Trade Name
Argentina		
Ducilo	6	Ducilo
Extavia	6	Perfilon
Hisisa	6	Hissilon
Minue-Medenyl	6	
Prenyl	6	Prenylon
Australia		
Allied Polymer	6	Caprolan
British Nylon Spinners	66	BNS
Belgium		
Union Chemique	66	Fabelta
Brazil		
Nylbrasil, S.A.	6	Nailonsix
Rhodiaceta	66	Rhodianil
Grillon, S.A.	6	Grillon
Rilsan	11	Rilsan
Matarazzo	6	Textilion
Canada		
Du Pont	66	Du Pont Nylon
Chile		
Sumar	6	Perlon
Colombia		
Vanylon	6	Vanylon
Egypt		
Misr Rayon	6	Misrnylon
France		
CTA	6	
Rhodiaceta	66	Rhodiaceta
Valentinoise	11	Rilsan
West Germany		
Bayer	6	Perlon
Phrix	6	Perlon
Bemberg	6	Perlon
Rhodiaceta	66	Rhodia
Hoechst	6	Perlon-Hoechst
Zellendorf	6	Perlon
Glanzstoff	6	Perlon
Greece		
Hellenic	6	Synthl

TABLE 3.2 (*Continued*)

Country and Producer	Type	Trade Name
India		
Century Rayon	6	
Gharivare Nylons	6	Garflon
Nanubhai	6	Nirlon
Israel		
Rogosin Industries	6	
Italy		
Bombrini	6	Delfion
Chatillon	6	Helion
Bemberg	6	Ortalion
Mangelli	6	Forlion
Snia Viscosa	6	Lilion, Rilsan
Rhodiatoce	66	Nailon
Japan		
Asahi	6	
Teikoku	6	
Toyo Rayon	6	Toray-nylon
Kanegafuchi	6	
Kureha	6	
Nippon Rayon	6	Nitiray
Kurake	6	
Mexico		
Celanese	6	Duracel
Fibras Quimicas	6	
Nylon de Mexico	6	Nylfil
Netherlands		
AKU	6	Enkalon
Peru		
Peruana	6	Glamour
Spain		
Quimicas	6	Tecron
Perlofil	6	Dayan
Safa	66	Safa nylon
Sweden		
Konstsilke	6	Cornyl
Switzerland		
Feldmuhle	6	Bodanyl
EMS	6	Grilon
Viscose Suisse	66	Nylsuisse
United Kingdom		
Enka	6	Enkalon
British Nylon Spinners	66	BNS

TABLE 3.2 (*Continued*)

Country and Producer	Type	Trade Name
United States		
Du Pont	66	
Chemstrand	66	
Allied	6	Caprolan
Firestone	6	Nyloft
Enka	6	
Uruguay		
Hisisa	6	Hisilon
Venezuela		
Sudalon	6	Sudalon

[1] Free world only.

length of the polymer chain, that is, the magnitude of x, is determined by a number of process conditions and can be controlled quite accurately. The average molecular weight for 66 textile nylon is in the range of 12,000 to 14,000 and in the range of 17,000 to 19,000 for high tenacity industrial yarn.

The second method is the catalytic opening of a lactam ring followed by polymerization as illustrated in the following equation:

Aminocaprolactam is the major starting material so that y equals 5, and the resulting polyamide is known as 6 nylon. The molecular weight of commercial 6 nylon is about the same as that of 66 nylon.

A slight variation of this second method of manufacture is illustrated in the preparation of 11 nylon through self-condensation of aminoundecanoic acid.

$$H_2N—(CH_2)_{10}—COOH \rightarrow$$

$$H_2N \left[—(CH_2)_{10}—\underset{\underset{O}{\|}}{C}—\underset{\underset{H}{|}}{N}— \right]_x (CH_2)_{10}—COOH$$

This nylon is available commercially from France and is sold under the trade name Rilsan.

Nylon fiber is prepared by melting the bulk polymer with a controlled moisture content in the absence of oxygen and pumping the viscous melt through the holes of a spineret. The molten filaments are solidified by a flow of cooling air as they fall vertically from the spineret and are wound up on a bobbin.

The long polymer chains in the as-spun filaments are randomly arranged with very little orientation in line with the longitudinal axis of the filament. Accordingly, the filaments have little strength. A second step in the fiber manufacturing process accomplishes this objective by drawing or stretching the filaments about two to five times their original length. The polymer chains become oriented along the major axis of the filament with an accompanying decrease in filament diameter. In addition, it is possible to develop a relatively high degree of lateral order (crystallinity) of the polymer chains by heat or solvent treatments.

The filaments assume the cross-sectional configuration of the spineret hole which is usually circular, although nonround cross sections can be achieved. The drawing step leaves the circular cross-sectional configuration unchanged but it reduces the sharpness of a nonround cross section. For the most part, then, the paper industry has available to it nylon fibers with relatively smooth surfaces and circular cross sections (Figure 3.1).

The drawing operation is carried out on a large number of filaments collected together in a bundle called tow. After drawing, but in one continuous operation, the tow can be mechanically crimped and cut into lengths of 1.5 to 6 in. This cut product is called staple and is supplied to the textile industry. For the paper industry the fibers must be straight, and the crimping step is eliminated. Much shorter lengths are also required. Cutting is a critical step in papermaking, since a high proportion of long cuts or fused ends will lead to poor sheet formation.

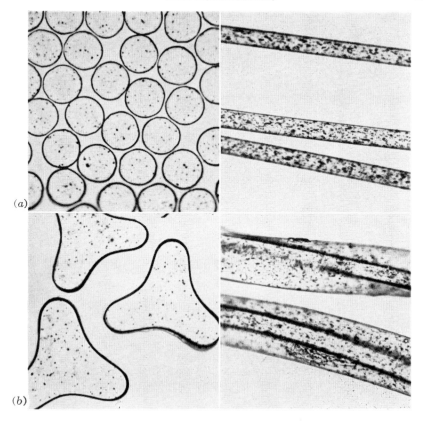

Figure 3.1. Cross sections of nylon filaments: (a) 3.1 denier per filament semi-dull luster, round; (b) 18 denier per filament semidull luster, trilobal.

PHYSICAL AND MECHANICAL PROPERTIES

Certain physical properties are dependent on polymer variables and processing conditions. These include tenacity, modulus, elongation, denier, cut length, and luster.

Denier, a common textile term, is the measure of yarn or filament size and is defined as the weight in grams of 9000 m. of the yarn. In actual practice, the weight of a measured length of a multifilament yarn bundle is determined and the denier of a single filament is calculated. The diameter of a filament is directly proportional to the square root of the denier. At constant denier the diameters of two filaments of different polymers are inversely proportional to the

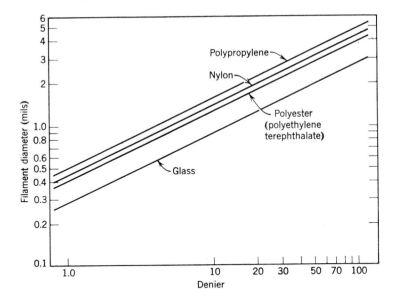

Figure 3.2.   Filament denier versus diameter.

square roots of these respective densities. This relationship is illustrated in Figure 3.2 in which the log of filament diameter is plotted against the log of filament denier for a number of different fibers. This relationship holds specifically for circular cross section filaments, and only the melt spun fibers are included.

A tabulation of the important physical properties of nylon fibers is given in Table 3.3. Since a wide variety of processing conditions is employed in the manufacture of nylon yarns, a wide range of physical properties can be developed. However, only the average properties of short-cut ($\frac{1}{8}$ to $\frac{3}{4}$ in.) fibers currently being supplied to the paper industry are given in this table.

The moisture regain of nylon compared with other man-made fibers over a range of relative humidities is given in Figure 3.3. When thoroughly wet, nylon absorbs about 9% water, and its tenacity falls to about 90% of its dry strength.

In comparison with other fibers, nylon is one of the strongest, and its great toughness provides high resistance to wear, flex, and abrasion. It has a low moisture absorption and excellent tensile and work recovery at elongations as high as 10%, as illustrated in Table 3.4.

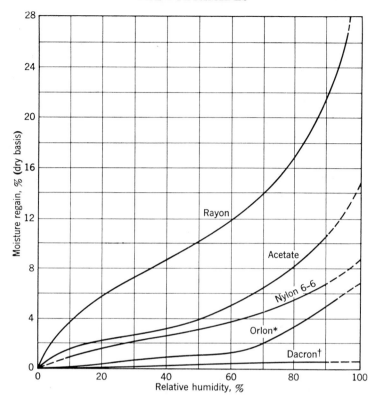

Figure 3.3. Moisture regain versus relative humidity of various fibers at 75°F.
* DuPont's registered trade mark for its acrylic fiber. † DuPont's registered
trademark for its polyester fiber.

Each sample was held at maximum elongation for 30 sec. at 60%
R.H. and 70°F. before it was allowed to relax.

CHEMICAL PROPERTIES

At room temperature nylon is quite resistant to attack by many
chemicals. The amide linkage is more susceptible to attack by acids
than by alkalis and this is especially evident at elevated temperatures. Nylon melts quite sharply at 480°F. (250°C.) and will ignite
at 989°F. (532°C.) but will not support combustion. It is subject to
oxidative degradation which is accelerated by heat and ultraviolet

TABLE 3.3
Physical Properties[1] of Nylon Fibers

Density	1.14 gm./cm^3.
Tenacity	
70°F. and 65% R.H.	4.1 gm./denier
70°F. and 93% R.H.	3.1 gm./denier
70°F. water	3.5 gm./denier
210°F. water	3.0 gm./denier
Break Elongation	
70°F. and 65% R.H.	61%
70°F. water	63%
Work-to-Break	
70°F. and 65% R.H.	1.62 gm. cm./denier cm.
70°F. water	1.33 gm. cm./denier cm.
Moisture Regain	
75°F. and 65% R.H.	4%

[1] Average properties of nylon fibers currently available for papermaking.

TABLE 3.4
Tensile and Work Recovery of Fibers

	Tensile Recovery (%)				Work Recovery (%)			
	% Elongation				% Elongation			
	1	3	5	10	1	3	5	10
Nylon	90	90	89	86	66	57	55	52
Dacron polyester fiber	98	79	65	51	82	49	35	24
Orlon acrylic fiber	89	66	51	—	63	33	20	—
Acetate	96	65	45	25	80	33	18	9
Rayon	72	40	31	25	49	14	14	10

light. This degradation occurs by rupture of the polymer chain and manifests itself by a discoloration (yellowing) of the fiber and loss in tenacity, elongation, and flex endurance (embrittlement).

A summary of the chemical resistance of nylon fiber is given in Table 3.5.

The amine and carboxylic acid groups present at the ends of the nylon polymer chains show the characteristic reactions of these groups. For example, the amine group reacts with acid dyestuffs to form a stable bond and similarly the carboxyl group can react with basic

TABLE 3.5

Chemical Resistance of Nylon Fiber

Chemical	Conditions			Effect On Tensile Strength (% loss)
	Concentration (%)	Temperature (°F.)	Time (hr.)	
HCl	1	70	1000	20
	10	70	10	20
	1	160	10	20
	37	70	0.1	Soluble
H₂SO₄	1	70	1000	20
	10	70	10	44
	1	250	1	33
	1	250	10	90
	70	70	0.1	Soluble
HNO₃	10	70	10	10
H₃PO₄	10	70	10	5
HCOOH	90	70	10	Soluble
NaOH	1	70	10	0
	10	70	10	0
	1	210	100	25
	10	210	10	5
	40	210	10	16
H₂O₂ pH-7	0.4	70	10	10
Organic solvents				(essentially unaffected)
Phenol	100	210	0.1	Soluble
Air (O₂)		250	100	31
		250	1000	37

dyestuffs. Cross-linking agents such as formaldehyde can convert nylon into an insoluble gel structure.

SHORT-CUT NYLON FIBERS

Nylon fibers for use by the paper industry are cut into short lengths to permit the attainment of good sheet formation. Long fibers tend to become entangled and to cause clumps in the final sheet. This entire subject of dispersion and web formation for papermaking has been treated quite broadly in Chapters 2 and 9, but suffice it to say that nylon fibers are cut to lengths of about $\frac{1}{8}$ to 1 in. The exact length is dependent on the denier, hence the stiffness of the fiber.

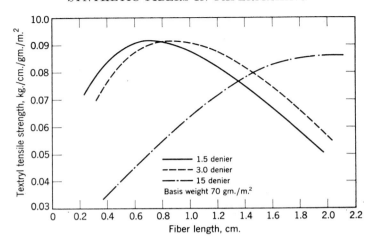

Figure 3.4.   Tensile strength versus fiber length for nylon textryls (3).

Using tensile strength of textryls* as a measurement of sheet uniformity, L. A. Auspos and E. B. Winn (2) developed data in Figure 3.4 for nylons of different denier and different cut lengths. These data were developed under conditions optimum for sheet formation; that is, low fiber consistencies (0.05%) and laboratory handsheets. The maxima for these curves are tabulated in Table 5.6 with calculations of the ratio of fiber length to diameter.

TABLE 3.6

Nylon Fiber l/d Ratio for Maximum Textryl Strength

Fiber Diameter and Length at Maximum Tensile Strength

Denier	Diameter (d) (cm.)	Length (l) (cm.)	l/d
1.5	13.6×10^{-4}	0.63	460
3	19.2×10^{-4}	0.94	490
6	27.2×10^{-4}	1.27	470
15	43.0×10^{-4}	1.90	440
		Average	465

Optimum sheet formation, hence optimum physical properties, is obtained for papers of 100% nylon fibers when the fibers have an l/d ratio of about 465. At higher ratios, that is, at greater lengths

* Textryl is a generic term for papers of synthetic fibers bonded with fibrids.

for a constant diameter, the fibers are more likely to bend and become entangled with one another and lead to poorer sheet formation. At lower ratios the fibers are shorter and cannot attain the higher sheet tensile strength, in part because of fewer bond points per fiber.

This relationship is affected by water viscosity (temperature) and fiber consistency. Because of the relationship of fiber diameter to denier, the optimum l/d ratio developed for nylon can be converted into a ratio of length in inches to filament denier.

$$\text{fiber length (inches)} = 0.2 \sqrt{\text{denier}}$$

This equation is the basis for the nylon fibers offered by the producers for sale to the paper industry. Although an unlimited range of cut lengths could be obtained for each denier, the following are currently available commercially:

1.5 denier, $\frac{1}{4}$-in. length	3.0 denier, $\frac{3}{8}$-in. length
6.0 denier, $\frac{1}{2}$-in. length	15.0 denier, $\frac{3}{4}$-in. length

In addition, special water-dispersing finishes are applied to the nylon fibers, for they are hydrophobic and would not otherwise disperse in water (3).

BINDER SYSTEMS

Some type of binder or adhesive is necessary to hold the nylon fibers together in a sheet structure, since nylon is not self-bonding as cellulose is. Nylon cannot be fibrillated by beating. In fact, beating or vigorous agitation of even a dilute suspension of nylon fibers can cause them to ball or rope together.

A number of different systems for bonding nylon fibers have been developed, but again they are treated lightly because the subject has been covered thoroughly in Chapter 9. One of the earliest systems (4,5) made use of hydrotropic salts, such as calcium thiocyanate, which in highly concentrated solutions are solvents for nylon. A waterleaf is impregnated with a dilute solution of the salt and the water is subsequently evaporated. The salt solution concentrates and tends to localize preferentially at the crossover point of the fibers. The surfaces of the fibers, swollen and partly dissolved, lead to a welding of the fibers. The practical difficulties associated with this technique are pointed out in Chapter 9, and there is no commercial application of salt bonding today.

A second more useful method employs synthetic polymers as bonding agents. Usually, these polymers are chemically similar to the fiber—for example, a polyamide binder for nylon papers. The technique involves impregnation of the waterleaf with a water dispersion of the polymer. The treated paper is then dried and the binder again seeks the cross-over points of the fiber matrix. The bonding process is completed by application of heat and pressure (160°C. and 200 p.s.i. for 30 seconds for a Type 8 polyamide). Another more practical version of this technique is the fibrid binder system (6) which leads to the maximum in nylon-paper properties. Still another method uses polyvinyl alcohol fibers as the bonding agent (7).

PAPERMAKING

Nylon fibers sold to the paper industry today are for the most part ready for use without further treatment. The fibers will readily disperse in water at room temperature with minimum agitation. Consistencies of the order of 0.5 to 1.0% are optimum to avoid fiber entanglement. The stock should not be passed through Jordans, disc mills, or similar refining equipment. Since the nylon-fiber stock drains so rapidly, the consistency is still further reduced to 0.05 to 0.1% in the headbox. Under these conditions, good sheet formation is possible with most standard papermaking equipment. An inclined wire Fourdrinier machine or a Rotoformer seems to give better formation with lightweight papers—basis weight, 5 to 15 lb.—but conventional flat wire Fourdriniers are handling 100% nylon papers successfully today.

For blends of nylon with cellulosic pulps, the nylon can be added to the beaten pulp in the beater or at the stock chest if sufficient agitation is available. Good sheet formation can be achieved with flat wire Fourdriniers or Rotoformers.

PROPERTIES OF PAPERS CONTAINING NYLON FIBERS

The physical and chemical properties of papers containing nylon fibers are strongly dependent on a number of factors, of which the most important are (1) the properties and relative proportions of the fiber and pulp components, (2) the type and extent of interfiber bonding, and (3) the presence of a saturating resin. In this section an attempt is made to show the effects of these variables on sheet properties.

First of all, let us consider papers in which the only fibrous material present is nylon, or what can be called 100% nylon papers. In Table 3.7 data are summarized on the properties of various nylon

TABLE 3.7
Properties of 100% Nylon Papers[1]

No.	Fiber Description	Binder Type	Binder Weight % of Final Paper	Basis Weight (gm./m.^{2})	Tensile Strength (lb./in.)	Elongation (%)	Tear Strength (gm.)	Burst Strength (p.s.i.)	MIT Fold Endurance	Treatment
1	Kraft control (wet strength)	—	—	85	12	3	280	35	1.2 m.	— (4)
2	3 d.p.f., $\frac{3}{8}$ in. nylon 66	ZnBr$_2$	10%	85	32	15	1056	67	52 m.	340°F. hot pressed (4)
3	3 d.p.f., $\frac{3}{8}$ in. nylon 66	T-8 nylon	5%	85	33	33	1228	88	700 m.	340°F. hot pressed (4)
4	3 d.p.f., $\frac{1}{4}$ in. nylon 66	Fibrid 101	15%	67	20	33	1021	110	>1.5 mm.	380°F. hot calendered (9)
5	3 d.p.f., $\frac{1}{4}$ in. nylon 66	Fibrid 101	30%	67	34	44	1226	144	>1.5 mm.	380°F. hot calendered (9)

[1] Papers Nos. 2 and 3 were made in the laboratory, whereas 1 and 2 were commercial grade papers and 4 and 5 were made on a 30-in. inclined-wire Fourdrinier at 50 ft./min.

71

papers reported in the literature. Examination of these data reveals that 100% nylon papers which are as much as four times stronger (tensile, tear, burst strength) than high-grade commercial kraft papers can be made. The best of these nylon papers is tougher than the best cellulosic papers by several orders of magnitude, as measured by flex endurance.

The best paper properties are obtained with a polyamide fibrid as a binder, the reasons for which are discussed in Chapter 9. A commercial nylon paper called Syntosil is reported as being used for maps and currency (8).

BASIS WEIGHT

The high strength of nylon makes it possible to produce lightweight but strong papers. Better strength and opacity are obtained with lower denier fibers. Auspos and Winn (2) developed the data shown in Figure 3.5 for nylon textryls, using 30% 101 fibrid binder.

The decrease in tensile strength as basis weight is decreased is explained by a decrease in the number of layers of fibers that are bonded together. The ultimate would be a single layer of fibers bonded only to others in the same plane. With multiple layers of fibers, most are bonded to those in adjoining layers, thereby greatly increasing sheet strength.

Further consideration of these data led to the conclusion that

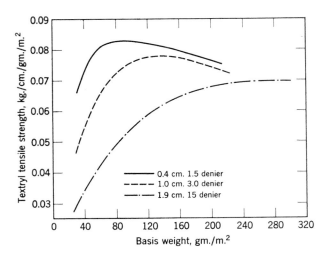

Figure 3.5.   Tensile strength versus basis weight for nylon textryls (3).

maximum nylon textryl strength is achieved when the basis weight is 6.7×10^4 times the fiber diameter at optimum l/d. This is illustrated in Table **3.8**.

TABLE 3.8

Ratio of Basis Weight (B) to Fiber Diameter (d) for
Nylon Textryls of Maximum Tensile Strength

| Fiber | | Basis Weight (B) at Maximum Tensile | |
Denier	d, cm.	Strength (g.s.m.)	B/d
1.5	13.6×10^{-4}	90	6.6×10^4
3.0	19.2×10^{-4}	134	7.0×10^4
6.0	27.2×10^{-4}	190	7.0×10^4
15.0	43.0×10^{-4}	270	6.3×10^4
		Average	6.7×10^4

TEAR STRENGTH

An outstanding property of nylon papers is tear strength. Tear strengths higher than those displayed by certain woven cotton fabrics have been achieved. As might be expected, tear strength is quite dependent on fiber length (see Figure 3.6) and type and amount of binder. In Table 3.9 are summarized some pertinent data taken from published literature (9). Various test methods for tear strength were considered at an ASTM symposium in 1958 (10), and valuable data on nylon papers have been reported.

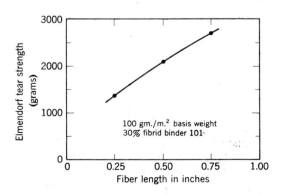

Figure 3.6.   Effect of fiber length on tear strength of nylon textryl.

TABLE 3.9
Tear Strength of Various Papers

Paper	Basis Weight (gm./m.^{2})	Elmendorf Tear Strength (gm.)
High wet-strength kraft	56	72
Nylon		
1.5 d.p.f., $\frac{1}{4}$ in.	100	637
3.0 d.p.f., $\frac{3}{8}$ in.	100	1035
15.0 d.p.f., $\frac{3}{4}$ in.	100	2720
Cotton fabric[1]	100	1092

[1] Dress goods sample (construction plays an important role in determining fabric properties).

NYLON FIBER—CELLULOSIC-PULP BLEND PAPERS

The most important commercial papers containing nylon fibers produced in the United States today are blends of nylon with cellulosic pulp (mainly wood). This is largely because these papers cost considerably less than 100% nylon papers, hence are better able to compete for markets with other paper, fabrics, and films. Generally, the sheet is saturated with a resin off the paper machine, but binder resins can be and are added to the stock chest (11, 12). A binder of some sort must be used because of an almost complete lack of bonding of the nylon fibers either with themselves or with the cellulosic-pulp fibers. Even with the best of binders, the great dissimilarities in fiber properties do lead to values at certain blend levels which are lower than those of either of the two homo-fiber sheets.

As mentioned in Chapter 9, wood pulp is a good binder for nylon fiber in the wet waterleaf, and completely satisfactory paper-machine performance can be achieved with a minimum of 5 to 10% of cellulosic pulp in the blend (13).

In Table 3.10 is a summary of some of the properties of nylon-cellulosic-pulp blend papers reported by McLeod (14) in 1958. The influence of nylon-fiber content on these same four key physical properties is nicely illustrated in Figures 3.7 and 3.8, taken from the literature (15). These data were developed on handsheets made in the laboratory with 1.5 d.p.f., $\frac{1}{4}$ in. and wood pulp. The sheets were dried, treated with a polyamide dispersion so that 22% by weight of the final sheet in every case was binder, and cured at 160°C. and at

TABLE 3.10
Some Properties of Nylon-Cellulosic Blend Papers[1] (14)

Paper Composition	Basis Weight (gm./m.²)	Tensile Strength (lb./in.)	Burst Strength (p.s.i.)	Elmendorf Tear Strength (gm.)	MIT Fold Endurance
40% nylon/40% rag/20% acrylic dispersion	84	23/17	50/30	168/108	40,000/13,500
High wet strength map paper	89	44/25	50/30	85/94	1,410/1,300

[1] The properties are given in both machine and cross-machine directions; for example, tensile of 23/17 lb./in. means 23 lb./in. in machine direction and 17 lb./in. in cross direction.

200 p.s.i. The 100% wood-pulp sheets were also treated with the binder in the same manner.

Examination of these data reveals that fold endurance and tear strength increased directly and substantially with increasing nylon fiber content. This is not the case for tensile strength and burst strength which show minimum values in the curves. Similar data have been developed by the Société de la Viscose Suisse in Switzer-

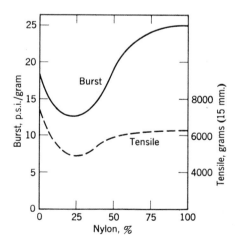

Figure 3.7. Physical properties. Nylon pulp blends—22% polyamide binder (3.8-gm. handsheets).

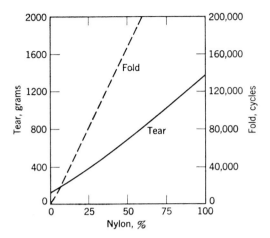

Figure 3.8. Physical properties. Nylon pulp blends—22%, polyamide binder (3.8-gm. handsheets) (16).

land (16) and by Papeterie de France (17) with Rilsan. The Japanese have also been active in studying the properties of nylon-cellulosic-pulp blend papers (18).

The direct improvement in fold endurance and tear strengths is explained on the basis that fiber length is the principal factor affecting these sheet properties and interfiber bonding is of minor importance. Clark (19, 20) has shown that the following relationship exists.

$$\text{tear strength} = k\frac{L^{1.5}}{d}$$

in which L = weighted average length of pulp fiber
d = density of sheet
k = constant

Since the nylon fibers are considerably longer (roughly three times) than the cotton fibers, the tear strength of the sheet goes up rapidly as the nylon content is increased. Fold endurance is also related to fiber, as is evident in the superior fold endurance of rag papers over kraft.

Before broad sweeping conclusions are drawn on the tensile and burst-strength properties of blend papers developed in Figure 3.7, previously unpublished data (21) in which a more effective binder

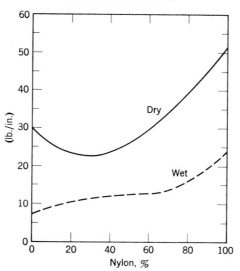

Figure 3.9. Nylon-kraft paper blends.

system is employed should be examined. Using a polyamide fibrid binder, workers at Du Pont have developed the data shown in Figures 3.9 and 3.10. Here minima are evident in both curves, but the tensile strength of the 60% nylon–40% pulp blend sheet is equivalent to that of the 100% pulp sheet, and with increasing nylon content the

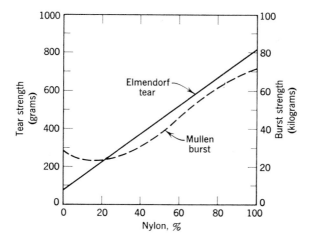

Figure 3.10. Nylon-kraft paper blends (22).

TABLE 3.11
Properties of Resin-Saturated Nylon/Pulp Blend Papers

Paper Composition	Basis Weight (gm./m.²)	Tensile Strength (lb./in.)		Elongation (%)	Toughness (in. lb./in.²)	Elmendorf Tear (gm.)	Burst Strength (p.s.i.)	MIT Fold Endurance (cycles)
		Dry	Wet					
100% sulfite (Freeness 590)	55	16/9	0.4/0.3	1.9/3.1	0.21/0.21	110/102	18	15
77% sulfite/23% Rhoplex B-15[1]	71	23/17	9.0/6.5	4.7/5.6	0.72/0.66	59/63	41	1,500
70% sulfite/30% nylon, 15 d.p.f., $\frac{3}{4}$ in.	55	8/5	0.3/0.2	1.5/2.6	0.09/0.11	164/164	13	—
58% sulfite/25% nylon, 15 d.p.f., $\frac{3}{4}$ in./17% "Hycar" 1577 resin[2]	64	15/14	4.9/4.1	3.2/5.3	0.38/0.57	530/495	34	10,000
55% sulfite/22% nylon, 15 d.p.f., $\frac{3}{4}$ in./23% Rhoplex B-15 resin	69	13/11	5.4/4.8	4.5/7.8	0.55/0.67	601/570	40	2,500
55% sulfite/22% nylon, 15 d.p.f., $\frac{3}{4}$ in./23% Rhoplex HA-8 resin[3]	69	12/8	5.5/3.7	5.5/7.1	0.52/0.49	601/82	34	700
70% sulfite[4]/30% nylon, 3 d.p.f., $\frac{1}{4}$ in.	55	6/4	0.1/0.1	1.4/2.8	0.07/0.07	91/77	8	2–3
55% sulfite/22% nylon, 3 d.p.f., $\frac{1}{4}$ in./23% Rhoplex B-15 resin	69	13/11	7.4/6.0	7/10	0.81/0.93	0.25/0.25	39	2,900

[1] Rhoplex B-15 is Rohm & Haas' trademark for its polyacrylate dispersion.
[2] "Hycar" 1577 is B. F. Goodrich's trademark for its butadiene/acrylonitrile dispersion.
[3] Rhoplex HA-8 is Rohm & Haas' trademark for its polyacrylate dispersion.
[4] Freeness 630.

tensile strength continues to increase, eventually reaching a value of 51 lb. for the 100% nylon sheet. The minimum in the burst-strength curve is not so pronounced as it was in the earlier work (Figure 3.7). It is apparent that there is a lot to be learned about the mechanism of interfiber bonding in synthetic fiber-cellulosic-pulp blend systems.

Resin saturation of a nylon-pulp blend paper after the paper has been formed and dried is another common method for obtaining interfiber bonding. A recent study (21) of resin-saturated papers of nylon and cellulosic pulp pointed out the importance of the resin to the properties of the structure. For nylon blends the preferred resins as far as paper strength is concerned included polyacrylates, melamine-formaldehyde resins, polyamide resins, and polyvinyl acetate. The choice among these classes of resins can be based on considerations other than strength; that is, softness, stiffness, and electrical properties. Some data from these laboratory studies are given in Table 3.11.

The papers were prepared by adding the nylon fibers to the refined pulp under conditions of good agitation. Consistencies in the range of 1 to 2% are satisfactory. On commercial equipment, open impeller pumps are used to transfer the stock mixture, for the long synthetic fibers clog the closed impeller type. Screens and other stock cleaners should be bypassed to prevent plugging by the nylon.

The nylon-plus-resin binder improved significantly the wet tensile strength, elongation, toughness, tear strength, and fold endurance of the softwood pulp paper. The only property sacrificed by the incorporation of nylon fibers was the dry tensile strength. The tear strength and fold endurance of the nylon-reinforced paper are high enough to permit the paper to be useful for certain textile applications in which the resin is important to the aesthetics of the structure. Papers of this type are of growing interest to industry and are opening up new markets for products made on papermaking equipment.

REFERENCES

1. *Polymer Processes,* Chapter 7, Interscience Publishers, 1953.
2. L. A. Auspos and E. B. Winn, *TAPPI,* **45,** 741–744 (1962).
3. U. S. Patent 2,869,435.
4. J. K. Hubbard, F. H. Koontz, J. R. McCartney, and R. A. A, Hentschel, *TAPPI* **38,** 257–261 (1955).
5. U. S. Patent 2,869,973.
6. U. S. Patent 2,999,788.
7. Parapu Kami, *Koggo Zasshi,* No. 1, 44–46 (1958).
8. *Textil-Rundschau,* **15,** 674, 677 (1960).

9. New Product Technical Information, NP-19 Du Pont Technical Service Section Publication, December 1960.
10. F. H. Koontz and J. K. Owens, *ASTM* Special Publication No. 241, 14–25 (1958).
11. U. S. Patent 2,653,870 (1953).
12. U. S. Patent 3,057,772 (1962).
13. Canadian Patent 599,158 (1960).
14. G. L. McLeod, *TAPPI,* **41,** 430–433 (1958).
15. J. R. Emery, J. D. Howell, S. Sands, *TAPPI,* **39,** 781–786 (1956).
16. *Textil-Rundschau,* **13,** 721–722 (1958).
17. French Patent 1,198,190 (1959).
18. Insatsu Kyoku, *Kenkyusho Hokoku,* No. 1, 13–18 (1957).
19. J. d'A. Clark, Paper Trade J., 115, No. 26: T. S. 328 (1942)
20. J. d'A. Clark, Paper Trade J., 116, No. 1: T. S. 1 (1943).
21. Unpublished data from the Du Pont Company.

4

THE POLYESTERS

DOUGLAS G. BANNERMAN

Market Development Manager
Textile Fibers Department
E. I. du Pont de Nemours & Co., Inc.
Wilmington, Delaware

Polyester fibers had their origin in the basic work of Dr. W. H. Carothers. Two of his first U. S. patents (2,071,250 and 2,071,251) granted in 1937 broadly cover all superpolyesters. Picking up these early leads, J. R. Whinfield and J. F. Dickson of Calico Printers Association, Ltd., between 1939 and 1941 developed the first commercial polyester fiber from ethylene glycol and terephthalic acid.

The rights to manufacture this fiber were sold to Imperial Chemical Industries (I.C.I.) and the trademark Terylene was adopted. E. I. du Pont de Nemours & Co. bought the United States patent rights and after 10 years of research and development opened up a commercial plant in 1953. Dacron* was established as its trademark.

Since then, several other polyester fibers have been introduced and a summary of world producers is given in Table 4.1. These fibers are not all identical chemically, but most, if not all, are based on aromatic or cycloaliphatic dibasic acids and aliphatic glycols. Polyester fibers are growing rapidly in importance (see Table 3.1) because of their versatility.

MANUFACTURING METHODS

Polyester fibers are prepared by condensation polymerization in a manner roughly similar to the preparation of 66 nylon. In polyethylene terephthalate an excess of ethylene glycol is reacted with

---

* Du Pont Registered Trademark.

TABLE 4.1
World Producers of Polyester Fibers[1]

Country and Producer	Trade Name
Argentina	
Duperial	Terylene
Forti	
Petroquimica	Dicrolene
Sudamtex	Acrocel
Brazil	
Rhodiaceta	Tergal
Canada	
Canadian Industries Ltd.	Terylene
France	
Rhodiaceta	Tergal
West Germany	
Hoechst	Trevira
Glanzstoff	Diolen
Huls	Vestan
Spinnfaser	Diolen
India	
Chemicals & Fibers Ltd.	Terylene
Israel	
Rogosin Industries	Vycron
Italy	
Rhodiatoce	Terital
Japan	
Teikoku	Teijin-Tetoron
Toyo Rayon	Toray-Tetoron
Nippon Rayon	
Toyo Spinning	
Kurashiki	
Netherlands	
AKU	Terlenda
Spain	
Safa	Teriber
La Seda	Enkalene
United Kingdom	
I.C.I.	Terylene
United States	
Du Pont	Dacron
Enka	
Celanese	Fortrel
Eastman	Kodel
Beaunit	Vycron

[1] Free world only.

dimethyl terephthalate in the presence of a catalyst and at elevated temperatures first of all to exchange glycol with methanol (Equation

$$H_3COOC\!-\!\langle\ \rangle\!-\!COOCH_3 + 2HOCH_2CH_2OH \rightarrow 2CH_3OH$$

(1)

$$+HOCH_2CH_2OOC\!-\!\langle\ \rangle\!-\!COOCH_2CH_2OH$$

$$\underset{\text{catalyst}}{\overset{\Delta}{\downarrow}}\!-\!HOCH_2CH_2OH$$ (2)

$$HO\!-\!\Big[\!-\!CH_2CH_2OOC\!-\!\langle\ \rangle\!-\!COO\!-\!\Big]_x\!-\!CH_2CH_2OH$$

1) and then eliminate glycol (Equation 2). To promote the attainment of desirably high molecular weights, the polymerization is carried out in the absence of oxygen under very low pressures (less than 1 mm. Hg) (1).

Polyester fibers are prepared and spun by procedures similar to those used for nylon (see Chapter 3). The bulk polymer is melted in the absence of oxygen and moisture and the viscous melt is pumped through the holes of a spinneret. The molten filaments are solidified by a flow of cooling air as they fall vertically from the spinneret and are wound up on a bobbin.

The long polymer chains in the as-spun filaments are randomly arranged with very little orientation in line with the longitudinal axis of the filament. Accordingly, the filaments have little strength. A second step in the fiber manufacturing process accomplishes this objective by drawing or stretching the filaments about two to five times their original length. The polymer chains become oriented, with an accompanying decrease in filament diameter, along the major axis of the filament. In addition, it is possible to develop a relatively high degree of lateral order (crystallinity) of the polymer chains by heat or solvent treatments.

The filaments assume the cross-sectional configuration of the spinneret hole, which is usually circular, although nonround cross sections can be achieved. The drawing step leaves the circular cross-sectional configuration unchanged, but it reduces the sharpness of a nonround cross section. For the most part, then, the paper industry has available to it polyester fibers with relatively smooth surfaces and circular cross sections (Figure 4.1).

The drawing operation for polyester fibers is carried out on a large number of filaments collected together in a bundle called tow. After drawing, but in one continuous operation, the tow can be mechani-

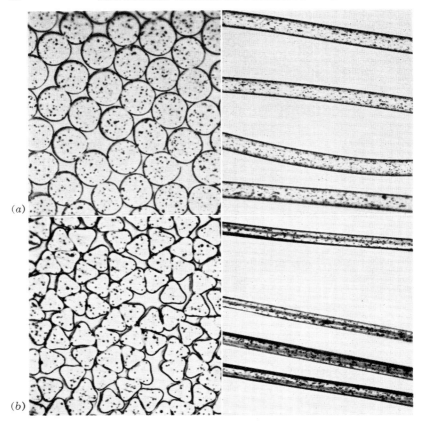

Figure 4.1. Polyester fibers. (a) 3.0 denier per filament semidull luster, round. (b) 1.4 denier per filament semidull luster, trilobal.

cally crimped and cut into lengths of 1.5 to 6 in. This cut product is called staple and is supplied to the textile industry. For the paper industry the fibers must be straight, and the crimping step is eliminated. Much shorter lengths are also required. Cutting polyester fibers is a critical step in papermaking, for a high proportion of long cuts or fused ends will lead to poor sheet formation.

PHYSICAL AND MECHANICAL PROPERTIES

As in nylon fibers, certain physical properties are dependent on polymer variables and processing conditions. Both continuous filament and staple polyester yarns are produced, and the different processing conditions give rise to different physical properties. Since the fiber supplied to the paper industry is made by the staple route, the average physical properties of the short-cut ($\frac{1}{8}$- to $\frac{3}{4}$-in.) staple product are given in Table 4.2.

TABLE 4.2
Physical Properties[1] of Polyester Fiber

Density	1.38 gm./cm.^{3}
Tenacity	
70°F. and 65% R.H.	3.8 gm./denier
70°F. and 93% R.H.	4.0 gm./denier
70°F. water	4.1 gm./denier
210°F. water	2.9 gm./denier
Break Elongation	
70°F. and 65% R.H.	45%
70°F. water	48%
Work-to-Break	
70°F. and 65% R.H.	1.03 gm. cm./denier cm.
70°F. water	1.25 gm. cm./denier cm.
Moisture Regain	
75°F. and 65% R.H.	0.4%

[1] Average properties of Dacron polyester fibers currently available for papermaking.

The extreme toughness of Dacron polyester fiber is best illustrated in its high value of work-to-break (cotton has a work-to-break of about 0.1 gm. cm/denier cm. at 70°F. and 65% R.H.). The polyester fibers generally have higher initial moduli (less stretch at equivalent stress) than the nylon fibers. Dacron exhibits good recovery from stress, although not quite so good as nylon (see Table 3.4).

The moisture regain of polyester fibers is extremely low (see Figure 3.3) and is reflected in a high degree of insensitivity of the fiber to water. The wet strength of the fiber is essentially equivalent to its dry strength and the dimensional stability of the fiber is outstanding. In Table 4.3 data are summarized on the increase in length of various preshrunk fibers resulting from an increase in relative humidity from 0 to 100% at room temperature. The fibers returned to their original lengths when conditioned again at 0% R.H.

TABLE 4.3
Effect of Relative Humidity on Fiber Length

Fiber	Average Per Cent Increase in Length of Samples Tested[1] (0 to 100% R.H.)
Rayon	3.4
Nylon	2.4
Acetate	2.1
Orlon[2] acrylic fiber	0.3
Cotton	0.2
Dacron polyester fiber	0.1
Glass	

[1] In some cases significant differences were noted with different samples o the same fiber.

[2] Du Pont Registered Trademark.

CHEMICAL PROPERTIES

The ester linkage is more susceptible to attack by alkalis than the amide linkage, but conversely it is more resistant to attack by acids. Polyesters of aromatic or alicyclic dibasic acids are among the stablest and, for this reason, plus a high melting point, polyethylene terephthalate and its close relatives are commercially successful synthetic polymers for fibers, films, and plastics.

The polyesters as a class are quite resistant to oxidative degradation, whether catalyzed by heat or ultraviolet light. Polyester fibers are comparatively difficult to dye because of the absence of reactive chemical groupings in the molecule. Terminal carboxyl or hydroxyl groups are reactive, but the concentration of these groups is low. A summary of the chemical properties of polyester fibers is given in Table 4.4.

SHORT-CUT POLYESTER FIBERS

Polyester fibers for use by the paper industry, are cut into short lengths, generally ranging from $\frac{1}{4}$- to $\frac{3}{4}$-in., in order to obtain good sheet formation. Good sheet formation is essential to the attainment of maximum physical and mechanical properties of paper, and the latest technology developed for synthetic-fiber web formation is discussed in Chapter 9 of this book. Since certain paper properties, such as tensile strength, are also dependent on fiber length, a balance must be sought between the two opposing requirements; that is, shorter lengths for better sheet uniformity and longer lengths for

TABLE 4.4

Chemical Resistance of Polyester Fiber[1]

	Conditions			
				Effect on
Chemical	Concentration (%)	Temperature (°F.)	Time (hr.)	Tensile Strength (% loss)
HCl	1	70	1000	3
	10	70	1000	13
	37	70	0.1	7
	37	160	10	20
H_2SO_4	70	70	100	0
HNO_3	10	70	10	0
NaOH	1	70	10	0
	10	70	10	0
	40	70	10	0
	1	210	10	16
	1	210	100	70
H_2O_2 (pH-7)	0.4	160	10	0
Organic solvents		(essentially unaffected)		
Phenol	100	210	0.1	Soluble
Air (O_2)	—	250	1000	7
	—	350	100	12

[1] All of these data were determined for Dacron polyester fiber.

better tensile strength. Auspos and Winn (2) have studied the effect of fiber length on the tensile strength of papers of 100% Dacron polyester fiber (Figure 4.2) and have showed that the maximum paper strength is reached by a constant ratio of fiber length to diameter (Table 4.5).

TABLE 4.5

Polyester Fiber l/d Ratio for Maximum Textryl Tensile Strength

Fiber Diameter and Length at Maximum Tensile Strength

Denier	Diameter (d) (cm.)	Length (l) (cm.)	Ratio (l/d)
1.5	12.4×10^{-4}	0.63	510
3.0	17.5×10^{-4}	0.94	540
6.0	24.8×10^{-4}	1.27	515
		Average	520

In Figure 4.2 it can be seen that sheet tensile strength increases rapidly as fiber length increases from 0.3 cm.; it then reaches a maximum value before falling off, quite sharply in the case of 1.5-denier-

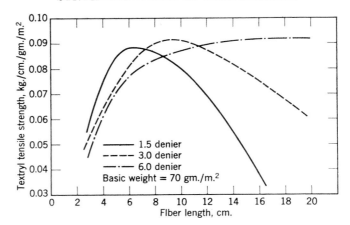

Figure 4.2.   Tensile strength versus fiber length for textryls of Dacron (3).

per-filament Dacron.   These parabolic curves are explained as follows. Under constant papermaking conditions sheet formation progressively deteriorates with added fiber flexibility, which is, in turn, a function of fiber length at constant diameter.   Sheet tensile strength improves with fiber length but, since it is an average measurement of many fibers, it is dependent on sheet uniformity.   As fiber length continues to increase, imperfections in the sheet appear and tensile strength begins to fall off solely because of the presence of weak spots in the sheet associated with nonuniform fiber formation.   Maximum tensile strength is the same for all filament deniers, but the maximum value is attained at different cut lengths.

The l/d ratio calculated in Table 4.5 is affected by water viscosity (temperature) and fiber consistency.   Because of the relationship of fiber diameter to denier, the optimum l/d ratio developed for Dacron polyester fiber can be converted into a ratio of length in inches to filament denier.   This turns out to be the same as that developed for nylon.

$$\text{Fiber length (inches)} = 0.2 \sqrt{\text{denier}}$$

This experimentally determined ratio is the basis for the polyester fibers offered by the producers for sale to the paper industry.

1.5 denier, $\frac{1}{4}$-in. length
3.0 denier, $\frac{3}{8}$-in. length
6.0 denier, $\frac{1}{2}$-in. length

BINDER SYSTEMS

Some type of binder or adhesive is necessary to hold the polyfibers together in a sheet structure, since they are not self-bonding as cellulose is. In this respect polyester fibers are similar to nylon. For further discussion of this general subject the reader is referred to Chapter 9 and to the section on binder systems in Chapter 3 of this book.

PAPERMAKING

Polyester fibers sold to the paper industry are generally ready for use without further treatment. They should be handled in a manner identical to that of nylon fibers of comparable denier and cut length. The fibers will readily disperse in water at room temperature with minimum agitation. Consistencies of the order of 0.5 to 1.0% are optimum to avoid fiber entanglement (3). The stock should not be passed through Jordans, disc mills, or similar refining equipment. Since the polyester fiber stock drains so rapidly, the consistency is still further reduced to 0.05 to 0.1% in the headbox. Under these conditions good sheet formation is possible with most standard papermaking equipment. An inclined wire Fourdrinier machine or a Rotoformer seem to give better formation with lightweight papers (basis weight, 5 to 15 lb.), but conventional flat-wire Fourdriniers are handling 100% polyester-fiber papers successfully today.

For blends of polyester fibers with cellulosic pulps, the polyester fiber can be added to the beaten pulp in the beater or at the stock chest if sufficient agitation is available. Good sheet formation can be achieved with either flat-wire Fourdriniers or Rotoformers.

PROPERTIES OF PAPERS CONTAINING POLYESTER FIBERS

Papers of 100% polyester-fiber composition, excluding binder, and those consisting of blends of polyester fibers with cellulosic pulps are in limited commercial production today (4). Obviously, papers of 100% polyester fibers are strongly dependent on the binder, and this is clearly shown in Table 4.6. The best values are obtained with 25% polyester fibrid (see Chapter 2). Papers of 100% polyester fiber are almost as strong as those of nylon and actually compare favorably with nylon in most physical properties. The elongation is lower, which again is a direct reflection of the lower elongation of the fiber.

TABLE 4.6
Properties of Papers of 100% Polyester Fibers

Paper	Binder	Basis Weight (gm./m.^{2})	Tensile Strength (lb./in.)	Elongation (%)	Tear Strength (gm.)	Burst Strength (p.s.i.)	MIT Fold Endurance
Kraft (6)	—	67	12	3	280	35	1,200
100% Dacron, 2 d.p.f., $\frac{1}{2}$ in. (6)	10% Mg(CNS)$_2$	83	22	8	384	132	68,000
100% Dacron, 3 d.p.f., $\frac{1}{4}$ in. (7)	25% 201 fibrid	100	46	33	680	156	—

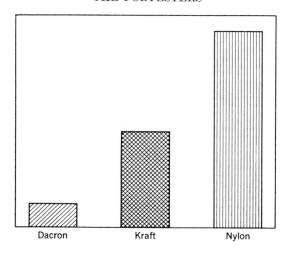

Figure 4.3. Hygroexpansivity of synthetic-fiber papers (6).

In addition to being about equal to nylon in most physical and mechanical properties, papers of 100% polyester fiber have several important advantages. Perhaps the most outstanding are related to the low moisture absorption of polyester fibers, which is reflected in superior wet strengths and dimensional stability. These properties are illustrated in Table 4.7 and Figure 4.3, respectively.

TABLE 4.7
Dry and Wet Strengths of Synthetic-Fiber Papers

Paper	Binder	Basis Weight (gm./m.^{2})	Tensile Strength[1] (lb./in.)		Ratio Wet/Dry
			Dry	Wet	
Kraft	—	100	25	2	0.08
High wet strength map paper	—	89	35	13	0.37
Nylon, 3 d.p.f.– $\frac{1}{4}$ in.	30% fibrid 101	100	51	28	0.55
Dacron polyester fiber, 3 d.p.f.– $\frac{1}{4}$ in.	25% fibrid 201	100	46	42	0.91

[1] Average of machine and cross directions.

Papers of 100% Dacron polyester fiber bonded with polyester fibrid 201 retain 91% of their dry strength when wet at room temperature, whereas nylon paper bonded with polyamide fibrid 101 retains only 55% of its dry strength. This is obviously orders of magnitude better than cellulosic papers (8% retention of dry strength when wet) even if treated with a good wet-strength resin (37% retention). These high values of wet strength are also a reflection of the excellent bonding of the fibers by the synthetic polymers (fibrids).

The hygroexpansivity data plotted in Figure 4.3 show that papers containing polyester fibers, specifically textryls of Dacron, are extremely stable to changes in relative humidity compared to kraft or nylon papers. Over wider ranges of humidities this same general relationship also holds. The dimensional stability of polyester fiber paper is useful in maps, apparel interlinings, electrical insulation, computer tapes, and tracing paper.

The resistance of polyester fibers to attack by certain chemicals is carried over into paper. With an equally resistant binder, papers of polyester fibers are unaffected or only slightly affected by solutions of many common acids. For example (5) a textryl of Dacron composed of 75% 3-denier, $\frac{1}{4}$-in. Dacron and 25% polyester fibrid 201 showed no loss in tensile strength after exposure for one week at 122°F. in 10% solutions of hydrochloric acid, nitric acid, and hydrogen peroxide. On the other hand, it was disintegrated completely by a similar exposure in a 10% sodium hydroxide solution.

Another important property of polyesters is good electrical insulation. Fibers of polyester polymers such as Mylar* polyester film are widely used for electrical insulation because of the combination of good electrical properties—for example, high dielectric strength—and outstanding mechanical toughness. Papers of Dacron polyester fiber impregnated with anhydride-cured epoxy resins are in commercial production today (8).

POLYESTER FIBER–CELLULOSIC PULP BLEND PAPERS

Polyester fibers are used in blends with cellulosic pulp almost solely for the purpose of imparting improved dimensional stability to the sheet. Although other properties of pulp sheets, such as tear strength and fold endurance, can be significantly improved by adding long polyester fibers, these same improvements can be effected just as easily and even somewhat better with nylon fibers. The work of McLeod (9) and the data given in Table 4.8 abstracted from his

* Du Pont Registered trademark.

TABLE 4.8

Properties of Polyester Fiber[1]-Cellulosic Pulp Blend Papers (9)

Paper	Basis Weight (gm./M.²)	Tensile Strength (lb./in.)	Tear Strength (Gm.)	Fold Endurance (cycles)	Expansivity per 15% R.H. Change (% maximum)
High wet strength map paper	89	44/25	85/94	1,410/1,300	0.07/0.21
40% Dacron/40% rag/20% acrylic binder	98	27/22	151/14	14,300/11,300	0.06/0.10
40% nylon/40% rag/20% acrylic binder	85	23/17	168/108	40,000/13,500	0.20/0.28

[1] Dacron polyester fiber.

TABLE 4.9
Properties of Resin-Saturated Polyester-Cellulosic Pulp Blend Papers (10)

	Basis Weight (gm./m.²)	Tensile Strength (lb./in.)		Elongation (%)	Toughness (in. lb./in.²)	Elmendorf Tear (gm.)	Burst Strength (p.s.i.)	MIT Fold Endurance (cycles)
		Dry	Wet					
100% sulfite (Freeness 555)	50	17/10	0.36/0.30	2.1/3.3	0.285/0.247	104/114	20	100
70% sulfite/30% Dacron, 6 d.p.f.—½ in.	58	10/9	0.29/0.25	1.6/2.2	0.120/0.147	231/245	19	25
91% sulfite/9% Everflex A resin[1]	53	24/19	2.5/2.4	2.6/4.3	0.500/0.630	91/86	36	260
64% sulfite/27% Dacron, 6 d.p.f.—½ in./9% Everflex A resin	56	17/16	3.3/2.9	2.6/3.4	0.368/0.430	326/372	36	25,000
64% sulfite/27% Dacron, 6 d.p.f.—½ in./9% Hycar 1577 resin[2]	49	12/10	3.4/3.2	2.8/2.5	0.264/0.199	365/300	35	120
64% sulfite/27% Dacron, 6 d.p.f.—½ in./9% Rhoplex AC 200 resin[3]	56	13/11	1.7/2.1	4.6/3.0	0.195/0.188	363/344	24	300

[1] Everflex A resin is a trademark of Dewey & Almy.
[2] Hycar 1577 resin is B. F. Goodrich's trademark for its butadiene/acrylonitrile dispersion.
[3] Rhoplex AC 200 resin is Rohm & Haas's trademark for its acrylate dispersion.

article readily show this. More recent unpublished data (10) from experiments using more effective resin binders but still following the procedure of saturating the dried waterleaf are tabulated in Table 4.9. These data were obtained by using longer fibers ($\frac{1}{2}$-in. 6 d.p.f.), and higher values would certainly be expected, especially in tear strength and fold endurance. Examination of the data clearly shows the need for an effective binder, since the second example, which contains no resin, is deficient in all properties except tear strength when compared with a 100% sulfite pulp sheet.

The reader should compare the data in this table with that reported for nylon-pulp blend sheets in Table 3.11. It is apparent that the selection of resin is very important. Generally speaking, nylon is a somewhat more effective reinforcing agent than Dacron polyester fiber as far as these mechanical and physical properties are concerned. However, as stated in the introduction to this section, the greatest contribution of Dacron, and perhaps the sole justification for its use over nylon, is to impart substantially improved stability of the paper to changes in relative humidity. McLeod demonstrated this stability, and again more recent unpublished data confirm it (Table 4.10).

TABLE 4.10

Hygroexpansivity of Dacron-Cellulosic Pulp Blend Papers (10)

Paper Composition			Hygroexpansivity (% length change)	
			Conditioned to Low	Low to High 10% to
% Pulp	% Dacron	% Resin	50 to 10% R.H.	90% R.H.
Blend kraft (450 Freeness)	6 d.p.f., $\frac{3}{4}$ in.			
100	0	0	0.158	0.425
80	0	20% Rhoplex HA-12[1]	0.146	0.365
75	25	0	0.111	0.204
60	20	20% Rhoplex HA-12	0.109	0.183
60	20	20% Rhoplex HA-8[2]	0.058	0.167
60	20	20% Hycar 1561[3]	0.051	0.114

[1] Rhoplex HA-12 is Rohm & Haas's trademark for its acrylate dispersion.
[2] Rhoplex HA-8 is Rohm & Haas's trademark for its acrylate dispersion.
[3] Hycar 1561 is B. F. Goodrich's trademark for its butadiene/acrylonitrile dispersion.

REFERENCES

1. *Polymer Processes*, Chapter 7, Interscience Publishers, 1953.
2. L. A. Auspos and E. B. Winn, *TAPPI*, **45**, 741–744 (1962).

3. German Patent 1,130,685 (1960).
4. H. F. Arledter, *TAPPI,* **39,** 299–303 (1956).
5. New Product Technical Information, NP-19 Du Pont Technical Service Section Publication, December 1960.
6. J. K. Hubbard, F. H. Koontz, J. R. McCartney, and R. A. A. Hentschel, *TAPPI,* **38,** 257–261 (1955).
7. R. A. A. Hentschel, *TAPPI* **44,** 22–26 (1961).
8. G. R. Traut, R. C. Berry, and N. L. Greenman, *Mater. Design Eng.,* **55,** 12–13 (1962).
9. G. L. McCleod, *TAPPI,* **41,** 430–433 (1958).
10. Unpublished data from the laboratories of the Du Pont Company.

5

GLASS FIBERS

GAMES SLAYTER

Vice President, Research
Owens-Corning Fiberglas Corporation
Granville, Ohio

Glass fibers, one of the more unusual man-made fibers now being used commercially to prepare special papers, are inert, or insensitive, to most outside influences; they will neither rot nor burn; they do not absorb moisture, and they are verminproof. Because of the physical nature of these fibers (see Table 5.1), the properties of the glass-fiber papers are, of course, unique and differ from those of all-cellulose papers.

At least two basic types of glass fibers are currently being used as raw materials for papermaking: (*a*) drawn glass filaments, the less expensive of the two, available in a wide range of diameters up to 9 μ, and (*b*) blown glass fibers. Sand (silica), plus other glass-forming materials, are melted down to form marbles about $\frac{3}{4}$ in. in diameter which are then remelted (Figure 5.1) and drawn to form continuous filaments. One of these marbles, if drawn out into typical commercial paper fiber, would produce filaments many hundreds of miles long, varying in diameter from 9 μ down to about 0.05 μ. (A human hair has an average diameter of about 26 μ, which is more than 150 times as large as some of the glass microfibers used for papermaking.) A pocketful of these marbles, if converted into filaments and then fashioned into a fibrous mat, could readily make a featherweight blanket large enough to cover a football field.

Blown glass fibers are produced by directing a high velocity stream of very hot gas onto a relatively coarse primary fiber; this results in fibers of random lengths of one to a fraction of an inch in diameter varying usually from 0.5 to 3 μ (Figure 5.2). Glass fibers of the order of 1 μ are so fine that a single pound of them laid end to end

TABLE 5.1

Miscellaneous Properties of Fiberglas Type E-Glass[1]

Physical Properties

Specific gravity	2.55 (note for bulk glass of same composition value is 2.58)
Hardness	6.5 Moh scale
Angle of contact (water)	0 Degrees for *clean* glass
Coefficient of friction (with glass)	1 For *clean* glass

Mechanical Properties

Tensile strength	400,000 p.s.i.
Modulus of elasticity (tension)	10.5×10^6 p.s.i.
Bulk modulus	5×10^6 p.s.i.
Poisson's ratio	0.22
Hysteresis	None
Creep	None
Resilience modulus	7600 in.-lb./in.^{3}

Thermal Properties

Coefficient of thermal expansion	2.8×10^{-6}/°F.
Coefficient of thermal conductivity	7.2 Btu-in./sq. ft./hr./°F.
Specific heat	0.19

Electrical Properties

Dielectric constant	6.43 @ 10^2 cycles
	6.11 @ 10^{10} cycles
Loss tangent	0.0042 @ 10^2 cycles
	0.0060 @ 10^{10} cycles

Acoustical Properties

Velocity of sound	18,000 ft./sec.
Acoustical impedance	1.4×10^6 gm./sq. cm./sec.
Velocity of crack propagation	5040 ft./sec.

Optical Properties

Refractive index	1.548 (at 550 mμ at 32°C.)

[1] *TAPPI*, **40**, No. 9 (September 1957).

would extend about 150,000 miles. They have a silky or suedelike feel and, contrary to expectations, will not pierce the skin or initiate itching or a brash feeling—a characteristic long associated with glass fibers of a much larger diameter, such as those used for glass-wool insulation. The development of these superfine fibers did much to

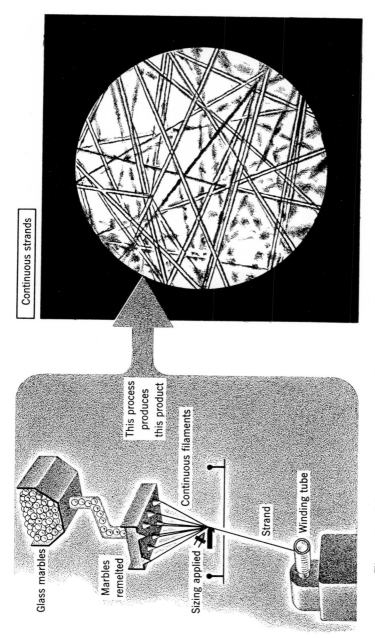

Continuous strands

This process produces this product

Continuous filaments

Glass marbles

Marbles remelted

Sizing applied

Strand

Winding tube

Figure 5.1. Schematic drawing showing how glass marbles are remelted to form continuous filaments.

99

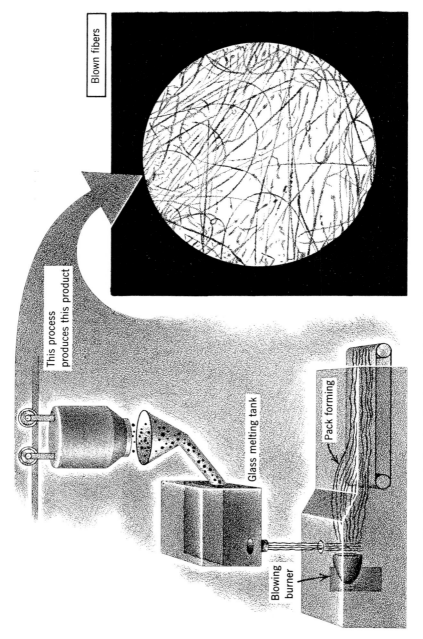

Blown fibers

This process produces this product

Glass melting tank

Blowing burner

Pack forming

Figure 5.2. Schematic drawing showing how blown glass fibers are produced from coarse primary fibers.

expand the use of glass fibers in papermaking. Table 5.2 contains a general description of several inorganic synthetic glass-type fibers.

TABLE 5.2

General Description of a Selection of Inorganic Synthetic Fibers[1]

	Quartz-Glass	Na-Glass	Aluminum Silicate	E-Glass
Chemical composition	100% SiO_2	78.2% SiO_2 21.8% $Na_2O(K)$	49% Al_2O_3 49% SiO_2 1% B_2O_3 $\frac{1}{2}$% Na_2O	54.3% SiO_2 15.5% Al_2O_3 16.3% CaO 9.9% B_2O 4.7% Na_2O
Softening or melting point, °C.	1500–1600	~570	1560–1750	750–800
Dielectric constant, 50 H.	3.5–4.2	6–7	5–6	5–6
Dielectric losses, 20°C.	0.000	0.01–0.03	—	0.0018–0.005
Dielectric losses, 200°C.	0.01–0.05	Not measurable	—	~0.01(—)
Volume resistivity, 20°C. in $\Omega \cdot$ cm.	$>10^{16}$	5×10^{11}	$>10^{14}$	10^{14}
Volume resistivity, 200°C. in $\Omega \cdot$ cm.	3×10^{13}	$<10^8$ (not measurable	$>10^{13}$	~10^{12}

[1] *TAPPI*, **37**, No. 7 (July 1954).

Some of the first successful 100% glass-fiber papers were made from filaments with diameters of approximately 0.75 μ on conventional papermaking equipment at the National Bureau of Standards in September 1950. This milestone gave great encouragement to the exploration of glass fibers for a wide range of specialized applications.

Although their composition may vary from a soft potassium glass to that of hard borosilicate glass, the borosilicate fibers are usually preferred because of their good electrical properties and outstanding resistance to weathering, heat, and chemicals. In addition to composition, the length, diameter, and surface treatment of the fibers are important in determining the physical properties of the final paper. Early in the development it was concluded that the glass fiber most suited for papermaking should have a length of approximately $\frac{1}{4}$ in., a diameter of about 9 μ, and a binder coating. The papers were made on wet lap cylinder machines, various Fourdrinier machines, and on Rotoformers. Data by Arledter showing the effect of the Fiberglass diameter on the basis weight, porosity, and tensile properties of glass-fiber paper are given in Table 5.3.

TABLE 5.3
Comparison between Glass-Fiber Paper Made of 0.75, 3, and
5.5–9 μ Glass Fibers[1]

Paper Grade

	HP 0-935	HP 0984-3	HP 0-786
Diameter of glass fibers, μ	0.75	3	5.5–9
Basis weight (24 × 36–500), lb.	40	68	133
Thickness, mil	10	19–22	40–45
Binder, %	6.0	8	6.5
Specific gravity	~0.26–0.24	0.23–0.21	0.22–0.19
85 l./min./100 cm.^{2} air resistance, mm. H$_2$O	110.0	11.0	1–1.5
400 ml. densometer $\frac{9}{32}$ in. hole	42	2.4	~0.4
High viscosity resin penetration	Fair	Good	Excellent
Tensile, gm./in.	2000–2500	3000–5000	3600–5500
Bursting strength, lb.	4	8	8

[1] *TAPPI*, **39**, No. 5 (May 1956).

Blends of these glass fibers—such as staple fibers, spun roving, or continuous filaments—were originally used in combination with highly beaten sulfite pulps, newsprint furnishes, bagasse pulps, and even muslin rags. Many coating and dispersion problems had to be solved, and it was not until the special surface binder was developed (a so-called soft chrome material which could bind the glass fibers together for processing, yet allow the fibers to disperse readily when blended with a pulp slurry) that real progress was made.

The introduction of glass fibers in the paper industry was made because of a strong demand for a new and better filter material. At that time the fibers were pliable enough to be twisted, woven, or knitted, and they had been enjoying a measure of success in the textile industry, in which they were particularly useful for fire- and ageproof draperies, weatherproof insect screens, and similar applications.

A unique property of glass-fiber filters is their ability to trap smoke, bacteria, and dust particles with remarkable efficiency. Because they can be made with numerous combinations of void sizes, these papers can be designed to permit high rates of flow for both gases and liquids. It has been observed, for example, that in a smoke-filled room only one particle of smoke (about 0.2 μ, or 8 millionths of an inch) in 100,000 is able to pass through the filter in a gas mask—and there is no increase in the normal breathing resistance of the mask. Many commonly known bacteria measure up to 50 μ, and one paper made from glass microfibers was reported to possess such remarkable filtration efficiency that only one bacterium in 500 million was able to get through.

The next step was the application of these papers in filtration problems concerned with atomic installations and radioactive particles, since radioactive dust can be readily removed from air, and finely divided precipitates from water suspension, with as much ease as coarse particles. Another reason for the success of glass-fiber filters is their ability to withstand elevated temperatures (up to 1200°F., except for special types which are resistant to temperatures as high as 1700°F.). This factor is important in pharmaceutical manufacturing and in hospitals in which sterile handling conditions are necessary, in food processing in which the paper can be sterilized as part of the equipment, and in electronic equipment fields in which organic materials, such as cellulosic papers, had previously been unable to stand up under severe conditions of temperature, moisture, and chemical attack.

Before glass-fiber papers were produced many of the available components in electronic equipment were limited to a top operating temperature of about 200°F., or the approximate maximum temperature that the cellulosic papers, used as barrier materials, could withstand. Another limitation of cellulosic papers was their frequent failure when abnormal conditions of high humidity were encountered.

When impregnated with suitable oils or resins, Fiberglas papers have excellent dielectric strength. Their temperature-resistance and low density, plus the absence of metallic impurities, make them an efficient electrical insulating material.

BLENDS OF GLASS FIBER WITH CELLULOSIC FIBERS

During the early study of glass fiber for paper it was found that, because of the inertness of glass to water, the addition of a small amount (5 to 10%) of glass fibers in a cellulosic-fiber furnish speeded up the drying rate of the paper, with a significant reduction in steam cost. This, of course, brought about greater production capacity when drying time was the main bottleneck. It was also observed that the presence of a small percentage of Fiberglas reduced the shrinkage across the web and resulted in increased yardage per ton. Comparisons between cellulosic-base absorbent papers and glass-fibered-base absorbent papers, and their blends, are based largely on Arledter's classical studies. These data are provided in the following tables:

Table 5.4: Cellulose Absorbent Paper versus Glass Absorbent Paper.

Table 5.5: Comparison between Pigmented White Absorbent Cellulose Paper and Pigmented White Absorbent Glass-Fiber Paper.

Table 5.6: New Decorative Absorbent Paper (Glass-Fiber) versus Standard Decorative Absorbent Grades.

Table 5.7: Electrical Properties of Glass versus Alpha-Cellulose Paper Laminates Made with Paraplex P-43 (Before and After Soaking in Water for 24 hr.).

Table 5.8: Laminates Made of Glass-Base Paper versus Cellulose-Base Paper.

Table 5.9: Comparison of Alpha-Cellulose and Glass-Fiber Papers Using Melamine Resin.

Table 5.10: Comparison of Flameproof Paper versus Glass-Fiber Papers and Cellulose Paper.

When glass fibers are added to cellulosic furnishes, there are important noticeable effects.

1. An increase in the freeness of the stock—or, to put it another way, a speeding up of the drainage rate—usually in direct proportion to the percentage of glass present.

2. Faster drying rate because of the inertness of glass to water.

3. A greater wet web strength without leading to a less porous paper—especially when submicron-diameter glass fibers are added. With glass fiber-cellulosic blends, therefore, both high wet strength and porosity can be obtained at the same time, but for cellulosic fibers alone it is well known that one of these properties can be improved only at the expense of the other.

4. Improvement in the porosity of the dry blended sheet.

5. Significant reduction in shrinkage, both in machine and cross-machine directions, because glass fibers do not change in dimension when going from the wet to dry state. One investigator reports less shrinkage on the order of 5 in. on a 200-in.-wide machine.

6. Dimensional stability of a cellulosic paper web can be greatly increased by adding a small percentage of glass fiber, as shown in

TABLE 5.4
Cellulose Absorbent Paper versus Glass Absorbent Paper[1]

	I	II	III	IV	V	VI	VII
Fiber material	Cellulose	Cellulose	Glass	Glass	Glass	Glass	Glass
Binder designation			A	B	D	C	None
Basis weight (24 × 36–500), lb.	88	81.5	61	65	60	56.7	36
Thickness, mil	10.4	9.8	11	12	12	10.32	8.4
Specific gravity	0.512	0.54	0.35	0.34	0.326	0.36	0.28
Density, gm./cm.^{3}	8.4	8.3	5.5	5.2	5.0	5.5	4.3
Densometer, $1\frac{1}{8}$ in.	22.2	23.4	0.5	0.6	4.8	1.2	6
Dry tensile, gm./in.	9950/5650	9300/5800	2750/1500	1400/1100	2350/1500	1650/1150	700/400
Tear, gm.	96/120	104/112	32/40	28/32	40/48	28/32	40/48
Klemm	10	14	8	None	12	None	32
Schopper wet tensile, gm./in.	400	400	1150	950	425	1400	540
Penetration, sec.							
Melamine (50% water)	3	2	Inst.	None	Inst.	None	Inst.
Phenolic (alcohol + benzol solvent, $s = 0.95$)	2	1	Inst.	Inst.	Inst.	Inst.	Inst.
Low-pressure resin solution (P-43 + 12% styrene)	6	22	22	Inst.	Inst.	22	Inst.
Wet stretch, %	2/0.4	3.4/0.7	0.0	0.0	0.0	0.0	0.0
Tensile, gm./in. (wetted with resin solution for 60 sec.)							
Melamine (50% water)	520	550	800–900	—	300	1100	580
Phenolic (alcohol + benzol solvent, $d = 0.95$)	2100	2100	Poor	300	500	450–600	580
Low-pressure resin solution (P-43 + 12% styrene)	3500	4200	Poor	500–600	1100–1800	200	650
Light fastness	Good	Good	Good	Fair	Fair	Poor	Excellent

[1] *TAPPI*, **37**, No. 7 (July 1954).

TABLE 5.5

Comparison between Pigmented White Absorbent Cellulose Paper
and Pigmented White Absorbent Glass Fiber Paper[1]

	I Cellulose	II Glass	III Glass
Basis weight (24 × 36–500), lb.	97.5	69.5	66
Thickness, mil	7.9	13.1	11.6
Specific gravity	0.806	0.345	0.37
Density, gm./cm.^{3}	12.3	5.3	5.7
Densometer, sec.	75.6	2	1.4
Dry tensile, gm./in.	7900/4300	2400/1900 1700/1680	2150/1500
Tear, gm.	72/96	24/40	32/40
Klemm	10	31	None
Schopper wet tensile, gm./in.	1400	550–900	1350 No penetration
Ash (filler), %	16.4	18	18
Penetration, sec.			
Melamine (50% water)	5	5	No penetration
Phenolic (alcohol + benzol solvent, $d = 0.95$)	2	0.5-inst.	2
Low-pressure resin solution (P-43 + 12% styrene)	52	28–17	18
Wet stretch,			
Machine	0.6	0.00	0.00
Cross	2.9		
Bursting strength, lb.	16.8	—	—
Opacity	Good	Good	Good
Light fastness	Good	Good	Fair
Tensile, gm./in. (wetted with resin solution for 60 sec.)			
Melamine (50% water)	1700	620	No penetration
Phenolic (alcohol-benzol solvent, $s = 0.95$)	3430	400	440
Low-pressure resin solution (P-43 + 12% styrene)	5000	400	400
Binder	—	A	B

[1] *TAPPI*, **37**, No. 7 (July 1954)

TABLE 5.6

A New Decorative Absorbent Paper (Glass-Fiber) versus Standard
Decorative Absorbent Grades[1]

	I New Glass	II Standard Cellulose	III Standard Cellulose
Basis weight (24 × 36–500), lb.	82.5	103	64
Thickness, mil	9	8.8	5.6
Melamine penetration 50:50, sec.	1.5	5.4–20	2.1
Low pressure resin penetration, sec.	12	72	25
Wet stretch, %	1.2	3.2	2.5
Oil test, sec.	1.2	4	5
Opacity:			
High pressure laminate	Very good	Good	Good—(fair)
Low pressure laminate	Good	Very good	Good—(fair)
Water absorption in laminate:			
24 hr., 25°C.	0.9	2.4	—

[1] *TAPPI*, **37**, No, 7 (July 1954)

Table 5.11 for register grade paper and in Table 5.12 for chart paper. This fact is of increasing importance in view of the growing use of automation for processing coated-paper documents at high speeds when dimensional stability of the paper is essential. Other properties improved by the use of glass fibers are shown in Tables 5.13 and 5.14.

7. Resistance to mold and rot—important for legal records, documents, and other printed material of lasting value.

8. Better resistance to acids and chemical solutions. The main acids that attack glass fibers are hydrofluoric, hydrochloric, and hot phosphoric. C-glass, a special glass formulation, is more resistant to acids than E-glass.

9. Improved tear resistance by as much as 400% over pulp alone when glass fibers are blended with short-length fibers, such as groundwood and short fiber pulps. In fact, there is considerable interest in the possibility of using glass fibers which may permit an increase in the groundwood content and realize an over-all weight reduction, important because of the increasing postal rates for magazines. A groundwood study with small additions of Fiberglas is described in Table 5.15.

10. Improved thermal stability; especially useful when sterilizing.

11. Little or no effect is observed on the tensile strength, opacity, brightness, or burst strength from adding up to 10% $\frac{1}{4}$-in. glass fiber,

TABLE 5.7

Electrical Properties of Glass versus Alpha-Cellulose Paper
Laminates Made with Paraplex P-43[1,2]
(Before and After Immersion in H_2O for 24 hr.)

	Alpha-Cellulose Absorbent Paper	Glass-Fiber Absorbent Paper
Thickness of laminate, mil	62–68	78–83
Resin content, %	72.5	84.5
Dielectric constant "as is":		
60 cycles	4.6	3.6
10^3 cycles	4.2	3.5
10^6 cycles	4.0	3.4
Dielectric constant after immersion in water 24 hr., 25°C.:		
60 cycles	6.7	3.8
10^3 cycles	4.9	3.6
10^6 cycles	4.1	3.5
Power factor "as is":		
60 cycles	0.089	0.021
10^3 cycles	0.032	0.019
10^6 cycles	0.033	0.020
Power factor after immersion in water 24 hr., 25°C.:		
60 cycles	0.21	0.043
10^3 cycles	0.12	0.027
10^6 cycles	0.039	0.027

[1] Results obtained from Rohm & Haas Co.
[2] *TAPPI*, **37**, No. 7 (July 1954)

although the density is generally reduced. Actually, formation of the paper web may be slightly hindered by the addition of glass fibers, especially when they are added in higher proportions; for example, up to 25%. However, papers consisting of 90% glass fibers with 10% long-fibered cellulose as a carrier have been made.

As would be expected from the inherent brittle nature of glass fibers, even as little as 5% addition may reduce the fold endurance by as much as 50%. Table 5.14 shows the physical properties of chart paper with increasing amounts of Fiberglas. For the same reason, great care must be taken in calendering glass-bearing sheets, for crushing the glass fibers will destroy any inherent benefits they might otherwise contribute.

TABLE 5.8

Laminates Made of Glass-Base Paper versus Cellulose-Base Paper[1]

Fibers Used	Cellulose	Glass
Thickness, in.	0.062–0.068	0.078–0.083
Resin content, %[2]	72.3	84.7
Barcol hardness	55	63
Flexure test:		
Lengthwise ultimate strength, p.s.i.	19,300	18,400
Modulus of elasticity, p.s.i.	11.06×10^5	6.83×10^5
Crosswise ultimate strength, p.s.i.	14,500	15,500
Modulus of elasticity, p.s.i.	7.40×10^5	6.24×10^5
Water absorption, 24 hr.:		
25°C soak		
Solubles, %	Negligible	Negligible
Total gain, %	1.45	0.38
100°C. soak		
Solubles	1.95	3.54
Total gain, %	9.46	2.82
Appearance	Opacity around sanded edges	Became opaque

[1] *TAPPI*, **37**, No. 7 (July 1954)
[2] Resin binder—Paraplex P-43.

TABLE 5.9

Comparison of Alpha-Cellulose and Glass Fiber Papers
Using Melamine Resin[1,2]
(Melmac 405 resin, American Cyanamid Co.)

	Hurlbut Paper Co., Base Paper Grade	
	521	306
Fibers used	Cellulose	Glass
Thickness, in.	0.0165	0.016
Resin content, %	58.5	77
Impact strength, ft.-lb./in.	0.26	0.39
Flexural strength, av. p.s.i.	21,100	17,000

[1] Results obtained from Physical Testing Laboratory, American Cyanamid Co.
[2] *TAPPI*, **37**, No. 7 (July 1954)

TABLE 5.10

Comparison of Flameproof Paper versus Glass Fiber
Paper and Cellulose Paper[1]

	I Flameproof	II Cellulose	III Glass
Hurlbut Paper Co. laminates burning test	Does not burn	Burns readily	Burns readily
Is flame self-supporting?	No	Yes	Yes
TAPPI flammability test, height of destroyed area, in.	$\frac{1}{4}$ to $\frac{1}{2}$	2	1
Afterglow	None	Strong	Short
Structural strength of laminate 20-mil. gm./in. after exposure to 1500°F.	15,000	0	13,000
Electrical tests after exposure to moisture	Good	Poor	Good
Dimensional stability	Excellent	Fair	Excellent
Water absorbency (boiling water)	0–0.2	1.8–3.2	0–0.2

[1] *TAPPI*, **37**, No. 7 (July 1954)

TABLE 5.11

Dimensional Stability of Register Grade Paper Produced on
Commercial Machine Run

		No Glass Fiber	2% Roving	5% Roving
Basic weight of test specimens	MD	27.5	28.4	28.8
Thickness of test specimens, inches		0.0026	0.0028	0.0026
Lb. (24 × 36–500)	CD			
Dimensional stability (Neenah Expansimeter):				
% expansion	MD	0.21	0.20	0.18
25%–80% R.H.	CD	0.62	0.63	0.58
% Contraction	MD	0.28	0.25	0.21
80%–25% R.H.	CD	0.62	0.61	0.59

TABLE 5.12
Hygro Expansivity Study of Chart Papers

Per Cent Dimensional Movement from Oven Dry

		50% R.H.	80% R.H.	90% R.H.	97% R.H.
Control	MD	0.88	0.95	1.03	1.19
4981	CMD	1.37	1.98	2.60	3.83
5% Fiberglas	MD	0.42	0.44	0.48	0.57
4987	CMD	1.25	1.72	2.01	2.86
10% Fiberglas	MD	0.35	0.42	0.41	0.41
4988	CMD	0.53	0.92	1.06	1.47

($\frac{1}{4}$-in. chopped 9 μ Fiberglas).

TABLE 5.13
Physical-Properties Data Obtained from Production Machine
Run of Register Grade Paper

Grade Name Register	Control No Glass Fiber	2% Fiberglas	5% Fiberglas
Basis weight (24 × 36–500), lb.	27.5	28.0	29.1
Mullen, p.s.i.	13.3	12.8	13.5
Caliper, in.	0.0027	0.0030	0.0027
Porosity, sec./100 cm.^{3}	20	15	19
Opacity, %	70.4	71.6	74.2
Tensile (lb./in.) MD	12.2	14.3	15.8
(Thwing Albert) CD	8.5	7.3	7.1
Fold (Schopper) MD	32	20	27
CD	16	12	8
Tear (Elmendorf) MD	21	26	24
(GMS), CMD	23	35	36
Smoothness, felt	54	22	60
(R.D.) sec./5 cm.^{3}, wire	46	18	46
Brightness (G.E.) %, felt	74.9	74.7	74.3
wire	75.1	74.9	74.5

TABLE 5.14

Physical Properties of Chart Paper

Machine Run Data

	Canadian Freeness	Basis Weight (lb./3470 ft.^{2})	Density (gm./cm.^{3})	Mullen Burst (pts./lb./rm.)	Tear (gm./lb./rm.)	Tensile (lb./in.)	Fold Endur- ance	Porosity (sec./100 cm.^{3})	Opacity (%)
Control 4981	315	80.2	0.73	0.47	1.16	29.7	142	82	82.5
5% Fiberglas 4987	325	81.4	0.70	0.53	1.75	32.3	111	49	84.7
10% Fiberglas 4988	370	80.0	0.66	0.48	2.14	30.3	55	26	82.0

TABLE 5.15
Groundwood Study

Sample No.	Density (lb./ft.^{3})	Tensile (lb./in.)	Tear (gm.)	Mullen Burst	Fold Endurance
1598A		MD 6.91	29.0		12
60% Groundwood	24.7	CM 8.28	20.3	4.25	3
1598B		MD 8.94	28.8		6
Plus 2% Fiberglas	28.2	CM 3.49	24.7	2.7	0
1598C		MD 5.78	14.75		7
70% Groundwood	33.8	CM 3.44	14.75	4.15	2
1598D		MD 7.74	17.9		8
Plus 1% Fiberglas	28.7	CM 4.61	17.4	4.89	3

Note. 1. Sheet A not calendered as heavily as others. 2. Physical characteristics except fold calculated to 24 lb./3300 ft.^{2} Basis weight for direct comparison.

FIBERGLAS-PLASTIC LAMINATES

According to Arledter, glass-fiber papers should be considered for laminates if the following properties are desired:

1. Improved electrical performance under varying heat and moisture conditions.
2. High dimensional stability.
3. Low-moisture pickup of the laminate.
4. Improved chemical resistance.
5. Improved heat resistance.
6. Flameproofness of laminate.
7. High strength.
8. Superior resin pickup properties.
9. A decorative sheet with high penetration speed and improved over-all properties in comparison with cellulose base paper.

When, by using glass fibers, a completely inorganic paper sheet is desired—as in electrical insulation, thermal insulation, and plastic laminates—the preferred bonding agents are aluminum hydroxide, ferric hydroxide, cupric hydroxide, and water-glass or sodium silicate. If a completely inorganic requirement is not specified, then vinyl acetate, phenolic resins, polystyrene, ethyl cellulose, polyesters, melamine resin, or silicones may be used as effective organic binders.

Glass flake (Table 5.16), another electrical insulating material, can be used with various types of pulp as bonding media. As the per-

TABLE 5.16

Basic Properties of Glass Flakes

Property	Values
Flake thickness, in.	0.00003 to 0.00020
Flake size	Random, approximately $\frac{1}{2}$ in. in the maximum dimension
Density, gm./cm.^{3}	2.549
Hardness, moh scale	6 to 7
Tensile strength, p.s.i.	100,000
Modulus of elasticity, p.s.i.	10.5×10^6
Poisson's ratio	0.22
Dielectric strength, v.p.m.	up to 2800[1]
Dielectric constant at 10^2 c.p.s.	6.43
Dielectric constant at 10^6 c.p.s.	6.11

[1] Dependent on thickness, type, and % sizing.

centage of glass flake is increased, there is a corresponding rise in the dielectric strength, since each flake is in itself a dielectric barrier. A multitude of flakes interstacked forms a continuous lamellar dielectric barrier. Sheets constructed of 90% glass flake combined with 10% glassine grade pulp have exhibited dielectric strengths at least six times greater than similar constructions using the kraft-type pulps. Table 5.17 shows what can be expected from uncoated specimens of glass flake combined with glassine-grade pulp.

TABLE 5.17

Characteristics of Glass-Flake Glassine-Pulp Papers

Flake-Pulp Proportion, Per Cent		Dielectric Strength (v.p.m., max.)	Tensile Strength, (lb./in. width)	Tear Strength (gm.)
Flake	Glassine			
75	25	800	28.9	45
85	15	860	18.1	51
90	10	900	17.7	27
95	5	1040	15.7	16

Phenolic resin laminates with glass-flake paper as a reinforcement have shown improved properties—compared to other laminates—and were made with a standard electrical grade phenolic resin and paper composed of 85% flake and 15% glassine pulp, with a 50% resin pickup. Since these laminates were introduced, superior flake papers have been developed which indicate that the electrical and physical properties of laminates can be still further upgraded (Table 5.18).

TABLE 5.18
Comparative Property Values of Glass-Flake Laminate with Other Typical Reinforced Laminate Grades (circled for inclusion in index)

Reinforcement	Flake Paper	Continuous Filament Glass Cloth	Continuous Filament Glass Cloth	Continuous Filament Glass Cloth	Glass Mat	Continuous Filament Glass Cloth	Glass Mat	Glass Mat	Continuous Filament Glass Cloth	Kraft Paper	Cotton Fabric
Resin	Phenolic	Phenolic	Melamine	Silicone	Melamine	Epoxy	Polyester	Polyester Flame-retardant	Teflon	Phenolic	Phenolic
NEMA or ASTM Grade U.S. Military Type—MIL-P		G-3	G-5 15037-GMG	G-7 997-GSG	G-8	G-10 18177-GEE	GPO-1	8013B		XXXP 3115-PBE-P A	CE 15035-FBG A
AIEE Insulation Classification	B	B	B	H	B	B	B	B	H	A	A
Dielectric strength—perpendicular, Cond. A step By step, v.p.m.	1250	600	350	350	300	500	500 short time	500 short time	500	650	350
Dissipation factor, Cond. D24/23 (10^6 cycles)	0.012	0.065	0.060	0.008	0.033	0.020	0.020	0.020	0.001	0.027	0.060
Dielectric constant, as rec. (10^6 cycles)	4.6	5.0	7.2	3.4	6.5	5.3	4.5	4.5	2.6	4.2	5.2
Water absorption, 24 hr., ⅛ in. thick (%)	0.76	1.50	1.10	0.08	1.70	0.08	0.40	0.40	0.03	0.38	1.0
Compressive strength—flatwise (1000 p.s.i.)	37	50	70	45	60	50	30	40	20	28	38
Flexural strength—lengthwise (1000 p.s.i.)	22	25	48	30	28	75	18	34	14	21	18
Izod impact—edgewise (ft. lb./in. notch)	3.31	8.0	10.0	9.5	6.1	12.0	8.0	14.0	12	0.40	1.6

115

GENERAL RULES FOR ADDING FIBERGLAS TO PAPER

According to the manufacturers of Fiberglas, fibers may be admixed to paper by chopping directly into the paper machine at a choice of several points: fan-pump inlet, Jordan inlet, stock-consistency regulator-chest outlet, or by adding prechopped fiber glass to the stock chest.

FAN PUMP INLET

Fiberglas is chopped continuously into a chute from which it slides, or is washed down, to the pulp slurry entering the fan pump. If time and agitation are sufficient for bundle dispersion, this is the simplest method and usually the most convenient.

FINAL JORDAN INLET

The Jordan in this type of operation is operated with the plug backed off, acting only as a mixer and pump for the pulp-Fiberglas slurry. Fiberglas is chopped and metered in a continuous operation into a steep chute from which it slides, or is washed down, to the pulp-water mixture. The slide and pipes leading to the Jordan inlet must be free of obstructions and abrupt bends to prevent clogging.

STOCK-CONSISTENCY REGULATOR-TANK OUTLET

This point of Fiberglas addition has worked quite well in several applications. The cutter is mounted above the tank on a suitable platform with a metal chute to carry the chopped Fiberglas down into the pulp slurry. Agitation following the consistency tank is usually adequate to disperse the glass thoroughly in the pulp before it reaches the machine headbox.

GENERAL RULES

1. Fiberglas must be added to pulp after all refining has taken place. Refiners reduce the glass-fiber length to a point at which its effectiveness is lost.

2. Fiberglas must be added to the paper furnish at a point at which sufficient time and agitation exists for complete fiber dispersion in the furnish. This point varies with each machine and can best be determined by inspection and experiment.

3. Until Fiberglas is thoroughly dispersed in the machine furnish, it should not meet obstructions to flow or abrupt bends in piping; otherwise, hang up or clogging will occur.

4. Fiberglas, when dispersed in pulp and water, will pass through without removal or clogging the various types of pulp cleaning or screening devices encountered in most paper mills.

5. Experience has shown that, once dispersed in a conventional pulp furnish, a binder-treated paper-grade glass fiber will not settle out in mill equipment or clog machine piping.

Other inorganic fibers which have value and which have been used in papermaking are silica, aluminum silicate, and asbestos. Asbestos, of course, is a natural fiber and may not be strictly considered a synthetic material; nevertheless, as is pointed out in a later section, useful papers are made by fibrillating asbestos, which is chemically an inorganic material.

Vitreous (glasslike) silica fibers may be said to possess the most complete natural electrical insulating properties. The raw material for these fibers is generally a borosilicate glass which has been chemically leached and then fired, so that the final material is essentially pure SiO_2.

It should be pointed out that glass paper made from silica fibers has a limited utility for specialized uses. The reason is that the silica fiber papers are quite brittle and fragile; they are difficult to purchase in a homogeneous length; and in general their physical properties do not suit the purpose so well as those of glass fibers.

6

METAL FIBERS

HANNS F. ARLEDTER

Director, Hurlbut Research
Mead Central Research Laboratories
Chillicothe, Ohio

For many years paper manufacturers have dreamed of the virtues which might be expected from paper consisting of 100% metal fibers or combinations of metal fibers with conventional papermaking fibers. Felted products containing small amounts of metal fibers or steel wool were suggested a long time ago. Kirschbaum (1), for instance, added 10% by weight of steel wool to a mixture of asbestos and cellulosic fiber. Lechler (2) felted metal fibers and bonded them with plastic materials to obtain elastic gaskets. Basler (3) introduced heat-conducting fiberboards containing metal fibers.

A somewhat unusual departure from ordinary metallurgy helped Armour Research Foundation metallurgists to make a filter of high porosity by compacting short metal fibers instead of metal powder (4). At approximately the same time, the papermaker learned to handle organic and inorganic synthetic fibers. In quick succession, using pilot-plant paper machines, he was able to produce continuous synthetic fiber webs made of glass in 1950 (5), organic synthetic fibers in 1953 (6), and metal fibers in 1953. The first papermachine-made metal fiber paper was produced on a pilot-plant paper machine on May 4, 1953, by the Hurlbut Paper Company, South Lee, Massachusetts (7). Trials to produce air-deposited metal webs of mild steel fibers were successfully concluded a few years later.

The new "metal-fiber technology" (pioneered by Armour Research and others), developed during the last decade or so, is centered around the basic concepts of felting metal fibers, as in papermaking, and sintering the felted fibers, as in powder metallurgy. Methods for the manufacture of metal fiber papers are technologically well ad-

118

vanced and promise economical production of a multitude of new structures. Many research laboratories in the United States are now engaged in extensive surveys to explore the long-range potentials of metal fibers and metal webs or papers in a multitude of composite materials and applications. It appears that potential applications for bonded and unbonded metal fiber webs are being conceived far more rapidly than they can be evaluated; advancements in technology are introducing many new materials with which to work. Although some of these programs appear to be heading toward a successful conclusion, there are still many problems of a technical nature to be resolved, and the question how to produce suitable metal fibers at lower cost remains of predominant importance.

Since this field is still in the exploratory stages, it is possible that methods for producing less expensive, low-diameter metal fibers of controlled dimensions will become available in the future. If this should happen, the market for metal fibers and metal-fiber papers and webs should expand greatly, and today's limited practical interest in expensive metal fiber products should multiply several-fold within the next 10 to 25 years. Estimated annual metal-fiber usage is currently at the rate of less than 500,000 lb.

METAL-FIBER PRODUCTS TERMINOLOGY

Metal-fiber products are being developed in three fields of technology.

1. Papermaking.
2. Nonwoven textiles.
3. Metallurgy.

To establish an understanding of the rather confusing terminology of these new products, it becomes necessary to clarify the following product terms now in use and encountered in the literature: metal-fiber paper, metal-fiber web, metal-fiber felt, metal-fiber mat, nonwoven metal-fiber web, felt metal (8), fiber metallurgy, metal-fiber body, metal-fiber shell, fiber metals, fibrous metal, metal-fiber filter mat, metal-fiber reinforcing mat, metal-fiber absorbent paper, metal-fiber fabrics, etc.

Each investigator uses terms related to his technology. All terms used are interrelated and describe the same basic structural nonwoven material. Only the method of manufacture or the bonding technique may vary.

Webs, mats, and felts are terms related to the nonwoven sheet made without spinning, weaving, or knitting and comprise paper, nonwoven fabrics, and felts.

Papers are produced by a wetlay process: *nonwoven fabrics* are fibrous sheets produced by an airlay process.

Mechanical *felts* are made by the ancient process of felting.

However, the line of demarcation between specialty papers and nonwovens is no longer clear. The categories "nonwoven fabrics" or "paper" today include nonwoven fibrous sheets made by both non-woven airlay (textile) and wetlay (paper) processes or in combination.

All metal-fiber products described here are nonwovens; most are produced by wetlay processes, few so far by airlay web forming. The interlocking of fibers is achieved in both processes by a com-bination of mechanical work, chemical action, heat (sintering) and/or pressure by either textile or papermaking processes.

In the literature the use of the terms fiber metal, fibrous metals, fiber metallurgy, etc., is not limited to the sintered metal-fiber webs. Likewise, the papermaker does not exclude sintering of the paper web as a means of bonding. Therefore, it remains largely a matter of taste or preference when a term is chosen to describe a new product.

METAL-FIBER PRODUCTION METHODS

Until recently, the development of metal-fiber papers or nonwoven fabrics was severely restricted because of the unavailability of metal fibers with the necessary physical properties and dimensions for processing on conventional papermaking equipment. Now, metal fibers useful for papermaking or metal felting are beginning to emerge from the laboratories into commercial pilot-plant production, and a number of methods are in development. Progress has centered around new fiber materials utilizing almost any metal alloy which can be produced in a fiber size ranging down to 10 μ or less. Most of these fibers are still quite expensive and preclude many large-volume applications of metal fibers and webs.

SHAVING OR SKIVING METHOD

Fibrous metal of this type has been on the market for more than 60 years as metal wool, and one of the first machines for its manu-facture was developed around 1899 by Shaefer (9). The first machine to incorporate a fully automatic principle was patented in 1927 by the Brillo Manufacturing Company (10). Today, such machines are of the multiple-wire type, in which the wire is pulled across a large number of chisel-cutting tools to shave off small filaments of metal wire. Depending on the number of serrations per inch, different grades of wools are obtained. Fine steel wool, designated "0000," is manufactured with 400 serrations per inch. With decreasing numbers of serrations, the wools are coarser. This wire-shaving method is still the most popular for producing fibrous metals. Steel wool consists of strong, resilient steel shavings which are sometimes several feet long and generally of polygonal cross section, mainly triangular and sharp edged (11). The first metal fiber paper, produced in the Hurlbut Paper Company pilot plant, was made from 0000 steel wool (7). Metal wools can also be cut from sheet stock and from tube stock with conventional lathes. Lathe-produced metallic chips or metallic filamentary material is sometimes called tinsel.

EXTRUSION AND BLOWING METHODS

Kratky describes a process in which the molten aluminum or lead is forced from a melting pot under pressure of inert gases through small orifices (12). Morden reports that the fibers manufactured in this way were specifically useful in felting processes (13).

Another method of forming metal fibers and filaments was patented by Marvalaud, Inc. The metal is blown under pressure through an orifice and delivered to a high-speed gas stream. By proper regulation of the extrusion velocity and of the stream of gas, continuous filaments or fibers of substantially circular cross section may be prepared (14). Extrusion of continuous metal filaments is also described in U. S. Patent 2,976,590 (15). A method of extruding filaments of high vapor-pressure metals has been developed by R. B. Pond (16, 17).

Armour Research Foundation employed a method similar to that used for the manufacture of rock wool to produce metallic fibers. In this method the molten metal is impinged on a rapidly rotating disc and the centrifugal forces help to fiberize the liquid metal. Other centrifugal spinning processes were developed by Marvalaud, Inc.

BROACHING METHOD

In this method a stack of metal foils is broached to manufacture metal fibers. In another method aluminum foil passes under the blade of a rapidly rotating microtome. Rectangular fibers of different sizes can be produced, depending on the cutting and feeding rate of the foil (11).

FOIL SLITTING AND CHOPPING

Metal foils of any desired thickness are slit to a width of $\frac{1}{50}$, $\frac{1}{100}$ and $\frac{1}{220}$ in. and are chopped to a predetermined length, for instance, of $\frac{1}{4}$ or $\frac{1}{2}$ in. with rotating cutting knives. The width of the resulting fibers is limited to approximately 50 μ, and the thickness of such fibers can be as low as 5 μ. These metal ribbon fibers are already finding industrial applications (18).

WIRE CHOPPING METHOD

Metal wires with diameters as low as 12 μ can be chopped to a predetermined length, for instance, of 6 to 25 mm. Such metal staple fibers are finding applications in the reinforced plastics field. The drawing of metal wires is done by starting with a rod which goes through alternate drawing, annealing and cold-working steps until it finally becomes an extremely fine filament. When drawing refractory metals and superalloys, diamond dies are employed for the last drawing operation; this helps achieve roundness and consistency of the product.

In the "hot pin" method the fiber is pulled over a hot pin while under predetermined stress. This causes stretching and aligning of the molecular structure. Higher strength fibers are possible with this method.

Thin copper wires are manufactured by drawing a number of wires through the same die to reduce their diameter simultaneously. Another method of decreasing the diameter of the metal wires subjects the metal to chemical etching. Thus it has been reported that a copper wire placed in a nitric acid bath will dissolve uniformly to yield fibers less than 1 μ in diameter (19). Fibers produced in this way can be successfully made into paper (20). Electrolytic etching techniques are reportedly applied for the production of fine tungsten filaments (21).

WHISKER METHOD

Almost any crystalline substance, such as metals or metal oxides, can be formed into "whiskers" by vapor phase or by electrolysis of molten salt. A number of methods, based on chemical, physical, or electrical principles, have been developed for the production of metal whiskers. These methods are summarized in Table 6.1 (22). Whiskers possess a strength that is closely related to the diameter, and the thinner the whiskers, the greater their strength. Iron whiskers of approximately 2 μ diameter can reach a tensile strength of 2 million p.s.i., and one of the strongest alloys of iron, as a whisker approximating 4 μ in diameter, can reach a tensile strength of 600,000 p.s.i. A whisker of 10 μ diameter has a tensile strength of 100,000 p.s.i. (22–40). So far the greatest drawback to any widespread applica-

TABLE 6.1
Methods Used to Grow Metal Whiskers (22)

Metal	Method of Growth	Temperature
Cadmium	From plated coatings	Room temperature
Cobalt	Reduction of bromide	1290°F.
Copper	Reduction of CuI_2 and $CuCl_2$	800 to 1380°F.
Germanium	Decomposition of GeI_4	930°F.
Gold	Decomposition of chloride	460 to 1470°F.
Iron	Reduction of $FeCl_2$ and $FeBr_2$	1020 to 1470°F.
Mercury	Condensation	−81.4°F.
Nickel	Reduction of bromide	1290°F.
Platinum	Decomposition of chloride	460 to 1470°F.
Silicon	Reduction of $SiCl_4$	1470 to 1830°F.
Silicon	Condensation	2280°F.
Silver	Reduction of AgCl	1290 to 1470°F.
Silver	Condensation	1560°F.
Tin	From plated coatings	Room temperature
Zinc	From plated coatings	Room temperature
Zinc	Condensation	660°F.

tion is the high price. As will be shown later, whiskers can be made to possess the ideal length and diameter for the manufacture of paper (22).

METAL DEPOSITION ON INORGANIC OR ORGANIC FIBERS

Metal can be deposited on the surface of organic or inorganic fibers (23), but the nonmetallic fiber core will remain. Metal fibers with a glass fiber core containing 85% metal on the surface were tested by the author and found useful for papermaking purposes. If the metal is deposited on organic fibers, the base fibers can later be dissolved or burned off.

POWDER METALLURGY

Powdered metal in copper tubes can be sintered and drawn to a fiber. This method is specifically useful for refractory metals such as tungsten. Because of the drawing step, breakage frequently occurs and fiber length cannot be controlled, so that the fibers obtained are often short. Powdered metal can also be pressed through a die and sintered in the die.

OTHER METHODS

Electrodeposition of metal in grooves is one of many novel methods proposed for the production of fine metal fibers. Numerous other methods are said to be in process of development but have not yet reached the stage of disclosure.

PROPERTIES OF METAL FIBERS

Unique properties that may be obtained from metal fibers are as follows:

1. Exceptionally high heat conductivity.
2. Excellent electrical conductivity.
3. Chemical reactivity for use in such applications as batteries.
4. Magnetic properties.
5. Advantageous physical properties at very low and very high temperatures.
6. Reflection and/or absorption of light and electromagnetic radiations.

A compilation of the general physical properties of the more common metals which have been considered in fiber form for papermaking are shown in Table 6.2. Table 6.3 describes the properties of specific metal fibers in comparison with Type E-glass fibers and cotton.

TABLE 6.2
Physical Properties of Different Metals (6)

	Aluminum	Zinc	Stainless Steel	Bronze	Copper	Nickel	Lead
Specific gravity, gm./cm.³	2.702	7.14	7.755	7.50 8.8	8.92	8.90	11.34
Melting point, °C.	659.7	419.4	1510	—	1083	1452	327.4
Electrical Resistance:							
Grams per ohm at 20°C. Wire Gage No. 40 (0.0048 in.)	0.0024	—	—	—	0.013	—	—
Wire Gage No. 10 (0.134 in.)	2640	—	—	—	14,270	—	—
Wire Gage 0000 (0.454 in.)	6,000,000	—	—	—	1,100,000	—	—
Heat Conductivity:							
At 100°C. in calories for plate 1 cm. across 1 cm.² Temperature difference 1°C.	0.492	0.262	0.106	0.18 to 0.25	0.908	0.138	0.082

TABLE 6.3
Properties of Metal Fibers (41)

Fiber	Specific Gravity	Length (cm.)	Diameter (10^{-4} cm.)	Tensile Strength ($\times 10^{-3}$ p.s.i.)	Modulus of Elasticity (10^{-6} p.s.i.)	Heat Resistance (°F.)	Coefficient of Expansion
Steel	7.8	Filament staple	1–25	200–400	20–30	2920	8–10
Aluminum	2.8	Filament staple	4–20	60–90	10	1212	17–20
Tungsten	19.3	Up to 2.5	20	200	58	6150	4.5
Tantalum	16.3	Up to 1.25	5	70–90	28	5390	6.6
Molybdenum	10.2	Up to 1.25	5–20	—	42	4700	5.4
Magnesium	1.8	Filament staple	6–15	40	6	1200	8–20
Type E-Glass	2.6	Filament staple	0.1–15	400	10.5	1300	2.8
Cotton	1.6	Up to 5	16	50–110	—	325	—

As would be expected, inorganic and/or metal fibers possess important basic differences in physical properties over cellulose fibers. Some of these differences are advantages; others are disadvantages. A comparison of the two broad classes of fibers is given in Table 6.4.

TABLE 6.4
Comparison of Properties of Cellulose Fibers
versus Inorganic Fibers (42)

	Cellulose Fibers	Inorganic Fibers
Effect of acids	Fibers disintegrate	Depending on fiber material, effect is slight to appreciable
Effect of alkali	Swelling and reduced strength	Attacked
Effect of other chemicals	Attacked by strong oxidizing agents	None to slight
Water absorbency	27 at 95 % R.H. Total retention > 100 to 127 %	Up to 0.3 %
Effect of heat	Loses strength above 300°F. Decomposes at 350 to 450°F.	Not influenced up to 600 to 2200°F.
Burnability	Burns readily	Does not burn
Electrical properties	Good at low moisture content
Extremely bad at high relative humidity	Excellent at low relative humidity, good at high relative humidity

Two types of metallic fibers are compared in Fig. 6.1. One of these is the conventional polycrystalline wire; the other, the whisker. In the true sense the whisker is not a fiber but rather a single crystal with great strength owing to a high degree of crystalline perfection. For example, the strength of iron whiskers plotted in the uppermost portion of Figure 6.1 may reach the extent of 2 million p.s.i. a value that nears its theoretical strength. The curve also shows the tensile strength of cold-drawn tungsten fibers plotted against the diameter. After fiber diameter is reduced the strength increases significantly to as much as 600,000 p.s.i. for very fine 0.001-in. diameter wires (25 μ). If all or even part of this tremendous strength could be realized when the fibers are incorporated into engineering material, a superior product would result.

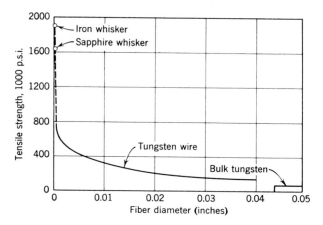

Figure 6.1. Strength of whiskers and fibers at room temperature. To date, the research at NASA has been confined to reinforcements made with fine wires.

More than 100 experimental and commercial metal fiber types have been studied by Hurlbut Research for their matting, felting, and papermaking properties. Figures 6.2 to 22 are a selection of photomicrographs which show a variety of metal fibers in comparison with unrefined kraft cellulosic fibers (Figure 6.2), 1½-denier viscose rayon fibers (Figure 6.3) and glass strand fibers (Figure 6.4). Ribbon fibers prepared from various metals are shown in Figures 6.5 to 7, whereas Figures 6.8 to 10 contain some of the types of metal fibers produced by American Viscose Corporation. Coarse metal fibers are shown in Figures 6.11 to 14, and Figures 6.15 to 18 illustrate steel fibers of varying types. Still other types of metal fibers are given in Figures 6.19 to 21, and Figure 6.22 shows metallized glass fibers.

Iron whiskers grown by reduction of a halide are shown in Fig. 6.23 (22). Note that some are twisted and kinked. The cross sections of the whiskers are usually polygonal, as demonstrated in Fig. 6.24. However, considerable variation in the cross-sectional shape of whiskers of the same metal is reported.

The relationship between metal-fiber cross sections (dimension in inches) and fiber strength has been reported (51). The considerable variations in cross-sectional shape of different fibers can be seen in Figures 6.8, 6.25 to 32 (215 ×) and Figure 6.33 (40 ×). Figure 6.33 shows the cross section of tungsten wires in a copper matrix (40 ×) (72).

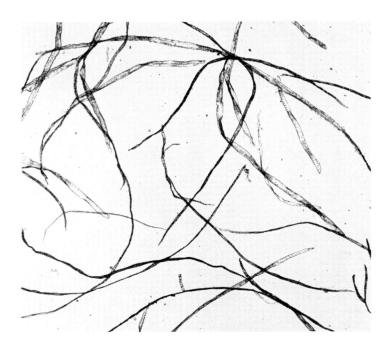

Figure 6.2. Unrefined kraft cellulose.

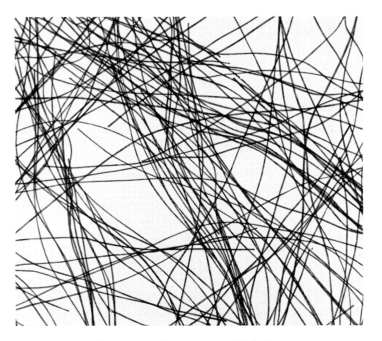

Figure 6.3. Viscose rayon 1½ denier.

Figure 6.4.   Glass strand fibers.

Figure 6.5.   Aluminum-ribbon fibers $0.0007 \times 0.004 \times \frac{5}{16}$ in.

129

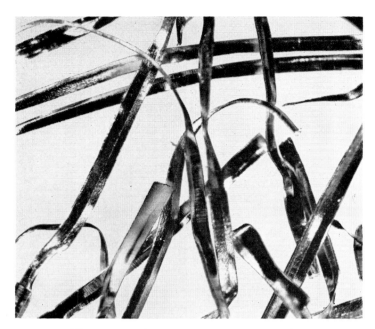

Figure 6.6. Aluminum $0.0005 \times 0.0008 \times \frac{1}{4}$ in.

Figure 6.7. Tin-Ribbon Fibers $0.001 \times 0.004 \times \frac{1}{4}$ in.

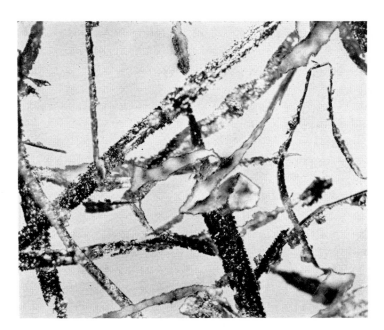

Figure 6.8.   Aluminum 3003, No. 249-43A (American Viscose Corp.).

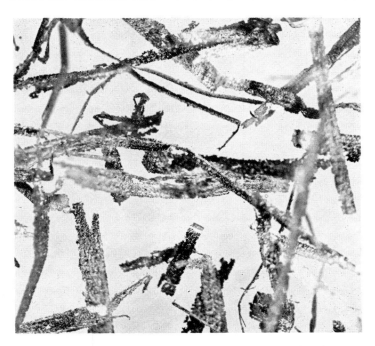

Figure 6.9.   Aluminum 1100 (American Viscose Corp.).

131

Figure 6.10. Antimonal lead (American Viscose Corp.).

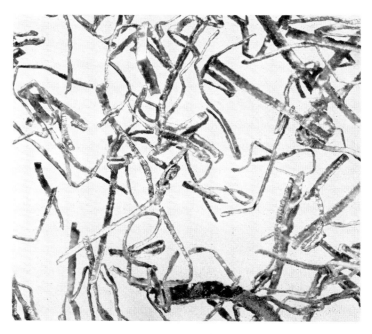

Figure 6.11. Aluminum 0.001 × 0.001.

132

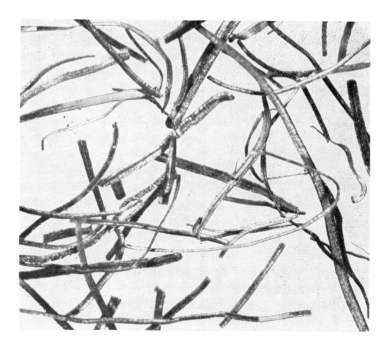

Figure 6.12.   Bronze 90–10 Type B.

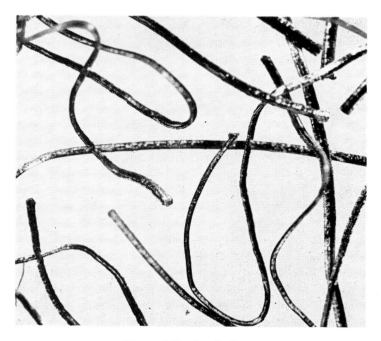

Figure 6.13.   Lead alloy.

133

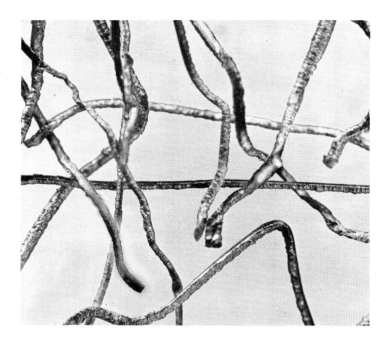

Figure 6.14. Aluminum.

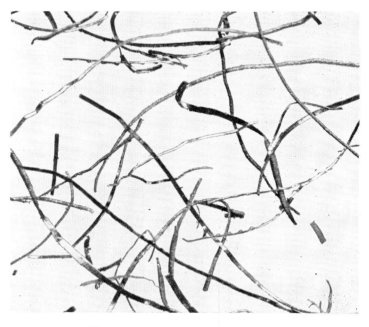

Figure 6.15. 430 stainless steel "B."

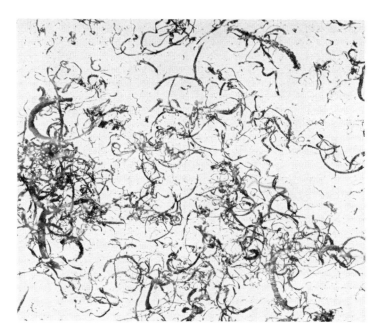

Figure 6.16. 302 stainless steel "A."

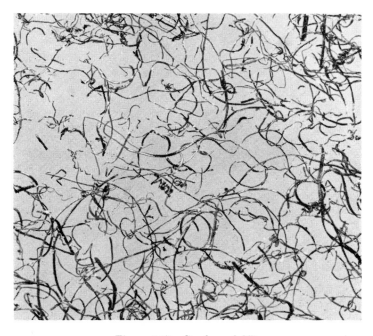

Figure 6.17. Steel wool SR.

Figure 6.18.   430 SS stainless steel "A" Fine.

Figure 6.19.   Aluminum.

Figure 6.20. Brass A : 80–20.

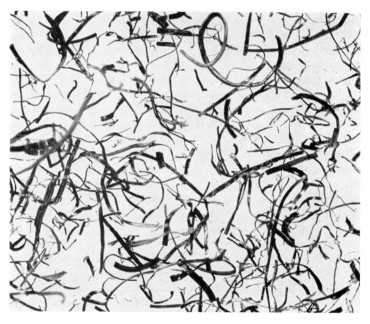

Figure 6.21. Bronze fibers, fine.

137

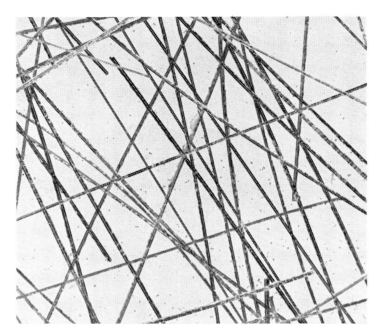

Figure 6.22. Metallized glass fibers (aluminum).

Figure 6.23. Iron whiskers grown by the reduction of iron bromide at 1330°F. (22).

138

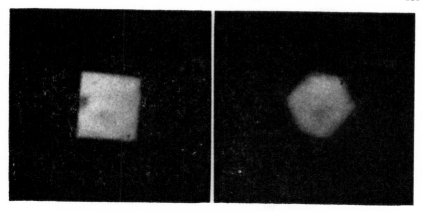

Figure 6.24. Cross sections of Two Iron Whiskers (2000 ×) (22).

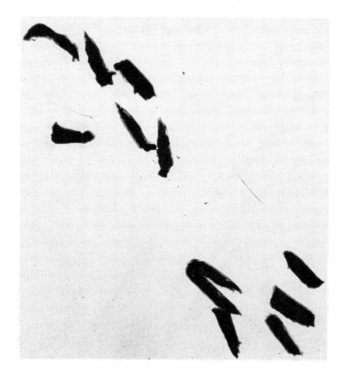

Figure 6.25. Aluminum 0.0007 × ½₂₂₀.

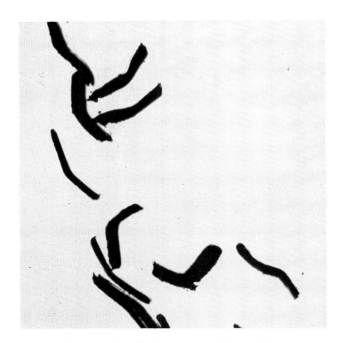

Figure 6.26.   R-Aluminum 0.0005 × 0.008.

Figure 6.27.   Aluminum 1100 249-40A.

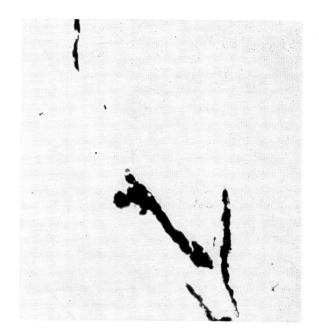

Figure 6.28.   Aluminum 1100 AV-249-40C.

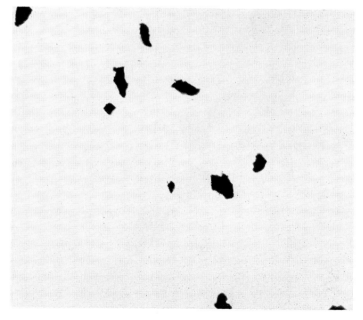

Figure 6.29.   SR steel wool.

141

Figure 6.30. Stainless steel fine 430 SS type A.

Figure 6.31. R-Lead alloy 0.002 × 0.004.

142

Figure 6.32. PD Aluminum 0.001 × 0.001.

TABLE 6.5
Properties of Experimental Metal Fibers

Producer	Type Metal	Fiber Thickness $(10^{-4}$ cm.)	Fiber Width $(10^{-4}$ cm.)	Fiber Length $(10^{-1}$ cm.)
Metal Fibers, Inc.	Aluminum	15	40–75	3–6
	Copper	15	25–100	3–6
Plastics Development and Research Corp.	Aluminum	50	125	6
Reynolds	Aluminum	11	250	6
SOS	Bronze	10–40	20–40	2–15
Joseph Bancroft	Aluminum	12.5	—	6
Clevite Corp.	Lead	9	—	6
Microfiber, Inc.	Al, etc.	50–100	—	6+
American Viscose Corp.	Tin	40	100	6–30

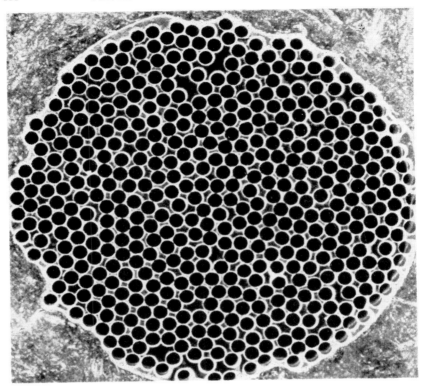

Figure 6.33. Transverse section of composite containing 483 tungsten wires in a copper matrix. In this research volumes of tungsten and copper were determined from area measurements (with a planimeter) of such photographs (80 ×).

TABLE 6.6
Properties of Experimental Al Fibers Produced by American Viscose Corp.

Code Number	Fiber Thickness (10^{-4} cm.)	Average Width (10^{-1} cm.)	Fiber Length (10^{-1} cm.)	Paper Maker Rating
249-44 A-3003A	6.3	4	2–6	Good
249-40 C-1100	9.0	2	3–10	Very Good
249-40 A-1100	11.5	2.7	3–8	Very Good
249-43 B-3003	11.5	3	4–10	Good
249-43 A-3003	16.3	2.5	6–15	Fair
249-42 A-3003	21	2.5	6–20	Poor

TABLE 6.7
Metal Fibers Produced by the Huyck Corporation[1]

Metal	Fiber Kind	Mean Diameter (μ)	Length (cm.)
302 Stainless steel	Type A	10–20	0.1–0.6
Stainless steel	Type B 430	50	Long
Stainless steel	Type B 17-4	100	0.6+
Brass 8020	Type A	10–20	0.1–0.6
Silver	Type A	15	0.1
Nickel	Type A	15	
Copper	Type A	10–20	0.1–0.6
Bronze 9010	Type B	30–60	Long

[1] In addition, Huyck has produced metal fibers from the following metals: tantalum, cobalt, tungsten, aluminum, alnico, and platinum. They have not (but could) produce fibers of tin, lead, zinc, gold, etc.

TABLE 6.8
Ribbon or Foil Metal Fibers

Metal	Producer	Thickness (in.)	Thickness (cm.)	Width (in.)	Width (cm.)	Length (in.)	Length (cm.)
Aluminum	Reynolds Metals Co.	0.0007	0.00175	$\frac{1}{220}$	0.0113	$\frac{1}{4}$	0.63
Aluminum	Reynolds Metals Co.	0.0004	0.001	$\frac{1}{220}$	0.0113	$\frac{1}{4}$	0.63
Aluminum	Revere Copper & Brass, Inc.	0.0005	0.00125	0.008"	0.02	$\frac{1}{4}$	0.63
Lead	Revere Copper & Brass, Inc.	0.002	0.005	0.004"	0.01	$\frac{1}{4}$	0.63
Tin	Revere Copper & Brass, Inc.	0.001	0.0025	0.004"	0.01	$\frac{1}{4}$	0.63
Nickel	—	0.0002	0.0005	0.008"	0.02	$\frac{1}{4}$	0.63

To establish a background for understanding the strength properties of metal-fiber paper or webs, either of the bonded or unbonded types, and products made therefrom, the individual fiber strength of metal fibers produced by different methods of manufacture was determined (51). Any fiber is as strong as its weakest point, and Figure 6.8 shows the irregular contour frequently observed. Fiber strength can vary to a considerable degree as a consequence, and typical ranges are shown in Table 6.9. For comparison, typical strength values of single organic fibers are listed in Table 6.10, and the average strength of various fiber materials is shown in Table 6.11.

Coarse metal fibers show limited strength properties with a range of 12,500 to 65,000 p.s.i., whereas 2 μ-36 μ iron whiskers show a value

TABLE 6.9

Fiber Strength—Metal Fibers (51)

| | Strength (gm.) | | |
Sample Identity	High	Low	Average
Aluminum Avisco 249-40 A	10	0	2.0
Aluminum Plastic Development & Research Corp.	22.9	7.8	13.1
Aluminum 0.0007 $\times \frac{1}{200}$ Reynolds	36.4	22.0	30.6
Aluminum 0.00045 $\times \frac{1}{100}$ Reynolds	59.0	44.5	51.7
Aluminum extra fine 0.002 $\times \frac{1}{4}$ in. Microfibre, Inc.	100+	24	78.5+
Tin Fibers 0.001 $\times$ 0.004 Revere	23.4	8.2	12.8
Steel Wool 000 Sunray	61	17.4	41.4
Stainless Steel, A SOS	77.4	32.9	57.3
Stainless Steel 430 SS, Type B	100+	34	61.1+

TABLE 6.10

Typical Strength Values of Single Organic Fibers (51)

| | Strength (gm.) | | |
	High	Low	Average
Loblolly pine exp. kraft (unbleached):			
Summerwood (45.7% yield)	64	10	32
Springwood (46% yield)	17	8	11
Nylon 3 denier	18	10	13
Reg. Rayon (3.75 denier)	13	10	11
Rayon, high strength (1.5 denier)	10	9	9

of 1 million p.s.i. Loblolly pine kraft fibers range from 42,000 p.s.i. for springwood fibers up to 105,000 p.s.i. for summerwood fibers. Thus some metal fibers are weaker than wood pulp fibers, although others are much higher in individual fiber strength.

Individual metal-fiber strength is known to depend on fiber size and the method of manufacture. Table 6.12 gives an indication how

TABLE 6.11
Average Strength of Fiber Materials

Fiber	Average Tensile Strength kg./mm.^{2}	Average Tensile Strength (p.s.i.)
Mild steel fibers	47	65,000
Iron whiskers (2 μ diameter)	725	1,000,000
Iron whiskers (5 μ diameter)	260	360,000
Copper whiskers (2 μ diameter)	225	310,000
Loblolly pine (summer)	77	105,000
Unbleached kraft (spring)	31	42,000
Aluminum (36 μ)	7.5	10,400
430 SS Fine A (28 μ)	23	32,000
000 steel (22 μ)	26	36,000
Aluminum 249-40 C.	3	4,000
Nickel wire (René 41)(12.5 μ)	200	280,000
Molybdenum wire (30 μ)	230	320,000

TABLE 6.12
Tensile Strength of Metal Wire as Related to Diameter

Molybdenum		Nickel-René 41		
Diameter of Wire (mils)	Maximum Tensile Strength (p.s.i.)	Diameter of Wire (mils)	Tensile Strength (p.s.i.)	Elonga-tion (%)
48	170,000	10	180,000	33
10	210,000	8	200,000	27
5	260,000	5	214,000	24
2.8	270,000	4	216,000	24
1.2	320,000	3	228,000	19
		1.5	256,000	16
		0.5	286,000	17

the tensile strength of annealed molybdenum wire and tensile strength and elongation of nickel superalloy wire are increased by drawing to smaller diameters. The dependence of strength on diameter of pure iron and pure copper *whiskers* is shown in Table 6.13. Fine metal wires or metal whiskers are, unfortunately, very expensive. For most papermaking operations the metal fibers must be inexpensive and ob-

TABLE 6.13
Average Strength of Pure Iron and Pure Copper Whiskers as a
Function of Diameter (41)

Diameter (mils)	Tensile Strength (p.s.i.)	
	Pure Copper	Pure Iron
0.08	320,000	1,000,000
0.1	270,000	850,000
0.125	225,000	660,000
0.25	130,000	300,000
0.5	100,000	100,000

tainable in large quantities before production on any reasonable scale can be achieved.

PAPERMAKING THEORY

RELATIONSHIP OF FIBER DIMENSIONS TO PAPER STRUCTURE

In the processed or beaten state papermaking fibers possess dimensions or geometry which cannot be easily defined in terms of numbers, available fiber surface, mean fiber diameter, number of fiber-to-fiber contact points, and the like. There are so many different fiber dimensions encountered in any fiber batch that a purely mathematical approach to the fiber-to-fiber relationship within the web defies definition.

Synthetic fibers, on the other hand, are man-made, and most of them possess a well-defined mean *fiber diameter, a fiber surface,* which can be calculated from cross-sectional and other observational factors, and a clearly defined length, which may be obtained by cutting strands or foils to the wanted dimensions or by mechanical fiber length classification.   This makes possible a more rigorous mathematical approach for assessing the internal fiber structure within a web, predicated on theoretical fiber-to-fiber relationships.

Experiments lead to the conclusion that the approximate mathematical definition of a synthetic-fiber paper web in terms of

1. specific external surface area per cubic centimeter of fibers,
2. theoretical number of fibers available in 1 cm.³,
3. theoretical number of fiber-to-fiber contacts per cubic centimeter,

4. theoretical fiber-fiber *contact area* per cubic centimeter,
5. theoretical number of fiber-to-fiber contacts for each fiber,
6. fiber length-to-diameter ratio,
7. theoretical number of fiber layers in paper,
8. relationship between caliper of paper and fiber diameter

becomes meaningful for predicting web properties such as heat conductivity, heat dissipation, electrical conductivity, filter-paper characteristics, development of chemical energy, and paper strength. Such an approach opens the door to a better understanding of metal-fiber paper characteristics and helps to solve

1. the problems of manufacture of the paper web, and
2. the design of synthetic paper webs for optimum properties for the new spectrum of metallurgical and other novel structures. It is no longer necessary to design around the limitations of more conventional structures.

Any mathematical analysis of a complex system with a large number of variables and with many sources of inaccuracies in the measurement and computation of results is bound to be only approximate. Despite such limitations, the outlined mathematical analysis and definition of the web has been of considerable value in the adaptation of such fibers to a host of product possibilities.

In Tables 6.14 and 6.15 the fiber dimension-paper structure mathematical relationships have been calculated for both circular and ribbon fibers of 0.5 to 100 μ diameter or thickness. These are the fiber parameters that the papermaker can consider for metal-fiber paper structures. The definitions of the variables presented in the tables are given below:

Average Fiber Diameter and Fiber Thickness (d). The term *mean fiber diameter* relates only to circular and oval shapes, and the term *mean fiber thickness* is employed only for rectangular and related fiber forms. There is no problem in defining the mean fiber diameter or fiber thickness for any fiber shape open to geometrical analysis. To assign an average fiber diameter or thickness to irregular-shaped fibers requires more elaborate statistical studies of microscopic cross sections to obtain the required approximations.

Fiber Length (l). A *fiber* is defined as having a length (l) to diameter (d) ratio of 10 to 10,000 as opposed to filaments or wires, which have very much larger l/d ratios. The mean fiber length is determined by the fiber-making process.

Theoretical Number of Fibers per Cubic Centimeter of Material (N) *or per Square Centimeter of Paper* (Np). Fundamental properties of the paper can be predicted from the values of N and Np. Tables 6.14 and 6.15 reveal that, depending on the fiber diameter or fiber thickness, the number of fibers per cubic centimeter (1-cm. length) can vary between 10,000 and 100 million. This factor can also be stated as the total length of fibers (in centimeters) available per cubic centimeter of fiber material. In addition, by introducing the specific gravity of the fiber material, the number of fibers per gram can be obtained as follows:

$$\text{number of fibers/gm.} = \frac{\text{number of fibers/cm.}^3, N}{\text{specific gravity of fibers}}$$

Specific External Fiber Surface Area (σ and σ_p). The specific external fiber surface area per cubic centimeter (σ) of fiber material is a recognized fundamental property of considerable importance in papermaking and is even more important in the development of metal-fiber paper webs intended for development of chemical energy, electrical properties, filter properties and others. For paper the external fiber surface area per squared centimeter (σ_p) is taken as (Np) times S. Tables 6.14 and 6.15 show that σ can vary between 400 and 80,000 cm.^{2} and for a 10-mil paper σ_p can be between 5 to 1000 cm.^{2}

THEORETICAL NUMBER OF FIBER-TO-FIBER CONTACTS:
C AND Cp

The strength of a wet and dry paper web depends on the number of fiber-to-fiber contacts. The number of contact points will further determine the electrical conductivity of a web, the heat transmission rate, and other vital properties, many of which are specific to metal-fiber webs. The values given in Tables 6.14 and 6.15 reveal the theoretically possible (astonishingly high) number of fiber-to-fiber contacts which vary between 10^4 an 10^{13} crossing points. Metal fibers of ductile and compressible nature will permit the attainment of most of this theoretical number.

FIBER PACKING DENSITY

The effective volume fraction α of fibers per cubic centimeter is equivalent to the packing density.

The void fraction Σ in 1 cm.^{3} of the paper then becomes

$$\Sigma = 1 - \alpha$$

The compressibility of the fiber material determines the packing density of the paper web during production on the paper machine (matting, wet-pressing, calendering) and during subsequent treatments (pressing, etc.). The compressibility is a function of a number of factors which include the average fiber diameter, the average fiber length, the fiber-length distribution, the stiffness of the fibers, the curling tendency of the fibers, and their flexibility, plasticity, and plastic recovery. As may be expected, the packing characteristics of the metal fibers are of vital importance to the manufacture of metal-fiber paper and the properties that can be obtained with them.

THEORETICAL FIBER-TO-FIBER CONTACT AREA

Parsons and Ratliff (**43, 44**) were able to estimate the fractions of the external surface area of cellulosic fibers entering into fiber-fiber bonding under various conditions of wet pressing, beating, and hemicellulose content. Among the many conclusions drawn from these data, the most significant is that the tensile and bursting strengths of paper are roughly proportional to the bonded area until saturation is reached. It was determined that in this region rupture is caused by intra- rather than interfiber failure.

It is a conclusion of unpublished experimental work with synthetic and metal fibers at Mead Central Research Laboratories that the same generalization holds for metal-fiber papers, provided fiber-to-fiber fusion (sintering) or bonding of the fibers with binder materials is obtained. It also appears that wet-web strength and the dry strength of unbonded compressed webs is a function of the fiber-fiber contact area (C_s), packing density, compressibility or ductility of the metal fibers employed, etc. The fiber-fiber contact area (C_s) also influences electrical conductivity, heat transfer rate, and other important properties of metal-fiber papers. It will be noted in Table 6.15 that for ribbon fibers C_s can vary between 25 and 250 cm.^{2} This fiber-fiber contact area can be enlarged by mechanical compression (calendering), and the ratio of *contact area* (C_s) to total *surface area* ($\square$) can be increased, in ductile metals to 50% and even up to 80% or more (see Table 6.14).

How the total surface area and the bonded area of cellulosic fibers

TABLE 6.14
Fiber Dimension Paper Structure Relationship-Geometry of Papermaking for Circular Fibers

Fiber Diameter d (10^{-4} cm.)	Fiber Volume (cm.^{3}) $V = (D/2)^2 \pi \cdot h$	Fiber Surface (cm.^{2}) $S = D \cdot \pi \cdot h$	Fiber Length to Diameter Ratio $R = L/D$			Theoretical Number of Fibers Available (cm.^{3}, $l = 1.0$) $N = 1/V$	Specific External Fiber Surface Area per cm.^{3} of fibers cm.^{2} $\sigma = N \times S$
			($l = 0.2$ cm.)	($l = 0.6$ cm.)	($l = 01.0$ cm.)		
100	7.8×10^{-5}	3.15×10^{-2}	20	60	100	1.28×10^{4}	4×10^{2}
50	1.96×10^{-5}	1.57×10^{-2}	40	120	200	5.1×10^{4}	8×10^{2}
25	4.9×10^{-6}	7.8×10^{-3}	80	240	400	2.04×10^{5}	1.58×10^{3}
10	7.8×10^{-7}	3.15×10^{-3}	200	600	1000	1.28×10^{6}	4×10^{3}
5	1.96×10^{-7}	1.57×10^{-3}	400	1200	2000	5.1×10^{6}	8×10^{3}
1	7.8×10^{-9}	3.15×10^{-4}	2000	6000	10000	1.28×10^{8}	4×10^{4}
0.5	1.96×10^{-9}	1.57×10^{-4}	4000	12000	20000	5.1×10^{8}	8×10^{4}

Fiber Geometry of a Paper of 10-mil Thickness (0.025 cm.) of Packing
Density 0.5—Fiber Length 1.0 mm.

Theoretical Number of Fiber-to-Fiber Contacts per cm.³ of circular fibers $C = (D/2)^2 \cdot K$	$Np = N/80$	σp cm.² $p = Np \times S$	$Cp = (Np)^2$	Theoretical Number of Fiber Layers in Paper $F = 1/D$
4×10^7	160	5	2.56×10^4	2.5
6.5×10^8	625	10	3.9×10^5	5
1×10^{10}	2500	20	6.25×10^6	10
4×10^{11}	16000	50	2.56×10^8	25
6.5×10^{12}	62500	100	3.9×10^9	50
4×10^{15}	1600000	500	2.56×10^{12}	250
6.5×10^{16}	6250000	1000	3.9×10^{13}	500

153

TABLE 6.15

Fiber Dimension-Paper Structure Mathematical Relationships for Ribbon Fibers

$(d = packing)$

$\sigma = N \times S$

d Fiber Thickness (10^{-4} cm.)	w Fiber Width (10^{-2} cm.)	l Fiber Length (10^{-1} cm.)	Fiber Kind Metal	$V = d \times w \times l$ Fiber Volume ($l = 1$ cm.) cm.^{3}	$S = 2W.L.$ Fiber Surface ($l = 1$ cm.) cm.^{2}	Specific External Fiber Surface Area (per gram of fibers) ($D = 1$)	$N = 1/V$ Theoretical Number of Fibers (1 cm. length in 1 cm.^{3})	$R = l/d$ Length to Thickness Ratio ($l = 0.6$ cm.)	$R = l/d$ Length to Thickness Ratio ($l = 1$ cm.)	C_A Specific Theoretical Number of Crossing Points (per cm.^{3}) ($D = 0.5$)	C_S Theoretical Fiber-Fiber Contact (area/cm.^{3}, packing density: 0.5)
5	2	6-10-up	Ni	1×10^{-5}	4×10^{-2}	4×10^3	10^5	1200	2000	6.25×10^5	250
10	1.13	6-10-up	Al	1.13×10^{-5}	2.26×10^{-2}	2.26×10^2	8.8×10^4	600	1000	9.7×10^5	123
12.5	2	6-10-up	Al	2.5×10^{-5}	4×10^{-2}	4×10^2	4×10^4	480	800	2.50×10^5	100
17.5	1.13	6-10-up	Al	2×10^{-5}	2.26×10^{-2}	2.26×10^2	5×10^4	350	580	5.5×10^5	70
25	1.0	6-10-up	(tin)Sn	2.5×10^{-5}	1×10^{-2}	1×10^2	4×10^4	240	400	5×10^5	50
50	1.0	6-10-up	Pb	5×10^{-5}	1×10^{-2}	1×10^2	2×10^4	120	200	2.5×10^5	25

154

is influenced by heating is shown in Table 6.16, in which Ratliff's results of a typical run in a Lampen Ball Mill (44), are used. The fraction of total area entering into bonding is surprisingly high for cellulosic fibers. It can be concluded from Table 6.14 that for metal fiber paper a similar high total bonded area cannot be achieved for metal-paper structures made of fibers of 10 μ diameter or above; however, with submicron fibers the total bonded surface area of cellulosic fibers can be approached.

TABLE 6.16

Ratliff's Data on Development of Total and Bonded
Area by Beating (44)

Beating Time (min.)	Exposed Surface (cm./gm.)	Percentage of Area Bonded
0	9,200	49
20	9,700	67
40	10,600	72
95	19,000	85

Continued studies of synthetic-fiber webs have added to our understanding of interfiber relationships, bonding, and theoretical maximum strength of paper. Metal-fiber paper can be made of fibers of a strength (whiskers) higher than that of cellulosic fibers. The possibilities for controlling the fiber-to-fiber bonding by various means (sintering) should be of great utility in the theoretical approach to the study of the concepts of *fiber strength* versus *actual paper strength* and idealized *theoretical paper strength,* to be accomplished only by ideal fiber orientation.

To analyze the relationship between fiber strength and paper strength, imagine an ideal sheet of paper in which half of the fibers are aligned in the MD and the other half are aligned at right angles to the first, both in the plane of the paper. Further, let us suppose that the interfiber bonding and fiber length is such that only the fiber will rupture (44) and there is no failure of fiber-fiber bonds.

The theoretical strength of such an idealized paper may be calculated as follows:

Idealized theoretical paper strength
$$= \tfrac{1}{2}(\text{number of fibers/cm.}^3 \times \text{av. fiber strength})$$

The papermaker calls the zero-span tensile strength of paper the "theoretical maximum paper strength." The ratio of 10-cm.-span tensile (actual paper strength) to zero-span tensile is often referred to as "per cent bonding." The values reported in Table 6.17 are based on representative data from available sources and represent the order of magnitude that might be expected.

It will be noted that properly sintered stainless-steel paper yields a theoretically higher strength than cellulosic papers. Should the favorable relationship in Table 6.17 for the steel-fiber paper be-

TABLE 6.17
Theoretical Paper Strength—Breaking Length (meters)

Test	Unbleached Kraft	Cotton Linter Paper	Sintered Stainless Steel Fiber Mat
Average 10 cm. Breaking length	6,700	3,100	7,000
Average zero Breaking length	12,500	9,200	14,000
Average theoretical Maximum breaking length	19,800	16,700	18,800

tween zero-breaking length, 10-cm. breaking length, and theoretical maximum breaking length hold true also for ideally bonded paper manufactured of micron whisker metal fibers, then metal-fiber paper structures of a breaking length of 100,000 meters or higher appear within the realm of possibility. Such a sheet of paper is hypothetical at this time. Also, the inherent problems of unreliability of conventional test methods (damage to paper and fibers at the grip) have to be considered in the proposed strength analysis of metal and synthetic fiber papers.

THE MANUFACTURE OF NONWOVEN METAL-FIBER STRUCTURES

The development of metal-fiber nonwoven fabriclike paper structures, to be made on papermaking equipment, is being actively pursued by a number of laboratories. It is typical of the paper and nonwoven industry that the manufacture of random or oriented paper and nonwoven webs involves a considerable amount of confidentially held technical know-how in the selection of equipment, its operation, and in the choice of fiber dimensions, fiber blends, and bonding techniques. Manufacturing methods play so large a part in determining mechanical web properties that modified processing techniques or new types of equipment are often required to handle new fibers. The knowledge to realize the full potential of new metal fibers is probably not yet fully developed, but it can be said that great strides have been made since the first pilot-plant papermachine-made metal-fiber paper paper, containing up to 100% metal fibers, was produced at Hurlbut Paper Company in 1953.

The basic technique of metal-fiber papermaking or of fiber metallurgy is to felt the metal fibers, as practiced in papermaking (wetlay process) or nonwoven manufacture (airlay deposition) and then to bond the felted fibers by various means. Figure 6.34 is a flowchart of the metal-fiber paper-manufacturing method used by Mead Central Research. An aluminum-fiber paper roll produced by this method is shown in Figure 6.35, and the metal-fiber paper surface, in Figure 6.36. A simple fiber metallurgy flowchart of the method developed by Armour Research (46, 47) is given in Figure 6.37.

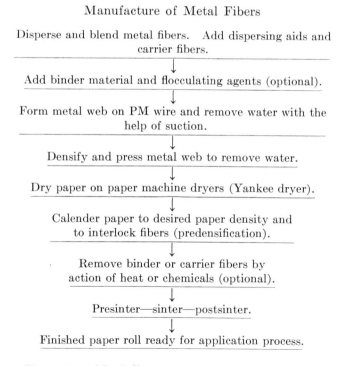

Manufacture of Metal Fibers

Disperse and blend metal fibers.   Add dispersing aids and carrier fibers.

↓

Add binder material and flocculating agents (optional).

↓

Form metal web on PM wire and remove water with the help of suction.

↓

Densify and press metal web to remove water.

↓

Dry paper on paper machine dryers (Yankee dryer).

↓

Calender paper to desired paper density and to interlock fibers (predensification).

↓

Remove binder or carrier fibers by action of heat or chemicals (optional).

↓

Presinter—sinter—postsinter.

↓

Finished paper roll ready for application process.

Figure 6.34.   Metal fiber paper manufacturing flowchart.

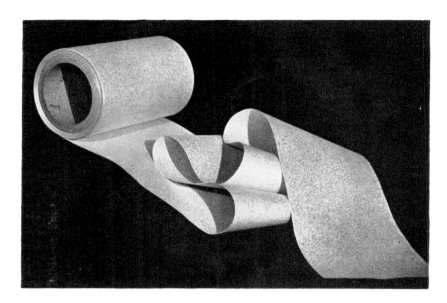

Figure 6.35. Roll of aluminum fiber paper.

Figure 6.36. Photomicrograph of steel-fiber paper.

The use of metal fibers introduces a number of new problems to papermaking. The papermaker, looking at metallic-fiber paper for the first time, will be puzzled by the fact that established concepts of paper basis weight, headbox stock consistency, wet-web moisture content at the wet press, paper-machine production, drying rate, speed, etc., are changed to a startling degree. Table 6.18 demonstrates the influence of specific gravity of the fibers on paper properties

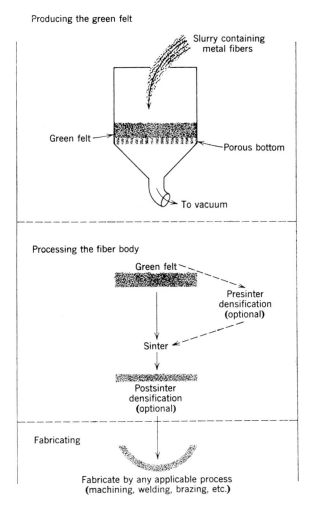

Figure 6.37. A simple fiber metallurgy flow chart.

TABLE 6.18

Influence of Specific Gravity of Fibers on Paper Properties and Papermaking Factors
(equivalent conditions)

Fiber Kind	Fiber and Paper Properties				Paper Machine Manufacturing Conditions		
Fiber Diameter: 15 to 20 μ Fiber Length 0.4 cm. (assumed equal)	Specific Gravity of Fibers	Thickness of Paper (cm.)	Paper Weight (gm./m.²)	Packing Density or Air Voids in Paper (uncalendered or calendered) (%)	Headbox Stock Consistency (gm./l.)	Wet-Web Moisture Content at Wet Press (%)	Paper-Machine Production and Drying Rate at Equal PM Speed (lb./hr.)
Polypropylene	0.92	0.025	115	50	2	80	1,000
Cotton	1.6	0.025	200	50	3.5	70	1,670
Aluminum	2.71	0.025	335	50	6.0	58	3,000+
Stainless steel	7.75	0.025	960	50	17	37.5	8,300+
Lead	11.34	0.025	1410	50	25	25	12,300+
Tungsten	19.3	0.025	2400	50	42	16	21,000+

and factors in manufacture. In reaching conditions comparable to running cellulose on the paper machine, the headbox stock consistency can shift from 2 to 42 gm./l., wet-web moisture content from 80 to 16% by weight, and the theoretical paper-machine production rate can skyrocket from 1000 to 21,000 lb./hr. as a result of the difference in specific gravity of fibers.

The papermaker also has to learn that the addition of binder or carrier fibers to the papermaking stock must be based on volume per cent solids and not on weight per cent. Table 6.19 shows binder and carrier, or blending fiber, equivalents based on theoretical calculations but approaching the experimental reality. Assuming that metal fibers with dimensions adjusted for the ultimate paper properties and manufacturing-process variables can be obtained, the production of metal-fiber paper is a fairly easy task. This is not generally true, however, because the less expensive types of metal fibers available today possess dimensions and specific gravities different from those observed on usual papermaking fibers. It is therefore necessary to use more sophisticated fiber-dispersion methods. The use of mucilaginous materials, such as polyvinyl alcohol, and carrier fibers, such as cellulose, submicron glass, or organic synthetic fibrillated fibers, to help disperse the metal fibers to reduce the incidence of excessive settling, to prevent fiber entanglement, and to bond the dry and wet sheet has been recommended. In some cases it may be advantageous to spin the metal fibers directly into the headbox water stream to prevent the possibility of fiber entanglement during storage and shipping.

There are two basic fiber structures possible for nonwoven fabrics or paper webs: oriented web structure and random web structure. In the oriented, the fibers are essentially parallel and result in a web with good strength properties in the machine direction but reduced strength in the cross (transverse) direction. The random web, on the other hand, is characterized by the lack of parallelism of the fibers and produces a material of essentially equal strength in all directions. Both highly oriented and random webs can be produced theoretically from metal fibers with modern techniques on papermaking or airlay equipment. The choice of paper-machine type depends on the degree of fiber orientation required and on fiber characteristics such as stiffness, fiber length, diameter, flexibility, surface conditions, resilience, dispersibility, abrasion resistance, compacting factor, and freeness. Any one of the Fourdrinier, cylinder, Rotoformer, or nonwoven machines may have the optimum potential for producing a particular result.

TABLE 6.19
Binder and Carrier Fiber Equivalents for Metal Fiber Paper

Fiber Kind	Specific Gravity of Fibers	Binder or Carrier Fiber Amount in Paper		Theoretical Equivalent Amount for Equal Performance		Theoretical Equivalent Glass Submicron Carrier Fibers for Approximate Equal Performance	
		% By Weight	% By Volume	% By Weight	% By Volume	% By Weight	% By Volume
Polypropylene	0.92	10	7.8	10	7.8	13.4	5
Chemical Cotton	1.6	10	14.8	6	7.8	8.15	5
Aluminum	2.71	10	20	3.85	7.8	5	5
Steel	7.75	10	34.2	1.35	7.8	1.80	5
Lead	11.34	10	51.0	0.95	7.8	1.25	5
Tungsten	19.3	10	64	0.56	7.8	0.73	5

Specific gravity of binder: 1.2
Specific gravity of carrier glass fibers: 2.71

Fibers with a length in excess of 1¼ in. are better utilized by the drylay processes; fibers with less than 1-in. length, or, particularly, very thin fibers, are best used with the wetlay process. The theoretical lower and upper limits of thickness and basis weight for the manufacture of metal-fiber webs depends entirely on the geometry of the available fibers (thickness and length), the flexibility and handling characteristics of these fibers, and the desired density of the paper web.

The probability of being able to form a paper web from metal fibers depends on fiber thickness, and this relationship can be assessed from Table 6.20. The wet- and dry-web strength of a synthetic-fiber web is a function of the available number of fibers per square centimeter, the number of fiber-to-fiber crossing points, the theoretical number of fiber layers that can be formed from these fibers, the fiber length, and other fiber characteristics.

In a mathematical survey it can be assumed that the fibers show the same degree of flexibility, forming characteristics, dispersibility, etc. This, of course, is not so in reality. With increasing fiber diameter, the stiffness of the fiber also increases. This will help dispersibility but, at the same time, will be detrimental to wet-web strength. The web of such a paper will be bulkier and the apparent density of the paper will be lower. Certain short metal fibers, for instance, require a minimum of 25 fiber layers per unit of *uncompressed* paper thickness to form a sheet well and to obtain the required minimum dry- and wet-web strength. Table 6.20 reveals that for such a fiber material an "off-machine" paper of 10-mil thickness would require fibers with a maximum diameter of 10 μ. The thickness of this paper can be reduced by compression to 5 mils or less. Metal-fiber webs made of ductile metals such as copper, tin, and lead, can be densified to a high degree. With increasing fiber length, the number of theoretical fiber layers per web thickness can be reduced, but will still maintain sufficient strength. Blending of coarse metal fibers with fine diameter metal, glass (submicron diameter), or other fibers is another way to reduce the metal-web thickness. Calendered metal-fiber papers of a thickness as low as 2 to 3 mil have been achieved. Some of the coarser metal fibers could be made into webs no thinner than 10 to 30 mils.

THE BONDING OF METAL FIBER WEBS

In contrast to cellulose fibers, which bond naturally by the mechanism of fibrillation, smooth metal fibers require a special treatment

TABLE 6.20

Relationship Between Paper Thickness and Fiber Diameter Based on Theoretical Number of Fiber Layers and Available Fibers per Squared Centimeter

d Paper Thickness (mil)	Paper Thickness (cm.)	F Fiber Thickness (10^{-4} cm.)	Theoretical Number of Fiber Layers d/F	Theoretical Number of Fibers of 1-cm. Length per cm.^{2} Apparent Density of Paper			Theoretical Number of Fiber-Fiber Crossing Points/cm.^{2} Paper. Apparent Density of Paper		
				0.5	0.25	0.125	0.5	0.25	0.125
1	0.0025	1	25	500	250	125	6.25×10^4	1.56×10^4	3.9×10^3
		5	5	100	50	25	2.5×10^3	6.25×10^2	1.56×10^2
		10	2.5	50	25	12.5	6.25×10^2	1.56×10^2	3.9×10^1
		25	1	20	10	5	1×10^2	2.5×10^1	6.25
10	0.025	1	250	5,000	2,500	1,250	6.25×10^6	1.56×10^6	3.9×10^5
		5	50	1,000	500	250	2.5×10^5	6.25×10^4	1.56×10^4
		10	25	500	250	125	6.25×10^4	1.56×10^4	3.9×10^3
		50	5	100	50	25	2.5×10^3	6.25×10^2	1.56×10^2
		100	2.5	50	25	12.5	2.5×10^2	1.56×10^2	3.9×10^1
100	0.25	1	2500	50,000	25,000	12,500	6.25×10^8	1.56×10^8	3.9×10^7
		5	500	10,000	5,000	2,500	2.5×10^7	6.25×10^6	1.56×10^6
		10	250	5,000	2,500	1,250	6.25×10^6	1.56×10^6	3.9×10^5
		50	50	1,000	500	250	2.5×10^5	6.25×10^4	1.56×10^4
		100	25	500	250	125	6.25×10^4	1.56×10^4	3.9×10^4

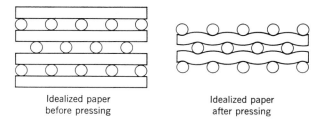

Idealized paper
before pressing

Idealized paper
after pressing

Figure 6.38. Idealized cross-sectional structure.

to develop the necessary strength for further processing in the form of paper. This strength can be attained by the formation of bonds in which individual metal fibers touch each other.

MECHANICAL INTERLOCKING

The properties of metal-fiber paper can be vastly changed by mechanical interlocking of the fibers accomplished by calendering the paper to a higher density. An idealized cross-sectional structure of a metal-fiber web, before and after pressing, is shown in Figure 6.38. The fiber-to-fiber contact area is small before pressing but increases considerably with pressing. This is particularly noticeable for cylindrical fibers, as illustrated in the idealized structural diagram Figure 6.39.

The mechanical interlocking of fibers not only increases the paper strength but can also increase the electrical conductivity of the web by a factor of 10^2 to 10^5. The use of fiber blends, specifically mixtures of soft ductile alloy-metal fibers in combination with harder alloy-metal fibers, can also improve the bonding strength. The compression bonding (calendering) of the metal-fiber web can be done before and/or after drying.

Before pressing

After pressing

Figure 6.39. Idealized fiber structure.

METAL ADDITION AGENTS

Addition agents may be used to promote superior bonds at points where the fibers come in contact. One example is the use of copper to braze iron fibers to improve the strength and ductility after a suitable heat treatment; another is the use of controlled reduction reactions during sintering. Additions to the fibers can be made by coating and sheeting techniques, such as electrodeposition or extrusion coating. Likewise, a lower-melting-point metal powder can be incorporated as a filler into the metal-fiber web during manufacture.

CHEMICAL BONDING

Metal-fiber paper can be bonded similarly to synthetic-fiber or cellulosic papers by the internal addition of a resin. Any suitable binders such as latex or acrylic resins can be used, as can fibrous binders such as cellulose, fibrillated acrylic fibers, nylon, or Dacron fibrids. The use of small percentages of thermoplastic fibers or resin powders has proved to be another useful bonding tool.

SINTERING

Sintering at optimum temperatures in inert or reducing atmosphere is the most effective way to increase the strength of a metal-fiber paper manyfold. Strength increases of 10 to 100 times, depending on sintering conditions and web speed, are reported. Pressure sintering, a technique employed for friction material, is sometimes useful (48). The strength of sintered metal-fiber paper is further increased by compression to expand the fiber-fiber contact area before the sintering.

COMBINATION BONDING

A novel method of producing metal-fiber webs utilizes combinations of bonding principles (49, 50). Metal fibers of optimum length are dispersed with the help of carrier and bonding fibers, which also provide the required wet-web and dry-web strength for paper-machine operations. The paper web, containing foreign binder fibers or materials, is then compressed by calender rolls to obtain interlocking of the long metal fibers and, in a secondary operation, is exposed to chemical action (49) or high heat (50) to remove the organic and/or inorganic binder and carrier fibers. Removal of binder and presintering of the paper web can be achieved in one operation. For example, continuous aluminum-fiber web of good handling strength and low electrical resistance (10^{-2} to 10^{-3} ohm cm.) was obtained by exposing a cellulosic bonded aluminum fiber web in a heat-treating oven at a temperature of 1200 to 1300°F. and a web speed of 6 ft./minute.

Among the many bonding systems investigated, none can be regarded as fully satisfactory for economy or other reasons. The problem of developing the most economical and practical bonding system of metal-fiber webs continues to be the concern of the manufacturer. The papermaking process has the advantage that metal-fiber papers can be made of almost any type of fibers and almost any combination of fiber blends and binder systems. The ability of the papermaker and metallurgist to engineer these products for specific applications will be an important factor in the future development of metal-fiber paper, nonwoven fabrics, and fiber metals.

PROPERTIES OF METAL-FIBER PAPERS AND FIBER METALS

The possibilities for the manufacture of metal-fiber paper were extensively investigated by The Mead Corporation and Hurlbut Paper Company, South Lee, Mass. (52). The properties of 100% aluminum-fiber paper, as well as blends of aluminum fibers formulated with relatively small percentages of cellulosic fibers as binders, are listed in Table 6.21 (53) and Table 6.22, respectively. Synthetic

TABLE 6.21
Properties of 100% Aluminum-Fiber Paper (53)

	A	B
Basis weight (24 × 36–500), lb.	250	210
Thickness, mils	10	9.5
Specific gravity	1.65	1.4
Pore volume, %	40	48
Densometer: 400 cm.³, sec.	85	15
Tensile strength, gm./in.	2200	1200
Burst, lb.	6	4

organic fibrous binders are especially valuable in conjunction with paper-grade metal fibers (see Table 6.23). The properties of a 2% rubber-bonded paper consisting of 94% aluminum fibers and 6% submicron glass fibers are reported in Table 6.24.

TABLE 6.22
Physical Properties of Paper Comprising Blends 85 and 92%
by Weight Aluminum Fibers

Paper Grade	0.2950	0.2950-C	O-2941	P-1055	P-1055-C
Aluminum by weight, %	92	92	85	85	85
Cellulosic fiber by weight, %	8	8	15	15	15
Basic weight (24 × 36–500), lb.	274	272	260	158	158
Thickness, mil	39	11	35	24.3	10
Tensile strength gm./in.	2500	1900	4600	6100	5900
Wet tensile, gm./in.	750	1050	1200	1500	2000
Bursting strength, p.s.i.	6	4.5	9	12	12
Volume % metal fiber	10	34	9.3	8.2	20

TABLE 6.23
Properties of Paper Made of Metal Fibers
and Organic Synthetic Fibers

Paper Grade	2955	2955-C
% Aluminum	84	84
% Organic synthetic fibers	16	16
Basis weight (24 × 36–500), lb.	202	196
Thickness, mils	43	12
Specific gravity gm./cm.^{3}	0.31	1.06
Densometer 400 cm.^{3} air	0.5	1
Tensile strength, gm./in.	2100	3500
Mullen, lb.	5.5	4
Pore volume, %	86	54
Fiber volume in paper, %	14	46

TABLE 6.24
Physical Properties of Paper Containing 94% Aluminum Fibers
and 6% Glass Fibers

Paper Grade	O-2949	O-2949-C	G-193
Basis weight (24 × 36–500), lb.	274	288	189
Thickness, mil	36	14	25
Tensile strength, gm./in.	2600	1400	4500
Mullen test, lb.	8.5	5	8.2
Volume % metal fiber	17.3	45	17.2

The data in Table 6.25 show how calender pressure influences the tensile strength and porosity of 92% steel fiber plus 8% cellulose-

TABLE 6.25

Influence of Calender Pressure on Properties of Paper Containing 92% Steel Fibers (53)

	I	II	III	IV
Calendering pressure, p.s.i.	None	2000	3000	4000
Weight, gm./m.^{2}	506	488	490	530
Thickness, mils	30	13.7	11.3	9.3
Specific gravity, gm./cm.^{3}	0.66	1.39	1.70	2.22
Tensile strength, gm./in.	1870	1950	1860	2250
Pore volume—air voids in paper, %	89	76.8	73.3	61

fiber paper. It will be noted that the tensile strength of the paper does not change appreciably. However, it was found that the metal fibers interlock on calendering densification, and the paper web develops sufficient handling strength for subsequent removal of the organic fibers by heat treatment, presintering and/or sintering of the remaining 100% metal web. The properties of a sintered 100% stain-

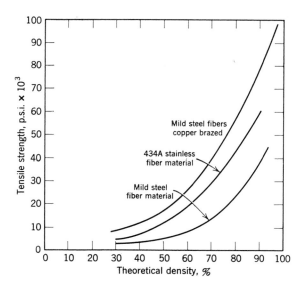

Figure 6.40. Tensile strength of porous fibre materials.

less-steel web are listed in Table 6.26. Read (46) reported the strength and porosity relationship of pressed and sintered steel-fiber mats shown in Table 6.27 and Figure 6.40. The impact properties of sintered-iron metal-fiber mats reported by Metcalfe et al. (4) are shown in Table 6.28. Electrical properties of certain aluminum metal-fiber process, which depend to some extent on the paper-proc-

TABLE 6.26
Properties of Sintered Stainless Steel Webs

Properties	I Stainless Steel A 302 SS (fine)	II Stainless Steel B 430 SS (coarse)
Basis weight (24 × 36–500), lb.	155	280
Thickness, mils	100	85
Volume % metal fibers	13	26
Densometer 400 ml./in.^{2} sec.	0.3	0.1
Electrical resistance ohm/cm.	0.01	0.04
Tensile strength gm./in.	16,000	80,000

(Tests by Mead Central Research Laboratories)

TABLE 6.27
Fiber Volume and Strength of Pressed and Sintered Steel-Fiber Mats

Ultimate Tensile Strength (p.s.i.)

Volume % Fibers	430 SS Fine	Mild Steel Fibers	Mild Steel Fibers, Copper Brazed
45	5,000	3,000	14,000
61	15,000	9,000	30,000
80	20,000	19,000	55,000

TABLE 6.28
Impact Properties of Sintered Iron Metal-Fiber Mats (4)

Volume % Metal	Izod Impact Strength (ft.-lb.)
15	1.0
30	2.0
55	4.0

ess variables, are listed in Tables 6.29 and Table 6.30. Metal-fiber webs, under the trade name "Felt Metal," are now available in pilot-

TABLE 6.29
Electrical Resistance of Aluminum Fiber Paper

Mead Research Pilot-Plant Grade	Metal Fibers Employed	Volume % Metal Fiber	Treatment of Paper Web	Electrical Resistance (ohm/cm.)
P-196	Avisco aluminum fibers	0.30	None (off paper machine)	2000
P-196 H	Avisco aluminum fibers	0.30	Web heat treatment 1300°F.	0.04
P-196 HT	Avisco aluminum fibers	0.30	P-196 H 40% resin content	0.04
P-258	Reynolds staple aluminum fibers	0.35	None (off paper machine)	300
P-258 H	Reynolds staple aluminum fibers	0.33	Web heat treatment 1200°F.	1.5
L-2995 L	SOS fine aluminum fibers	0.4	50% resin treated, laminated	0.002

TABLE 6.30
Electrical Resistance of Metal Fiber Paper (53)

	I	II	III
Metal fibers, %	100% aluminum	92% aluminum	80% aluminum
Resistance in ohms for 1 cm. distance 5 cm. length and specified contact pressure	0.3–1.0	1.0–1.5	6–14

plant quantities from the Huyck Corporation. "Felt Metal" may be considered a metallic analogy of paper.

METAL-PAPER OR FELT-METAL APPLICATIONS

Fiber-metal structures, metal-fiber papers, and metal fibers under development by Armour Research Foundation, Mead Central Research Laboratories, and many others have been available for several years in laboratory or pilot-sized quantities. This initiated considerable research to determine the merits and demerits of these unique engineering materials. Many new applications for these materials have been described in the literature.

STRUCTURAL AND DECORATIVE LAMINATES

A particularly advantageous use for paper made from metal fibers is in the laminated structural and decorative fields (53). Metal-fiber paper, when used on or below the decorative surface layer of a plastic laminate (table tops, etc.), shows much higher resistance to cigarette burns, and resists delamination better than metal foil laminates under severe conditions of heat and moisture exposure. One might project the possibility that such structural materials could be important in rocket and space technology.

Absorbent metal-fiber paper with uniform formation and electrical resistance can be manufactured, and laminates containing one or more layers of metal-fiber overlay paper, with 20 to 40% phenolic or melamine resin content, can be made with controlled electrical resist-

TABLE 6.31

Electrical Resistance of Laminates Surfaced with Melamine-Treated Metal-Fiber Paper Overlay (53)

Paper Grade	O-2955	O-2944-C	O-2949-C	O-2942-C
Resistance in ohms measured on embedded wires for 5.2-in. distance and 6-in. length	0.2	1.7	6.6	110
Volts to produce heating of surface to approximately 100 to 120°F.	2	3(−6)	13	25

ance (53), as shown in Table 6.31. This construction could be utilized in aircraft de-icing systems, heating panels, etc.

METAL-FIBER PAPER-REINFORCED PLASTICS

Early data obtained by Mead Central Research show that metal-fiber paper can be employed as a reinforcing medium for plastics in direct competition with glass mats, glass-fiber paper, and woven glass fabrics or synthetic-fiber paper. For maximum reinforcement metal-

fiber webs are made of medium- to high-strength metal fibers of
a length in excess of 4 to 6 mm., unless other properties, such
as fatigue strength, thermal and electrical conductance, magnetic
properties, wear resistance, and modulus of elasticity, are major
considerations. Absorbent papers produced of low strength or very
short metal fibers yield phenolic laminates with characteristics
similar to cellulosic paper laminates. Phenolic laminates of long-
fibered steel-fiber paper (50% volume) show equal or less impact
or flexural strength than comparable laminates reinforced with glass-
fiber paper. If the specific gravity of the laminates is taken into
consideration (steel 7.75, glass 2.7), there can be no doubt that glass-
strand reinforcement is favored by the results as far as flexural and
impact strengths are concerned.

Read (46) reported the results of metal-fiber reinforcements of
epoxy resins as listed in Table 6.32. His findings confirm the previous

TABLE 6.32
Metal Fiber Reinforcement of Epoxy Resins (46)

Metal Fiber	Volume (%)	Impact Strength (ft.-lb./in. notch)	Flexure Modulus of Rupture (p.s.i.)	Modulus of Elasticity (10^6 p.s.i.)
None		1	8,500	0.44
Aluminum	25[1]	3	10,000	0.7
	50[1]	6	12,500	0.9
	75[1]	8	17,500	2.1
430 stainless steel	25[1]	4	12,500	1.6
	50[1]	6	18,000	1.8
	75[1]	8	25,000	2.2
	83[2]	11.5	64,300	17.0
Mild steel	50[3]	5	59,900	16.3
Molybdenum	30[1]	32	62,000	4.3

[1] Unbonded fibers.
[2] Bonded (sintered) fibers.
[3] Unbonded, very long fibers perpendicular to applied stress.

conclusions for regular aluminum and 430 stainless-steel webs. The
values shown in this table for the *sintered* stainless-steel mat, the
long-fibered directional mild steel, and the molybdenum laminate
demonstrate the inherent potential of properly designed metal-fiber

webs to attain strength improvement for specific laminate applications.

The strength of a fiber-web reinforced plastic laminate is a function of the strength of the reinforcing fibers, the volume per cent of reinforcing fibers, and the fiber length. Both experiments and theory have supported the conclusion that, with proper adhesion between fibers and matrix using straight fibers, maximum strength can be obtained with the proper layup with a fiber length as short as $\frac{1}{2}$ in. The strength of the laminate decreases with decreasing fiber length below $\frac{1}{2}$ in. These facts will have to be considered for the manufacture of metal reinforcing mats or papers for laminates of optimum strength characteristics.

FIBER-REINFORCED METAL COMPOSITES

Many fiber-reinforced metal composites have been investigated in recent years (54–59). The tensile strength of pure magnesium in the

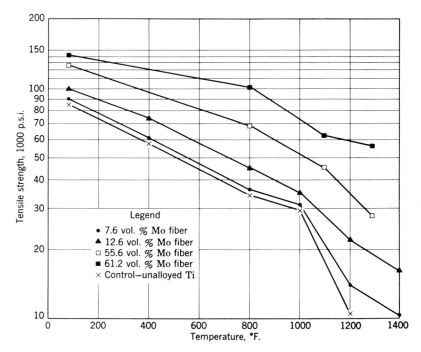

Figure 6.41. Tensile strength of staple molybdenum fibre reinforced unalloyed titanium (Clevite Research Centre), DMIC report 117, 1959.

as-cast condition can be increased by reinforcing with a steel fiber, as reported by Read (Table 6.33). Continuous metal-fiber webs can

TABLE 6.33
Strength of As-Cast Magnesium Reinforced with Steel-Fiber Body

% Steel Fiber (by volume)	Tensile Strength, (p.s.i.)	$\dfrac{\text{Tensile Strength}}{\text{Density}}$
0	7,600	4,370
4.5	10,700	5,350
9	18,950	8,430
27	39,870	12,100

be envisioned as running through a bath of molten magnesium or other metals to form metal-fiber-reinforced metal structures.

Among many others, titanium alloys reinforced with metal fibers have been extensively studied by the Clevite Research Center (54). The results are interesting because staple-fiber-reinforced titanium composite produced by Halladay by conventional powder-metallurgy methods could also be manufactured with new, but established, paper-making methods of producing webs of mixtures of metal fibers (molybdenum) and metal powder (titantium). These mixtures would then be compacted and vacuum sintered. Mead Central Research Laboratories has produced metal-fiber papers containing greater than 50 volume % of metal powders (aluminum).

In other experiments (55, 56) copper of a strength of 30,000 p.s.i. was strengthened to more than 120,000 p.s.i. by adding 35% wire-type tungsten fibers with a strength of 300,000 p.s.i. It is reported in the same source that this strength could also be obtained with very short lengths of fibers, and Carroll-Porczynski (19) speculates that if whiskers of a tensile strength of 2,000,000 p.s.i. could be employed the composite would have a strength of more than 1 million p.s.i.

CERAMICS REINFORCED WITH METAL FIBER

Several investigations have proved that the incorporation of a uni-form fine-metal skeleton in a refractory ceramic can improve thermal shock and impact resistance, flexural strength, etc. (61–68). Several metal-fiber ceramic composites have been patented in recent years (69, 70). Armour Research Foundation (46) prepared metal-fiber-reinforced ceramic rocket nose cones by felting refractory tungsten

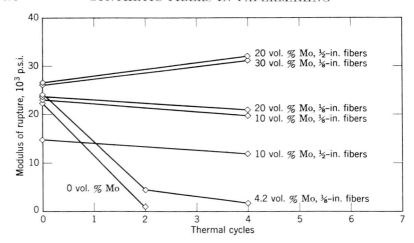

Figure 6.42. Modulus of rupture as a function of thermal cycling of molybdenum fibre reinforced ceramic (body 712).

metal fibers of 125 μ diameter and vacuum impregnating the shaped fiber-web skeleton with a ceramic dispersion. There is a good possibility that very open low-density metal-fiber paper webs can accelerate the development of new composite ceramic materials. Exploratory experiments with a molybdenum-fiber ceramic body consisting of 58.5 volume % mullite and 41.5 volume % alumina mixed with 0.43% molybdenum fibers of $\frac{1}{8}$- to $\frac{1}{2}$-in. lengths were reported by Swica et al. (62).

It may be observed in Table 6.34 that after four thermal shock cycles the composite structure containing 25 volume % fibers can have a modulus of rupture as high as 32,000 p.s.i. Among the many interesting results reported by Swica (62), the findings about the influence of fiber diameter, mixtures of fiber diameters, fiber length, and fiber volume are particularly noteworthy in connection with papermaking theories. Figure 6.42 shows, for example, that fibers $\frac{1}{2}$-in. long, at 20 volume % molybdenum fibers, provide greater reinforcing value than is obtained with $\frac{1}{8}$-in. fibers.

SOUND ABSORPTION OF METAL FIBER MATS

R. H. Read (46) reports that metal-fiber mats show promise as high temperature, high vibration, corrosion-resistant sound absorbers. Table 6.35 shows that stainless-steel metal webs compare favorably

TABLE 6.34
Exploratory Experiments with Molybdenum Fiber Body 712 (62)

Dimensions of Molybdenum Fiber (in.)	Volume % Fiber	Modulus E at r.t. (10^6 p.s.i.)	Modulus E Calculated (10^6 p.s.i.)	Modulus of Rupture After Four Cycles (p.s.i.)	% Total Stress Assumed by Fiber (calculated)	Stress Assumed by 712 (calculated) (p.s.i.)
$0.008 \times \frac{1}{4}$	30	40.5	36	27,900	35.0	18,150
$0.002 \times \frac{1}{8}$	30	35.7	36	30,700	35.0	20,000
$0.006 \times \frac{1}{4}$	43	36.5	37.5	36,800	48.8	18,900
0.006×3	25	35.4	35.9	32,000	29.0	22,735
$0.002 \times \frac{1}{8}$	4.2	32.2	34.2	1,400	5.24	(average stress: 19,946)
None	0	33.8	—	0		

TABLE 6.35
Sound Absorption (%)

Sound Frequency, (c.p.s.)	Sintered Stainless Fiber Body ($2\frac{1}{2}$-in. thick)	Unbonded Fiberglas Batt (3-in. thick)
250	47	39
500	80	69
1000	94	83
2000	93	95

with unbonded Fiberglas at room temperature. However, similar results were obtained up to 1500°F., as reported by Armour Research Foundation Laboratories.

VIBRATION DAMPING

Metal-fiber materials can absorb mechanical vibration, that is, they have a high internal damping capacity. Tests (46) showed that stainless-steel sheets of 20 and 24% fiber volume density had resonant magnification factors of 4.6 and 13, respectively, whereas an aluminum (1100) sheet of equivalent weight per unit area had a magnification factor of 27.

FILTER APPLICATIONS

For the filter engineer metal-fiber webs and metal-fiber paper provide a new spectrum of metallic or composite filter mats, with few limitations in material selection and with wide ranges of pore sizes, chemical resistance, heat resistance, and catalytic effects. Metal fibers becoming available now can be produced in mean diameters of 10 to 100 μ or more, and, if required, finer fiber diameters (still very expensive) can be manufactured. Thus metal fiber webs of average pore diameter as small as 5 μ and up to 100 μ at moderate densities are reported (see Table 6.36). Still finer pore sizes can be envisioned with metal fibers of 1 to 5 μ diameter or less.

TABLE 6.36

Filter Properties of Sintered Stainless-Steel Filter Paper Mats

Fiber nature	Fine	Coarse
Basis weight (24 $\times$ 36–500), lb.	160	280
Thickness, mils	100	85
Volume % stainless steel	13	26
Air porosity, ft.^{3}/min./ft.^{2} at 0.5 in. H_2O	44	140
Approximate pore size in microns	6	$\sim$100
Bubble point in H_2O	56	>4

(Tests by Mead Central Research Laboratories).

Filter structures of high temperature resistance and strength, with pore sizes below 5 μ can be obtained by using composite webs of fine metal fibers and high-melting-point ceramic fibers of 1 to 2 μ fiber diameter. Metal-fiber webs can show varying degrees of porosity, 10 to 50% or more packing density, and their air permeability can be adjusted over wide ranges; for instance, 10 to 200 c.f./ft.^{2}/minute at 0.5 in water pressure drop (A.S.T.M. method D-737-46), more or less, depending on fiber size, web thickness, and density (porosity).

Material in Design Engineering reports that the Purolator Company is now using metal-fiber filters for high temperature filtration of corrosive materials.

MAGNETIC SURFACES

A phenolic-melamine laminate surfaced with, or containing, one or more layers of an absorbent steel-fiber paper, with or without the addition of iron or ferrite powder filler, shows good magnetic surface properties and can hold permanent magnets (71).

THERMAL BARRIERS

Sintered metal-fiber felts or papers can serve as efficient thermal barriers. Read et al. (47) tested stainless-steel-fiber plates of equal weight per unit area, in comparison with nonporous plates of the same steel, with an oxyacetylene flame. They report that the time required to show heat damage is 10 times longer than with nonporous plates.

GASKETS

Increasingly severe conditions in novel machine designs have necessitated special gasketing materials of high temperature resistance, controlled compressibility, elastic recovery, and good resistance to spread under load. Metal-fiber paper and metal-fiber webs can be manufactured of heterogenous mixtures of metal fibers, asbestos, glass, metal powders, synthetic fibers (Teflon, etc.), and ceramic and plastic materials. In future developments the papermaker should be able to make his own contributions.

HEAT- AND SHOCK-RESISTANT METALLIC CLOTH

Fabrics and nonwoven materials of the future may be produced of stainless steel or metal wire of fibers drawn so fine that the flexibility of the products will approach normal textile fibers. Apparel made of such fabrics can either collect solar energy or they can keep the wearer cool in summer. Inexpensive metal fibers or wires of reduced thickness are required to achieve this goal.

Table **6.37** (**72**) shows the diameter of metal fibers required to

TABLE 6.37
Diameters of Materials With Flexibilities Equal to Nylon (72)

Material	Modulus of Elasticity (p.s.i.)	Diameter Required (μ)[1]
Nylon	400,000	19.0
Carbon	700,000	16.8
Fiberglas	8,000,000	9.1
Fused silica	10,000,000	8.6
Columbium	22,700,000	7.1
Iron, nickel	30,000,000	6.6
Tungsten, molybdenum	50,000,000	5.8

[1] To give flexibilities equivalent to 19-μ nylon filaments.

make a given material as flexible as 19 μ nylon fibers. In addition, the modulus is given for each material. Reducing the diameter of the fibers by one half will improve the flexibility by a factor of 16.

OTHER METAL-FIBER PAPER AND FELT-METAL APPLICATIONS

Metal-fiber paper and fibrous metal can serve many useful and attractive purposes in areas of which the potentialities are not yet fully assessed. Listed below are some representative applications pioneered by Armour Research Foundation and many others (1–3, 46, 47, 71–80):

1. Battery plates (60)
2. Fuel-cell electrodes
3. Catalysts
4. Heat exchangers
5. Capacitors
6. Porous self-lubricating bearing material
7. High-heat-resistant brake linings
8. Gas mixers or diffusers
9. Transportational cooling devices
10. Boundary layer control
11. Fluidized beds
12. Air bearings or conveyors
13. Gas-fired infrared burners
14. High-temperature and corrosion-resistant wicks
15. Radio frequency shielding
16. Waveguide channels
17. Sonar absorbers
18. Friction materials

PAPER-STEEL WIRE COMPOSITE

Paper and steel or metal wires have been combined in a new composite which can hold any shape or can be heated with electricity. It consists of fine steel or resistance wires incorporated into the paper (79) or laminated between two sheets of paper with a water-resistant bonding agent (80).

GLASS FIBERS WITH CONDUCTIVE SURFACE

Glass-fiber rovings rendered electrically conductive by surface treatment are made into a core in automobile ignition wires to suppress signals generated by the high-frequency pulsating current of the ignition system. These electrical conductive glass fibers were used in several 1964 passenger cars and trucks, thus demonstrating the increasing number of volume applications (82).

FUTURE OUTLOOK

The paper machine is a tool designed for mass production. The production rate of even a small pilot-plant paper machine of 12-in. width can reach metal-fiber paper production rates of several thousand pounds of paper per day, even at slow speed. The manufacture of metal-fiber paper with high-speed production paper machines will become a reality only when the price of the metal fibers can be reduced to make their utilization attractive for the application engineer. The papermaker is prepared to start mass production of felted metal-fiber webs when economical metal fibers of the required dimensions become available and when a market can be developed for these new engineering structures. A promising start has been made, and only time can tell if the new engineering tools created by the metallurgist and paper-maker will find the volume applications predicted for them.

ACKNOWLEDGMENTS

My most grateful thanks go to Dr. Bruce Brookbank and Mr. Stanley Knowles of the Mead Central Research Laboratories in Chillicothe, Ohio, who helped with the arrangement and grammatical clarification of the manuscript.

My sincere thanks are due Mr. E. L. Scott and Mr. F. P. Lee, Jr., for providing the photomicrographs used in this chapter and to Dr. D. C. McIntosh for data on the strength of metal fibers.

The assistance of co-workers, both at the Hurlbut Paper Company in South Lee, Mass., and the Mead Central Research Laboratories in Chillicothe, Ohio, in the preparation and testing of the samples reported herein, is gratefully acknowledged.

My special appreciation is due Dr. J. C. Redd, General Manager of Research, and the Mead Corporation for permission to publish.

REFERENCES

1. U. S. Patent 1,447,347, Steel-Asbestos Felts, Kirschbaum.
2. German Patent 695,579, Elastic Gaskets, P. Lechler.
3. H. Basler, "Heat Conducting Board," A.P.C. 291,499 (May 4, 1953).
4. A. G. Metcalfe, C. H. Sump, and W. C. Troy, *Metal Progr.*, 81 (March 1955).

5. Thomas D. Callinan, R. T. Lucas, and R. C. Bowers, "The Electrical Properties of Glass Fiber Paper," Naval Research Lab., May 1951, *NBC Tech. News Bull.*, **35**, 177 (December 1951).
6. H. F. Arledter, *TAPPI*, **41**, No. 4 (April 1958).
7. H. F. Arledter, "New Developments in Industrial Filter Paper," paper presented at American Chemical Society National Meeting, September 13, 1954.
8. Trade name of the Huyck Corporation.
9. G. Shaefer, German Patent 78,671, Wire-Wool Machine.
10. British Patent 268,244, Metal Wool-Making Machine, Brillo Manufacturing Company.
11. *Mod. Mater.*, Section "E" **1**, 181 (Academic, New York, 1958).
12. L. Kratky, *Hutnicke Listy*, **14**, No. 6, 499 (1959).
13. J. F. C. Morden, "Metallic Fibers," *Metal Ind.*, 496 (June 17, 1960).
14. British Patent 814,490, Forming Metal Fibers and Filaments, Marvalaud, Inc.
15. U. S. Patent 2,976,590, Marvalaud, Inc.
16. U. S. Patent 2,825,108, Centrifugal Spinning of Metallic Filaments, Marvalaud, Inc.
17. U. S. Patent 2,907,082, Production of Continuous Filaments of High Vapor Pressure Metals, Marvalaud, Inc.
18. Fibers produced by Reynolds, Revere Copper & Brass Company, and others.
19. C. Z. Carroll-Porczynski, *Advanced Materials*, Astex Publishing, Guilford, 1962.
20. H. F. Arledter, "Metal Fiber Paper," *Ind. Eng. Chem.*, **49**, No. 7, 26 (1957).
21. Chemical "Drawing" Produces Tungsten Filaments, Abstract from *Prod. Eng.*, **15**, (August 7, 1961).
22. G. W. Sears and S. S. Brenner, "Metal Whiskers," *Metal Progr.*, 85–89 (November 1956).
23. U. S. Patent 3,041,202, Metal-Coated Fibers and Treatments Therefor, H. B. Whitehurst, assignor to Owens-Corning Fiberglass, Inc.
24. G. A. Hoffman, "What Can We Do with Whiskers?," *New Scientist*, No. 216, 40 (January 5, 1961).
25. S. S. Brenner, "The Growth of Whiskers by the Reduction of Metal Salts," *Acta Met.*, **4**, 62 (January 1956).
26. P. D. Gorsuch, "On the Crystal Perfection of Iron Whiskers," *J. Appl. Phys.*, **30**, 837 (1959).
27. P. D. Gorsuch, Research Laboratory Report No. 57, RL01840 (General Electric Company, December 1957).
28. G. W. Sears, A. Gatti, and R. L. Fulman, "Elastic Properties of Iron Whiskers," *Acta Met.*, **2**, 727 (1954).
29. J. M. Margottet, "Reproduction des sulfure, selenivre et tellure de l'argent cristallisés et de l'argent filiforme," *C. R. Academic Sci.*, Paris, **85**, 1142 (1877).
30. H. W. Hohlschutter, "Über den Mechanismus der Haarsilberbildung auf Silbersulfid," *Z. Elecktrochem.*, **38**, 345 (1932).
31. C. Wagner, "Mechanism of the Reduction Oxides and Sulphides to Metals," *Trans. AIME*, **194**, 214 (1952).
32. R. Schenk et al., "Untersuchungen über metallische Fassern," *J. Phys. Chem.*, **139**, (1928).

33. C. Herring and J. K. Galt, "Elastic and Plastic Properties of Very Small Metal Specimens," *Phys. Rev.*, **85**, 1060 (1952).
34. K. G. Compton, A. Medizza, and S. M. Arnold, "Filamentary Growth on Metal Surfaces Whiskers," Corrosion, **7**, 327 (1951).
35. R. M. Fisher, L. S. Karken, and K. G. Carroll, "Accelerated Growth of Tin Whiskers," *Acta Met.*, **2**, 368 (1954).
36. R. W. DeBlois and C. D. Graham, "Domain Observations on Iron Whiskers," *J. Appl. Phys.*, **29**, 528 (1958).
37. R. V. Coleman and G. G. Scott, "Iron Whiskers," *Phys. Rev.*, **107**, 1276 (1951).
38. R. V. Coleman and G. G. Scott, "Magnetic Domain Patterns on Iron Whiskers," *J. Appl. Phys.*, **29**, 526 (1958).
39. I. A. Oding and I. M. Kopev, "Tensile Properties of Filamentary Whiskers," *Metalloved i Term. Obrabotka. Metal.*, No. 9, 44 (1961).
40. G. W. Sears, "A Mechanism of Whisker Growth," *Acta Met.*, **3**, 361 (1955).
41. D. V. Rosato, "Nonwoven Fibers in Reinforced Plastics," *I. a.EC*, **54**, No. 8, 31–37 (August 1962).
42. H. F. Arledter, "Uses of Inorganic Synthetic Fiber Paper," *TAPPI*, **37**, No. 7, 152A–156A (July 1954).
43. S. R. Parsons, *Tech. Assoc. Papers*, **25**, 360 (1942); *Paper Trade J.*, **115**, No. 25, 34 (December 17, 1942).
44. F. T. Ratliff, *TAPPI*, **32**, No. 8, 357–367 (August 1949).
45. S. S. Mason, *TAPPI*, No. 8, 403 (August 1950).
46. R. H. Read, "Fiber Metallurgy," *Mater. Design Eng.*, 104–106 (December 1959).
47. R. Read, W. Pollock, and S. W. McGee. "Fiber Metallurgy," *Precision Metal Molding*, **16** (April 1958).
48. A. G. Metcalfe, C. H. Sump, and W. C. Troy, "Fibre Metallurgy," *Metal. Progr.*, **84**, No. 26, 250 (March 1955).
49. H. F. Arledter, U. S. Patent 2,971,877, 1960.
50. H. F. Arledter, U. S. Patent 2,706,156, 1958.
51. D. C. McIntosh, The Mead Corporation, Chillicothe, Ohio.
52. The Mead Corporation and Hurlbut Paper Company, South Lee, Mass.
53. H. F. Arledter, *TAPPI*, **41**, 189–192 (April 1958).
54. J. W. Holladay, "Titanium Alloys for High Temperature Use Strengthened by Fibres or Dispersed Particles," DMIC Rep., 117 (August 31, 1959).
55. "Ultra-Strength Materials," *Aircraft Production*, 307 (August 1961).
56. "High Strength Alloy Obtained by Adding Fibres to Metals," *Corrosion*, **16**, 38 (1960).
57. R. Irmann, "Sintered Aluminum with High Strength at Elevated Temperatures," *Metallurgia*, **46**, 125 (1952).
58. E. Gregory, and N. Y. Grant, "High Temperature Strength of Wrought Aluminum Powder Products," *Trans. Amer. Inst. Mech. Engrs.*, **200**, 247, (1954).
59. N. Y. Grant, and O. Preston, "Dispersed Hard Particle Strengthening of Metals," *Trans. Amer. Inst. Mech. Engrs.*, **209**, 349, (1954).
60. H. F. Arledter, Pending German Patent Application, 1953.
61. "The Heat Treatment, Reinforcement and Cladding of Titanium Carbide Cermets," *WADC Tech. Rep. 55-82* (December 1954, Alfred University).

62. J. J. Swica, W. R. Hoskyns, B. R. Goss, J. H. Connor, and J. R. Tinklepaugh, "Metal Fibre Reinforced Ceramics," *WADC Tech. Rep. 58–452* (January 1960, Alfred University)
63. Y. Baskin, C. A. Arenberg, and J. H. Handwerk, "Thoria Reinforced by Metal Fibres," *Am. Ceram. Soc. Bull.*, **38**, No. 7, 345 (1959).
64. Y. Baskin, Y. Harada, and J. H. Handwerk, "Some Physical Properties of Thoria Reinforced by Metal Fibres," *J. Am. Ceram. Soc.*, **43**, No. 9, 489 (1960).
65. C. A. Arenberg, H. H. Rice, H. Z. Schofield, and J. H. Handwerk, "Thoria Ceramics," *Am. Ceram. Soc. Bull.*, **36**, No. 8, 302 (1957).
66. P. D. Johnson, "Behaviour of Refractory Oxides and Metals, Alone and in Combination, in Vacuo at High Temperatures," *J. Am. Ceram. Soc.*, **33**, No. 5, 168 (1950).
67. A. V. Levy, H. Legget, and S. R. Locke, "Composite Ceramic-Metal Systems for 3,000°–6,000°F. Service," paper presented at the American Rocket Society Annual Meeting (December 5, 1960).
68. J. I. Fisher, and R. L. Hodson, "Development of Metal Fibre-Ceramic Rocket Nozzles," Report 2177-3 (August 1959, Armour Research Foundation of Illinois Institute of Technology).
69. British Patent 638,767, Reinforced Refractories, Cleveland Magnesite and Refractory Company.
70. British Patent 733,061, Reinforced Refractories, B. T. H.
71. H. F. Arledter, "Progress Report on the Development of Metal Fibre Paper," *TAPPI*, **41**, No. 4, 189 (1958).
72. J. H. Ross, "Prospects for Use of Fibrous Metals," *Metal Progr.*, 93–130 (April 1962).
73. H. B. Nudelman, A. G. Metcalfe, and C. H. Sump, "Fibre Metallurgy—Its Use for Slip Ring Brushes," Aeron. Eng. Rev., **31** (December 1955).
74. R. H. Read, "Fiber Metals," *Frontier,* **1** (1959).
75. British Patent 821,690, Metal Fibre Articles, Armour Research Foundation.
76. A. I. P. Maszucchelli, "Metal Fibres Beef Up Plastic Dies," *American Machinist,* **102**, No. 2, 94 (1958).
77. "Aluminum Air Filters," Booklet (Carey Electronic Engineering Co., Springfield, Ohio).
78. "J-M Gasketing Tapes," Technical Data Sheet (Johns-Manville Corporation).
79. H. F. Arledter, *TAPPI,* **39**, No. 5 (May 1956).
80. *Chemical Eng. News,* 47 (December 11, 1961).
81. U. S. Patent 3,041,202, H. B. Whitehurst, June 26, 1962.
82. F. A. Mennerich, Mod. Textiles Mag., **43**, No. 12, 43–45. (December 1962).
83. D. L. McDanels, *Metal Progr.,* 118–120.

7

CERAMIC FIBERS

HANNS F. ARLEDTER

Director, Hurlbut Research

STANLEY E. KNOWLES

Associate Director, Hurlbut Research
Mead Central Research Laboratories
Chillicothe, Ohio

Legend tells us that the Emperor Charlemagne delighted in mystifying his dinner guests by throwing an asbestos tablecloth into a roaring fire and then removing it unharmed from the flames. It was thus demonstrated more than 1100 years ago that textiles could be made of mineral fibers. It was, however, only a decade or so ago that papers were developed which would have astonished Charlemagne's guests even more. These materials can be exposed to a blowtorch without harm, without color change, and without change in hand or feel.

To assess the progress being made in the development of inorganic fiber papers and to surprise even the experienced specialist, a revealing story is told.

A paper, presented by one of the authors in 1953 before the Electrochemical Society (1), disclosed properties of submicron glass and ceramic- and silica (quartz)-fiber papers and speculated on possible uses of these products. A certain reviewer of the paper was extremely skeptical and expressed the opinion that such products would be too weak for any possible commercial application. However, some of the 100% inorganic ceramic papers were already in production* and are representative of a series of papers that became most successful in industry.

This is only one example of the skepticism that has made the acceptance of synthetic-fiber paper an "uphill battle" over the last 10 years. When the first filter papers made of Dynel,† Teflon,‡

---

* Grades of Fiberfrax®, Trademark of the Carborundum Co.
† Union Carbide Chemicals Co.
‡ Trademark of E. I. du Pont de Nemours, Inc.

etc., were disclosed (2), one reviewer reasoned that hydrophobic fibers could not be dispersed in water and that usable paper could not, therefore, be made of such fibrous materials, despite the fact that the papers were well along the way toward commercial development.

These experiences should be a warning to everyone not to conclude that anyone could know exactly how it will all come about in the future. Our thinking is based on today's methods, markets, and concepts, but tomorrow's civilization will be profoundly changed by space-age technology, of which ceramic fibers are a part. New sets of values may open markets for all of these new products that may flower into a thriving industry in centuries to come.

WHAT ARE CERAMIC FIBERS?

The upper crust of the earth contains approximately the following amounts of chemical elements:

> 46.6% oxygen
> 27.7% silicon dioxide
> 8.1% aluminum
> 5.0% iron
> 3.6% calcium
> 2.8% sodium
> 2.6% potassium
> 2.0% magnesium
> 4.0% titanium

Ceramic-base materials are major constituents of the earth's crust. The most successful ceramic fibers have approximately the chemical composition represented by its three main elements; on the other hand, some of the more sophisticated ceramic-oxide fibers consist of elements found in minimum quantities.

The term ceramic fibers refers to products made of refractory materials used in the ceramics industry. It does not include basic glass, leached silica glass, or carbon or graphite fibers, mention of which is made for comparative purposes only. To separate ceramic fibers from glass, the amount of sodium, lithium, or potassium (with the exception of potassium titanate) in the final product is limited to less than 2%. Like glass, ceramic fibers can be produced in a translucent or transparent form.

Ceramic fibers include all refractory fibers made of alumina, zirconia, thoria, magnesia, fused silica, hafnia, berylia, titanium dioxide, potassium titanate, and their mixtures with and without SiO_2. By definition, mono-oxide ceramics such as alumina ceramics are composed of at least 80% oxides. More often they contain 90% or more base oxides; special products contain 99% and sometimes 100%. Mixtures of two or more oxides can vary in wide ratios over broad ranges. Such ceramics are tailor-made for a specific application or represent compromise solutions to suit manufacturing conditions. The main group of ceramic fibers is composed of SiO_2 in admixture with metal oxides such as aluminum and magnesium oxides, barium, and calcium.

THE MANUFACTURE OF CERAMIC FIBERS

Virtually any metal oxide can now be produced in fibrous form (3).

Ceramic fibers can be produced by numerous methods, including the following:

1. Blowing methods
2. Spinning methods
3. Continuous-filament methods
4. Colloidal evaporation processes
5. Vapor deposition single-crystal method and whisker method
6. Oxidation, crystallization, pseudomorphic alteration, and other methods

BLOWING METHODS

Blown ceramic fibers can be produced by several methods, from fused natural minerals, oxide-silica combinations (bauxite, kyanite, kaolin, borate tailings, baria, magnesia, calcia, etc.,), and others. The heat resistance and other properties of the wool produced is determined by the high ratio of alumina or other oxides to silica.

Refractory fiber compositions can be obtained by a Carborundum Co. process of melting mixtures of alumina and silica containing a small amount of modifying agents such as borax glass. An example is a mixture of 50 parts per unit weight of white alumina ore, 50 parts by weight of flint, and $1\frac{1}{2}$ parts of sodium borax glass. This mixture is melted in an arc furnace and forced as a small stream to meet a jet of compressed air or steam at about 80 p.s.i. As it joins the air jet at approximately a right angle, the stream of molten material is dissipated into a fine fibrous form and collected on a screen. The ceramic fibers are processed with water to remove pelletized material (4) (see Figure 7.1).

Short Staple Bulk Fiber
Process Flow Diagram (12)

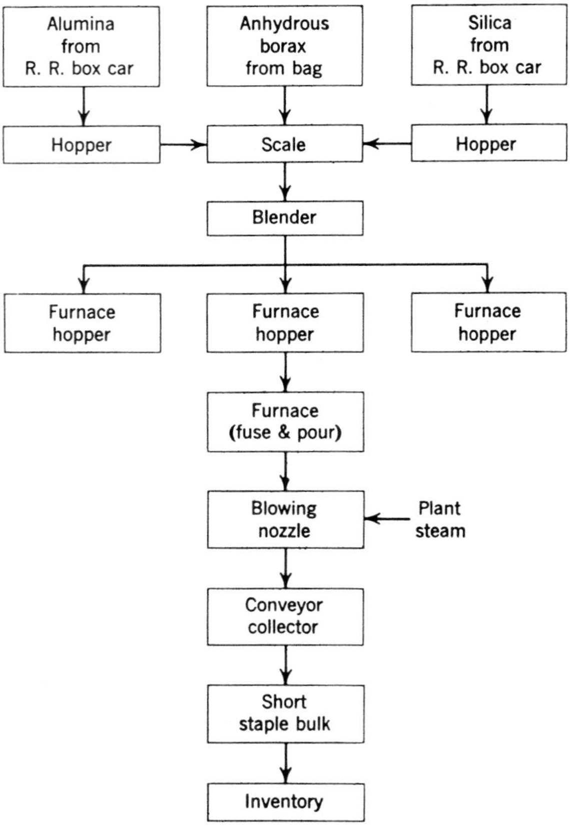

Figure 7.1

Babcock and Wilcox Co. produces Kaowool* by direct resistance heating of kaolin with an approximate molecular ratio of $2Al_2O_3$, $2SiO_2$, $2H_2O$. The molten material is blown into fibers and the pure white homogenous fibrous mass is collected on conveyors (5). To eliminate the possibility of fiber contamination by a refractory of a different composition, the kaolin melt is contained in unmelted kaolin. Alumina-silica fibers are also obtained from calcite, bauxite, and raw kaolin.

* Trademark of Babcock and Wilcox Co.

The Johns-Manville Corp. has developed a process for the manufacture of fibers made of kyanite ($3Al_2O_3$, $2SiO_2$) by using an electric furnace in which the molten liquid acts as a high resistance conductor for melting the kyanite rocks (6). Fibers made of a blend of 100 parts kyanite and 10 parts silica are described (7).

According to a process of making fibers invented by T. R. Hagland, bauxite is fused in an electrical furnace in the presence of iron oxide to effect reduction. Varying quantities of quartz are added. The melt is drawn off and blown by steam, at 8 atm., into a fibrous mass (8).

H. C. Smith describes the manufacture of ceramic fibers made of borate tailings consisting of B_2O_3, Al_2O_3, and SiO_2 (9). The partly dried tailings are mixed with finely divided limestone and fed to mineral-wool cupolas along with coke, melted in a reverberatory furnace and fiberized. The molten product is blown by a gaseous blast into mineral wool.

W. C. Heraeus Co. feeds 6-mm. quartz rods through a graphite guide and over an oxyhydrogen burner to reduce their thickness to 0.2 mm. (10). These fibers are then further reduced by passing through a graphite block and a bank of jet oxyhydrogen blow pipes to draw or blow the fibers into fine quartz wool. The Engelhard industry method passes quartz material into a flame at a temperature above the melting point of quartz, fiberizing the material by means of a high-velocity, high-pressure gas (11).

SPINNING METHODS

McMullen (13) describes a spinning method for producing ceramic fibers with a higher proportion of long silky fibers and containing a relatively low proportion of beads and pellets, comparable with blown types of fibers. In this method a stream of molten inorganic material is forced onto either side or the periphery of one or more rapidly rotating discs which throw off the molten material in a tangential direction, thereby transforming it into a fibrous form. For the manufacture of longer ceramic fibers another method is utilized. White alumina ore, white sand, and zirconia are fused and mixed in an arc furnace, which is tilted to allow the molten material to pour from the furnace into a small stream that impinges onto the periphery of one of two 12-inch rotors, rotating at 4200 r.p.m. Fibers of an average diameter of 4 μ can be produced in this way.

The Johns-Manville Corp. has also developed a special spinning apparatus for the production of refractory fibers (6, 7). This machine employs a plurality of rotating bodies which provides centrifugal force for transforming the molten material into long, fine fibers.

CONTINUOUS FILAMENT METHODS

The manufacture of continuous filaments of miscellaneous ceramic materials is described by the U. S. Department of Commerce (14). Several refractory glasses in the baria–alumina–silica, calcia–alumina–silica, and magnesia–alumina–silica systems were successfully drawn into continuous filaments in a dry inert atmospheric glove box which utilizes graphite and boron nitride as crucible and heater materials. The manufacture of continuous-filament ceramic and silica fibers is extensively covered by Silverman's patents (15).

Labino (16) produced continuous-filament, fused silica fibers of great uniformity and fineness by moving a quartz rod at a constant low velocity to a suitable hydrogen or illuminating gas flame. From the softened rod a thread is drawn at very high speed and wound on a polished drum. M. E. Nordberg (17) patented an apparatus suitable for the manufacture of fused silica filaments from a powder mixture instead of a solid rod.

The Bjorksten Research Laboratories have reported methods of obtaining multiple filaments (18) of fused quartz by means of electrical heating devices. The General Electric Co. has developed a production method for fused silica continuous-200-filament yarn (quartz yarn) of 10 μ filament diameter (0.0004 in.). A scientist at A. D. Little Co. suggested producing continuous filaments by rotating rods of zirconia (ZrO_2) or alumina (Al_2O_3) at high speed in the hot zone of solar or arc furnaces (19).

A fine-grained polycrystalline material in continuous form such as a roving can now be readily made in large quantities by the Hitco (H. I. Thompson Co.) process, details of which have not been disclosed (20).

COLLOIDAL EVAPORATION PROCESSES

The colloidal evaporation process is based on rapid drying of stabilized suspensions that results in the fiberizing action. The fibers are then subjected to heat treatment in Globar®* furnaces at maximum temperatures of 2700°F., or gas-oxygen furnaces at maximum temperature of 3200°F., in order to render them both thermally and

* Registered product of Carborundum Co.

mechanically stable (21). Fibers produced on a pilot-plant basis with this method have a tape or ribbonlike cross section and a maximum width of 1 m. or less. Successful development of fibers from colloidal suspensions has been achieved with ZrO_2, SiO_2, mixtures of the two, and Al_2O_3 and ThO_2.

Horizons, Inc., and Minerals and Chemicals Phillip Corp. developed a process to manufacture these fibers (20), and the Boeing Airplane Co. is studying the evaporation process under an Air Force contract (22).

General Electric Co. has been developing a process (23) in which inorganic materials are dispersed in organic film-forming medium. The dispersion is then poured in the form of a slurry on a glass plate to a thickness of about 5 mil. When dry, the thin film splits into a large number of narrow filaments, which are then ignited, leaving a coherent residue of high strength. R. A. Florentine et al. described magnesium oxides in fiber form obtained by extrusion of aggregated magnesium oxide in a magnesium acetate-methanol-water system. The fibers or filaments are then heat-treated (24).

VAPOR DEPOSITION AND WHISKER METHODS

Horizons, Inc., disclosed a method of producing fibers from vapor phase, based on the heating of high purity aluminum or aluminum-titanium melts, under controlled conditions in hydrogen atmosphere in the presence of moisture and traces of silicone, Ti, Cr, Si and Zr, to initiate fibrous growth of aluminum suboxides (25).

Whiskers are essentially single crystals and differ from polycrystalline aggregates. They possess a strength related to their diameter. Approaching the theoretical limits of atomic cohesion, they may be hundreds of times stronger than the bulk crystal. With increasing temperature they show less deterioration of strength than their corresponding bulk polycrystalline counterparts. Almost any crystalline oxide can assume the whisker form under suitable conditions. There are numerous methods of whisker growth proposed in the literature (26–31). Sapphire whiskers are grown by heating pure alumina to 2200 to 3000°F. in an atmosphere of hydrogen gas containing water vapor.

Hofmann (32) and Williams et al. (33) have recently compared the relative weight of equal-strength crystals (see Figure 7.2).

Whiskers are theoretically ideally suited to paper structures, but unfortunately their high price will retard any such development for

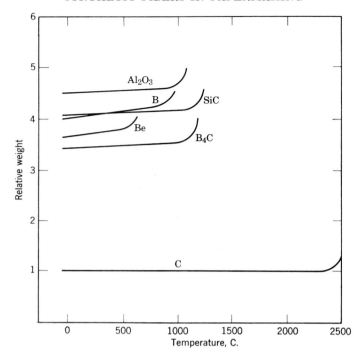

Figure 7.2.   Relative weight of equal strength crystals (44).

some time to come, that is, until the difficult volume production problem has been solved.

OXIDATION, CRYSTALLIZATION, AND OTHER CERAMIC-FIBER MANUFACTURING METHODS

Molybdenum oxide fibers can be produced by oxidizing molybdenum
wire at 500 to 550°C. in an electric field of 4000 volts.   It can be
speculated that other ceramic-oxide fibers can be produced by oxidizing metal in wire or slit-foil ribbon form.

Fibrous titanium dioxides can be grown synthetically by oxidation
of K_2TiO_6 (34), by crystallization in borate melts (35), by crystallization in cryolite melts (36), and by pseudomorphic alterations of
potassium fibers (37).

H. C. Gulledge (53) describes the synthesis and properties of potassium titanate.   These fibers are produced in irregular masses of

fibers or lumps but can be opened and dispersed to make paper or mats.

PREPARATION OF CERAMIC FIBERS FOR PAPERMAKING

To prepare ceramic fibers for the papermaking process, the fibers have to be adjusted in length, and some types such as blown fibers have to be cleaned. The adjustment of filaments to the requested length is achieved by chopping or other suitable means. The value of a refractory mineral fiber as a heat-insulating medium is affected by the nonfibrous impurities formed during fiber manufacture. Blown ceramic fibers, as produced, contain balled fibers and shots, slugs, coarse white or black sand, and other unusable deposits which must be removed.

The useful portion of the fiber, as a raw material for papermaking, can vary widely, and an analysis of a number of bulk fibers which have come into the authors' hands in the last 10 years have shown the following fractionation ranges:

fine fibers	20–70%
balled fibers	5–15%
shots, slugs, coarse white sand and unuseable deposits	80–34%

Typical Examples	a	b	c
Fine fibers	31%	62%	45%
Balled fibers	7%	4%	—
Shots, slugs, etc.	62%	34%	55%

From the viewpoint of the papermaker only the fiber portion (length/diameter ratio $>10/1$) has value. "Shots" are useless filler which weaken the sheet and prove harmful in other ways. Therefore fiber manufacturers have developed methods to "wash" the pulp and to remove the shots. A method that utilizes a wet-cyclone separation process to remove a substantial proportion of the nonfibrous particles from the fibers obtained according to the foregoing methods is described in the patent literature (38, 39, 40). Another U. S. Patent (41) describes another method and apparatus for opening the fibrous material, separating shots from fibers, and forming the open, clean material into a mat or blanket. In this process the fibrous material is fed into a high-velocity fluid stream which is directed onto the point of a conical baffle or barrier. As the high-velocity stream drives the material against the target, partial separation of the shot is effected as the lumps of fibers are opened. The lighter, loose fibers are carried into the collection chamber as the heavier bundles and shots bound off the barrier, strike the wall, and fall down on the screen, from which they are passed for future processing.

PROPERTIES OF CERAMIC FIBERS

Ceramic fibers show the following unusual properties:

1. High heat resistance and resistance to thermal shock.
2. Resistance to most chemicals, including strong acids.
3. Electrical properties favorable for flexible high-temperature electrical insulation.
4. Excellent acoustical characteristics at temperatures up to 2300°F. or higher.
5. Heat insulation by diffusion, reflection, and blocking of infrared radiation.

Most of the traditional inorganic fibers, such as glass, asbestos, and mineral wool, provide excellent heat insulation up to 1000°F. Above this temperature continuous exposure rapidly degrades these materials. Ceramic fibers were developed to extend the useful range to 2000 to 4000°F. There are projections for future temperature resistance up to 6000°F. for short exposure.

Engineers are engaged in continuous research to produce materials that withstand the severe demands of industrial and military applications. In this work they are constantly producing and evaluating new compounds, and the number of new products is bewildering. For example, National Berylia Corp. is reported in the laboratory stages of developing berylia ceramic fibers (42). The authors have examined more than 50 ceramic inorganic fibers of varying design since 1951. Complete physical and end-use data are usually not available, and in many cases the products will never leave the laboratory screening stage.

Table 7.1 compares approximate properties of various fiber materials that have reached production or pilot-plant production status. Table 7.2 shows basic properties of high-temperature ceramic oxides, which may eventually be fiberized.

TABLE 7.1
Comparison of Approximate Properties of Various Fiber Materials

Fiber Kind	Specific Gravity	Room Temperature Tensile Strength (p.s.i.)	Melting Point Softening Point
Zirconia	6.0	50,000–200,000 (est.)	4700°F.
Fiberfrax	2.73	180,000[1]	3200°F.+
Quartz fibers	2.2	130,000–350,000	3030°F.
Stainless steel	7.78	96,000	2650°F.
E-Glass	2.5	up to 300,000	1400°F.

[1] Approximate mean.

TABLE 7.2
Properties of Developmental High Temperature Ceramic Oxides
(which can be fiberized) (43)

Oxides	Melting Point (°F.)	Specific Gravity (Theoretical)	Tensile Strength (p.s.i.)	Thermal Expansion (in./°F. $\times 10^6$)	Thermal Conductivity (Btu/°F./ in./hr./ft.^{2})	Thermal Shock Resistance
Thoria ThO_2	6400	9.69	14,000	5.8	24	Very poor
Magnesia MgO	5070	3.58	12,000	8.9	43	Poor
Hafnia HfO_2	5020	9.68	—	3.5	—	—
Zirconia ZrO_2	4880	5.56	21,000	4.8	10	Poor
Berylia BeO	4650	3.00	20,000	5.3	108	Good
Alumina A_2O_3	3540	3.97	38,000	4.3	30	Good

TABLE 7.3
Properties of Developmental Ceramic Refractory Materials (44)

Refractory	Specific Gravity (gm./ml.)	Melting Point (°F.)	Maximum Working Temperature (°F.)	Tensile Strength (p.s.i.)
Zirconium carbide	6.3	6300	—	15,800 at 2200°F.
Titanium carbide	4.7	5700	—	17,200 at 800°F.
Tungsten diboride			5100	
Hafnia carbide	12.2		7000	
Silicon carbide	3.1		(inert) 4000 (oxidizing) 3000	25,000 at 2200°F.

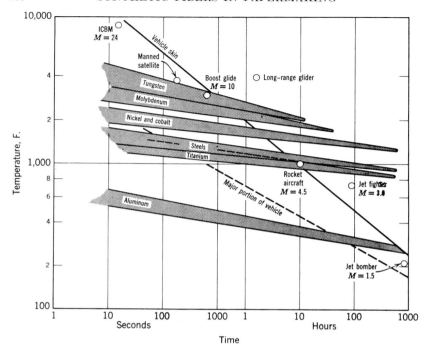

Figure 7.3. Temperature-time requirements of future air vehicles (black lines) compared with maximum use temperature ranges of various materials groups (gray bars). [Battelle Memorial Inst. (45).]

TABLE 7.4
Where High Temperatures are Encountered (45)

9000°F. (4982°C.)	Leading edges and nose cones of re-entry vehicles for a few seconds up to 30 sec.
5000°F. (2760°C.)	Solid-fuel rocket engines heat critical areas to this temperature.
3000°F. (1649°C.)	Manned satellites must have skins to meet this temperature.
2500°F. (1371°C.)	Turbojet combustion chambers and nozzle vanes, ram-jet flame holders and combustion sections are reaching temperatures of this order.
2000°F. (1093°C.)	All components of ram-jet engines.
1800°F. (982°C.)	Gas-turbine buckets, nozzle vanes, combustion chambers,
1500°F. (816°C.)	Compressor sections and turbine wheels of turbojets, combustion chambers of turbojets after burners, etc.

TABLE 7.5

Properties of Commercial Ceramic Fibers

	Fiberfrax Short Staple	Fiberfrax Long Staple (Medium)	Fiberfrax Long Staple (Fine)	Kaowool	J-M Ceramic Fibers
Producer:	Carborundum Co.	Carborundum Co.	Carborundum Co.	Babcock & Wilcox	Johns-Manville
Method of manufacture:	Blowing	Spinning	Spinning	Blowing	Blowing or spinning
Raw materials:	Alumina Flint Borax-glass	Alumina ore White sand Zircon	Same	Kaolin Al_2O_3, $2SiO_2$, $2H_2O$	Kyanite $3Al_2O_3$, $2SiO_2$, plus Silica
Appr. Chemical Analysis:					
Al_2O_3	51.2	51.3	51.3	45.1	42
SiO_2	47.4	45.3	45.3	51.9	50
ZrO_2	—	3.4	3.4	—	—
TiO_2	—	—	—	1.7	6.0
B_2O_3	0.7	—	—	0.08	—
Na_2O	0.7	—	—	0.2	—
Other	—	—	—	1.02	2.0
Specific gravity	2.73	2.73	—	—	—
Melting points (fusion point), °F.	3200°F.+	3200°F.+	3200°F.+	3182°F.	—
Use limits:					
Short periods, °F.	—	—	—	2300°F.	—
Continuous, °F.	2300	2300	2300	2012	2012
Fiber diameter, μ (average)	0.5–10 / 2.5	3–60 / 16	2–30 / 7	2.8	1–5 / 3.0
Fiber length, mm.	1–40 / Varies	12–250 / Av. 50–70	12–250	Varies max. 200	Varies short to long
Bulk density as received, lb./ft.³	4	2	2	—	4–5

It is of interest to note that the upper limit of temperature resistance of the available ceramic fibers with a present upper limit at the melting point of zirconia fibers (4700°F.) can be theoretically extended up to the melting point of thoria (6400°F.). If Table 7.3 is used for a purely theoretical speculation, a short exposure at temperatures up to 7000°F. (hafnium carbide) is not out of the question. This will become a reality, of course, only if fiberizing methods can be developed or adapted for these specific refractories. The question whether fibers of even higher temperature resistance will be required cannot be answered, but speculations based on Figure 7.3 are possible.

A comparison between Table 7.2, which shows the tensile strength of the nonfiberized materials, and Table 7.1, which shows tensile values of fibers, reveals the basic advantage of fibers in regard to strength.

Table 7.4 gives a list of major product applications wherein resistance to very high temperatures is a prerequisite property.

Properties of commercially available alumina-silica fibers are listed in Table 7.5. These are, thus far, the most successful ceramic papermaking fibers on the market. Superrefractory zirconia fibers, now commercially available, are described in Table 7.6. These fibers

TABLE 7.6
Properties of Superrefractory Zirconia Fibers (46)

	Zirconia	Zirconia A	Zirconia B
Source:	Hitco	Hitco	Hitco
Chemical composition:	99% ZrO + 1% SiO$_2$	94% ZrO$_2$ + 5% CaO	
Fiber character:	Polycrystalline circular	Polycrystalline circular	Polycrystalline circular
Specific gravity	6.0+	5.9	
Melting point		4700°F.	
Use temperature °F.	2000°F.+	3000°F.	
Fiber diameter, μ	2.5–12.5	2.5–12.5	2.5–12.5
Fiber length, mm.	50–250	6–100	50–300
Tensile strength, p.s.i.	50,000 (200,000), est.	200,000, est.	Unknown

undergo little or no change when exposed to temperatures between 3400 and 3500°F. for extended periods. Paper can be made of these fibers, and research to develop the products is under way.

TABLE 7.7
Properties of Various Ceramic Fibers

Type:	Titanium Slag-Flint Fibers	Baria-Alumina Silica Fibers	Calcia-Alumina Silica Fibers	Magnesia Alumina Silica	Alumina Silica	Silverman Ceramic Fibers	Bauxite Fibers	Bauxite Kaolin Fibers	Borate Tailing Fibers	Potassium Titanate Fibers	Fiber Frax #10 Experimental
Reference:	British Patent 758,312 746,417 Carborundum Co.	A. Silverman Patents	2,736,141 2,822,579	2,838,882		British Patent 495,654 T. R. Haglund		U. S. Patent 2,674,559 Babcock & Wilcox	Canadian Patent 455,781 H. C. Smith	Du Pont Tipersul	Carborundum Co.
Composition (%):											
SiO_2	46.99	82	80	81	44	53.8	24-53 %	26.5	42		49
Al_2O_3	43.19	8	15	12	56	38.9	76-47 %	68.1	15		49
TiO_2	7.55							2.7			
B_2O_3	1.28										
Na_2O	0.56					1.13					
Fe_2O_3	0.43					0.69		2.1			
BaO, CaO or MgO		10	5	7					28		
Other						5.44 ZrO_2			28 CaO—11% MgO	$K_2Ti_6O_{13}$	
Specific gravity	2.78					2.7			4	3.6	2.73
Melting point	3056°F.				3272°	Above 2500°F.	Above 2600°F. (no sintering)			2500°F. (sharp)	3000+
Tensile strength @ 1500°F., p.s.i.	132,000		77,600	83,400						24,000	
Average fiber diameter, μ	12.5	18	29	24						1	1.2
Fiber length, mm.	Varies	Varies	Varies	Varies	Varies	Varies	Varies	Varies	Varies	0.2	1-20

199

TABLE 7.8
Sound Absorption Coefficients of Ceramic Fibers

Noise Frequency Test Band	Thermoflex®			Tipersul[1]		
				(a)	(b)	(c)
Density, lb./ft.³	8	8	8	3.6	9.0	7.8
Thickness	1 in.	2 in.	3 in.	2.5 cm.	2.8 cm.	2.5 cm.
Cycles						
125	0.07	0.33	0.35	0.01	0.05	0.08
250	0.65	0.61	0.64		0.27	0.80
500	0.85	0.76	0.83	0.39	0.63	0.68
1000	0.87	0.93	0.97	0.81	0.63	0.73
2000	0.83	0.92	0.96	0.87		
4000	0.80	0.85	0.91			
NRC[2]	0.80	0.80	0.85			

[1] = E. I. du Pont de Nemours & Co.

[2] Noise reduction coefficient, average of middle four cycles.

(a) = fibers behind nylon mesh

(b) = behind nylon mesh, with pinholes $\frac{1}{4}$ in. O.C., $\frac{1}{2}$ in. deep

(c) = fibers in steel can, wire mesh fare

® Johns-Manville

200

Magnesia whiskers of 1 to 3 μ diameter, lengths up to 700 μ, and maximum strength 3.5 million p.s.i. in both brittle and flexible types, were obtained by Hulse (47).

Magnesium oxide materials of 99.4% MgO and a density of 2.6 to 2.8 have a melting temperature of more than 4532°F. Electrically fused aluminum refractories containing 90% alumina can be used above 3000°F.; at 99% alumina, above 3400°F.

Properties of various ceramic fibers described in the literature are listed in Table 7.7.

The properties of potassium titanate fibers, $K_2Ti_6O_{13}$, produced on pilot-plant scale under the trade name Tipersul* by Du Pont, are outlined in Table 7.7. These fibers can be dispersed in water, and paper of approximately 0.22 to 0.5 or higher specific gravity (gm./cm.³) can be produced in the normal manner with or without the use of binders.

An example of the acoustical properties of ceramic fibers is shown in Table 7.8 (48).

General properties of fused silica in comparison with E-glass are shown in Table 7.9.

TABLE 7.9
General Properties of Fused Silica and E-Glass

	Clear Fused Quartz	Typical E-Glass
Composition SiO₂, Content %	99.97	53.4
Al₂O₃, CaO, B₂O, Na₂O, and others	0.03	46.6
Density, gm./cm.³	2.20	2.53
Young's modulus, p.s.i.	10×10^6	12.7×10^6
Average coefficient of thermal expansion, 1°C., range 0–300°C.	0.55×10^{-6}	4.2×10^{-6}
Softening point, °C.	1670	∼840

The problem of high temperature is extremely complex. All properties are affected by the great sensitivity of high-temperature materials to the interrelated factors of composition and processing history (impurities, aging procedures, process variables, etc.). Although stress-strain temperature parameters are the focal points of material selection studies, the mechanical thermal, and environmental condi-

* Trademark of E. I. du Pont, de Nemours, Inc.

tions and the processing properties are other important considerations. It is mainly for this reason that fibrous, woven, and nonwoven fiber structures are required to achieve various specific goals.

PHOTOMICROGRAPHS OF CERAMIC FIBERS

The microphotographic analysis of fibers, which includes the measurement of fiber diameter and diameter distribution, determination of fiber, and fiber cross section, gives the papermaker the first conclusive evidence of the papermaking potential of a new fiber product. If the physical properties of the fibers are known, such as stiffness, resilience or compressibility, or tensile strength and toughness, the papermaker can predict the paper properties with some assurance. Figure 7.4 shows Fiberfrax short staple of average fiber diameter 2.5 μ and Figure 7.5 illustrates Fiberfrax No. 10 of average fiber diameter 1.2 μ. This pilot-plant product (Fiberfrax No. 10) demon-

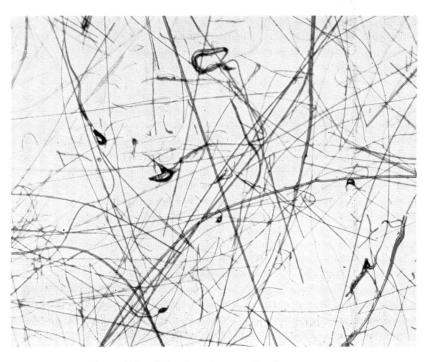

Figure 7.4a. Fiberfrax short staple fiber (225 ×).

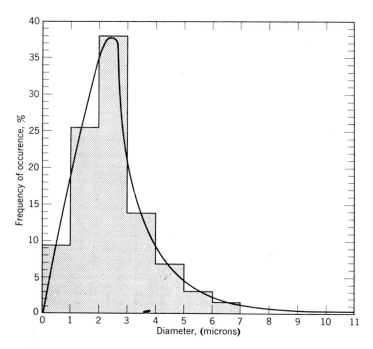

Figure 7.4*b*. Diameters of Fiberfrax short-staple fiber.

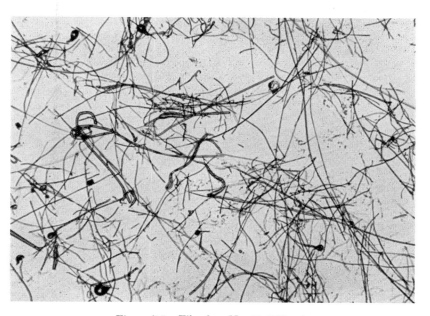

Figure 7.5. Fiberfrax No. 10 (225 ×).

203

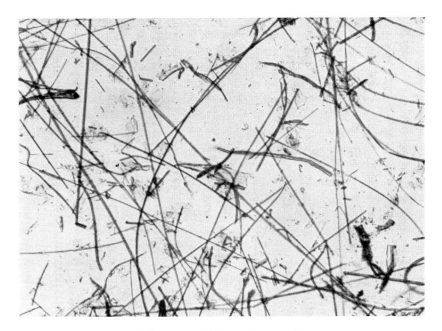

Figure 7.6. Kaowool (225 ×).

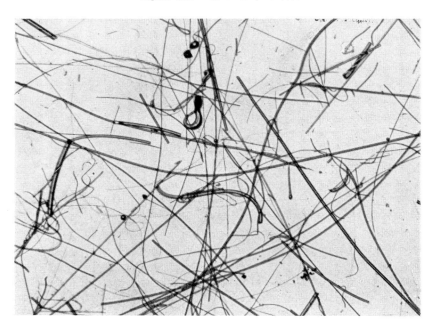

Figure 7.7. Code 112 J-M glass microfibers.

Figure 7.8. Tipersul (225 ×).

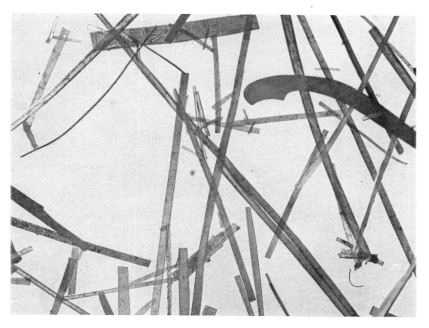

Figure 7.9. Zirconia (stabilized) (225 ×).

205

Figure 7.10. Alumina [long fibers dried and fired at $2800°$ F. $(225 \times)$].

Figure 7.11. Alumina [short fibers dried and fired at $2800°$ F. $(225 \times)$].

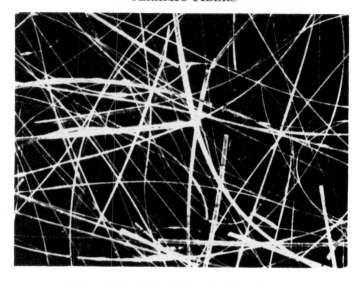

Figure **7.12**. "Hitco" zirconia fibers (40 ×).

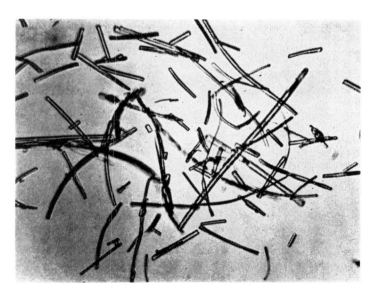

Figure 7.13*a*. Zirconium dioxide fibres (400 ×).

Figure 7.13b. Microstructure of zirconia-silica polycrystalline fiber heat treated at 1900°F. for ½ hr. (3500 ×).

Figure 7.13d. Microstructure of zirconia-silica polycrystalline fiber heat treated at 1900°F. for 3 hr. (3500 ×).

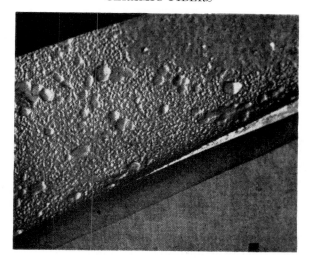

Figure 7.13c. Microstructure of zirconia containing calcia and silica. Sample treated at 1900°F. for 1 hr. (2800 ×).

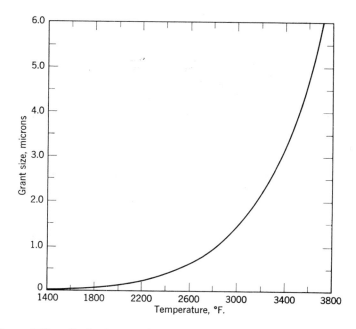

Figure 7.13e. Grain size as a function of temperature for a zirconia fiber.

strates the possibility of producing blown aluminum silicate fiber of fairly fine diameter.

Figure 7.6 shows Kaowool fibers. For comparative purposes, Figure 7.7 shows glass fibers, Code No. 112, of about 3 μ diameter. Potassium titanate fibers (Du Pont) can be seen in Figure 7.8, and ribbon aluminum oxide and zirconia fibers (Boeing Co.) are illustrated in Figures 7.9, 7.10, and 7.11. Zirconia fibers, produced by H. I. Thompson, are shown in Figure 7.12. Zirconium dioxide fibers produced by Minerals and Chemicals Phillip Corp. are shown in Figure 7.13 (20).

Figures 13a, 13b and 13c are photomicrographs of zirconia-silica polycrystalline fibers and microstructure taken at various periods of heat treatment and magnifications (76). An important factor in fiber strength is the size of grain, which can be inhibited by use of suitable additives and control of treatment time and temperature. Figure 7.13d gives the effect of temperature on grain size, as developed without inhibitor.

STRENGTH OF CERAMIC FIBERS

The determination of the individual fiber strength of submicron or micron fibers is difficult. McIntosh (49) has determined the tensile strength of Fiberfrax fibers of 2.5 to 11 μ. Based on his results and data reported in the literature, it appears that the trend of fiber strength increases with decreasing fiber diameter holds true for ceramic fibers, as it does for whiskers (see Table 7.10). Tensile

TABLE 7.10

Approximate Strength Values of Fiberfrax Short-Staple Fibers (49)

Fiber Diameter (microns)	Tensile Strength (p.s.i.)
2.5	370,000+
5	310,000
7.5	270,000
11	220,000
17	160,000

strength of 50,000 to 400,000 p.s.i. (quartz 400,000 p.s.i.) for regular ceramic fibers are reported, and alumina whiskers of a tensile strength of 3.5 million p.s.i. are mentioned in the literature. Dr. McIntosh measured one 2.5 μ Fiberfrax fiber with a tensile strength as high as 1.7 million p.s.i. (an isolated test, not typical).

Tensile strength of fibers alone does not determine the strength of resulting paper or laminates. Toughness, resiliency of the fibers, the fiber length, and the kind and amount of binder affect its strength and handling characteristics. The brittleness of alumina and certain silica fibers make manufacture of paper extremely difficult, (Table 7.11) but even this problem can be solved in modern papermaking by

TABLE 7.11

Influence of Aluminum-Silicate Fiber Diameter on Tensile Strength

Type of Fiber	Fiber Diameter (microns) (mean)	Tensile Strength (p.s.i.)
Short staple	1.3	—
Short staple	2.5	350,000 (49)
Long staple, fine	6	180,000
Long staple, medium	10	115,000
Long staple, coarse	20	50,000 (est.)

the addition of supporting organic fibers in the process and by later removing the carrier fibers by chemical action (50) or by burning (51). Table 7.12 indicates the resiliency of Fiberfrax fibers (52).

TABLE 7.12

Resiliency of Fiberfrax Refractory Fibers

Units of Compression	Degree of Resiliency[1] (as blown)
10	5
20	10
30	15
40	20
50	25
60	30
70	35

[1] As reported by Carborundum Co.

High-density pads of some ceramic fibers can withstand high compression loads without destruction. Du Pont states that a Tipersul fiber sample (binder-free) of a density of 102 lb./cf.[3] was compressed at 40,000 p.s.i. This gave 64.5% deformaton; however, when the pressure was released, there was an immediate 58% recovery of the deformation (53).

THERMAL CONDUCTIVITY OF CERAMIC FIBERS

The outstanding heat-insulating properties of ceramic fibers at high temperatures are the dominating factor that helped to boost their manufacture during the last 10 years. The K-value of fibers is not entirely a base material constant. It is determined to a greater extent by bulk factor, fiber form, fiber length, fiber diameter or cross section, number of fibers per unit volume, uniformity of fiber distribution, and shot content. Table 7.13 compares the K-value of different ceramic fibers for varying bulk densities and temperatures, as reported by the fiber suppliers. For comparative purposes Table 7.14 lists the thermal conductivity at room temperature of some other materials.

The insulation efficiency of bulk aluminum silicate ceramic fibers (Fiberfrax, Carborundum Co.) and the thermal conductivity of (Tipersul) potassium titanate at various densities can be observed in Table 7.13 and Figure 7.14. The low thermal conductivity of Tipersul is due in large part to the high refractive index of the fibers and their dimensions (1 μ); these qualities serve to block infrared

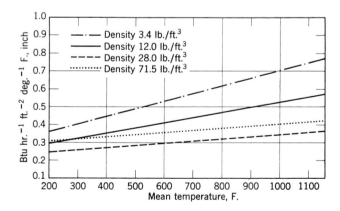

Figure 7.14. Thermal conductivity of Tipersul fibrous potassium titanate at various densities (52).

TABLE 7.13
Thermal Conductivity of Ceramic Fibers (20)

Thermal Conductivity Btu/hr.,/ft.²/°F,/in.

Mean Temperature (°F³)	Fiberfrax Bulk Fiber (6 lb./ft.³)	Fiberfrax Washed Fiber (6 lb./ft.³)	Kaowool (3 lb./ft.³)	Kaowool (5 lb./ft.³)	Kaowool (10 lb./ft.³)	J-M Ceramic Fibers (3 lb./ft.³)	J-M Ceramic Fibers (6 lb./ft.³)	J-M Ceramic Fibers (12 lb./ft.³)	J-M Ceramic Fibers (18 lb./ft.³)	Potassium Titanate Fibers Tipersul (3.4 lb./ft.³)	Potassium Titanate Fibers Tipersul (12 lb./ft.³)	Potassium Titanate Fibers Tipersul (28 lb./ft.³)	J-M Microquartz Fibers (3 lb./ft.³)
300	—	(0.30)	—	—	—	0.4	0.36	0.33	0.32	0.4	0.33	0.26	—
400	—	(0.36)	0.52	0.46	0.38	—	—	—	—	0.45	0.36	—	0.42
600	0.69	0.5	0.80	0.68	0.51	0.68	0.54	0.47	0.45	0.52	0.4	0.3	0.58
800	—	—	1.15	0.94	0.66	0.93	0.70	0.61	0.55	0.61	0.47	0.33	0.7
1000	1.24	0.86	1.57	1.29	0.83	1.25	0.89	0.76	0.65	0.71	0.53	0.35	1.2
1400	1.89	1.45											
1600	2.22												
1800	2.58	1.98											
2000	2.92	2.26											

213

radiation by diffuse reflectance (see Table 7.15). The heat-insulating properties of papers made of ceramic fibers are reported later in this chapter.

TABLE 7.14
Thermal Conductivity of Ceramic Materials

Insulating Material	Exp. K-Values at Mean Temperature, 54°F.	Bulk Density	
		(gm./cm.^{3})	(lb./ft.^{3})
Ultra fine SiC-A	0.15	0.041	2.55
-B	0.17	0.125	7.85
Silica gel	0.15	0.094	5.87
Calcined fine MgO	0.32	0.235	14.7
Sawdust	0.34	0.170	10.6
Aluminum-silicate refractory fibers	0.23	0.097	6.0

TABLE 7.15
Infrared Radiation Transmission of Fibrous Potassium Titanate (53)

Thickness (mils)	Transmission, % for Wavelengths, 0.9–2.4 μ
10	8.40
18	5.25
68	3.45

In conclusion it can be said that ceramic fibers supply a unique new insulating material in our progressing industry.

METHODS OF PRODUCING CERAMIC FIBER PAPER

Modern research programs are aimed at achieving new fibers, and paper materials made therefrom, to satisfy a number of many-phased requirements. With this in mind, considerable thought had to be given to ceramic fibers. Research must be concerned with how well fibrous materials will withstand other environmental conditions in addition to extreme heat. Furthermore, it had to be learned how they could best be formed into nonwoven or paperlike structures. Thus three general areas of research are involved:

1. Choice of the fiber base material to determine mechanical and chemical properties of the fibers.

2. Methods of manufacture to deposit materials as fibrous webs.

3. Principles of holding such fibers together with the aid of binders or other means.

Ceramic papers are produced in three basic versions:

1. Bonded with inorganic binders,
2. Bonded with organic binders,
3. Without binder.

Any paper grade must be developed to meet the functional properties specified for its end use. It is not necessary to exceed the strength needed for handling and use to provide satisfactory performance. Glass- and ceramic-fiber papers with little or no bonding possess limited but sufficient strength to meet many requirements. Any synthetic- or ceramic-fiber paper can be adjusted from its minimum, binder-free condition to substantial strength by addition of increasing amounts of binder.

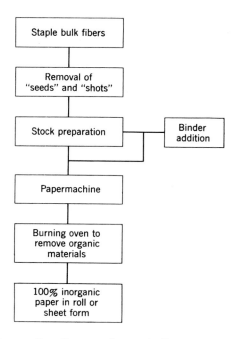

Figure 7.15. Process flow diagram of ceramic-fiber paper manufacture (51).

The manufacture of paper of ceramic fibers in general is not difficult when fibers are obtained with dimensions that can be adjusted to the ultimate paper properties and the manufacturing-process variables. The fibers must disperse well and should remain dispersed, with the aid of the proper mechanical motion, to the point of deposition and web forming. Basically, there appears to be no problem in the production of ceramic-fiber papers that cannot be solved on any conventional paper machine: Fourdrinier, uphill wire Fourdrinier, rotoformer, inverformer, or cylinder machine.

Hurlbut Paper Company developed two methods of manufacturing 100% inorganic binder-free papers to permit the use of fibers that otherwise could not be employed in papermaking processes. The paper is formed with the help of carrier or binder fibers or organic binders. This paper, produced on regular paper-machine equipment, is then exposed to chemical or burning action to remove the binder or carrier fibers (50) (see Figure 7.15).

BONDING OF CERAMIC-FIBER PAPERS

The selection of a binder for ceramic-fiber paper is complex, and both fibers and binders must be "tailored" to suit a given composite material. Numerous organic synthetic binders have been proposed for the manufacture of inorganic- and ceramic-fiber paper. Synthetic rubbers, neoprene, Geon* (vinyl chloride), Lustrex,* Styrene,* Acrysol,* Cascophen,* Ceglin,* Teflon,* fluro-carbon, polyester, Glyptal,* Formvar,* cellulose, silicone, to mention only a few, are cited in the literature (54) and have been evaluated by the authors.

Making paper of inorganic synthetic fibers is more complex than simply putting a binder on or into a fibrous mat. Each possible binder must be considered on the basis of its specific merits. Keim et al. (55) contend, for instance, that the choice of a thermosetting resin obtained by reacting a saturated aliphatic dicarboxylic acid with a polyalkylene polyamine is recommended because it improves the wet strength of a mineral-fiber paper. Good wet strength is obtainable, of course, in numerous other ways. Properties of synthetic-

* Geon is the trademark of B. F. Goodrich Chemical Co.
Lustrex is the trademark of Monsanto Chemical Co.
Acrysol is the trademark of Rohm and Haas Co.
Cascophen is the trademark of Borden Co., Chemical Division.
Glyptal is the trademark of General Electric Co.
Formvar is the trademark of Shawinigan Products Corp.
Ceglin is the trademark of American Viscose Corp.

fiber papers bonded with a small amount of synthetic Latex binder are described in Table 7.16.

TABLE 7.16
Physical Properties of Fiberfrax® Ceramic Fiber Paper

Fiberfrax Grades[1]

	970 C	970 A	970 F	970 J
Basis weight (24 × 36–500), lb.	35	97	160	320
Thickness, mils	10	20^2	40^2	80^2
Dry tensile, gm./in.	500+	1000+	1500+	2000+
Mullen, p.s.i.	—	4.5	7+	8+
% Binder	3–10	$3.5 \pm 1\%$	$3.5 \pm 1\%$	$3.5 \pm 1\%$

[1] The above Fiberfrax grades are manufactured by Hurlbut Paper Co.
[2] @ 8 p.s.i. on a Schopper thickness tester.

Paper strength increases with the amount of binder, and if a binder content of 10% is permitted, for example, the strength of a ceramic-fiber paper can be five times the value reported for a paper of the same nature containing only 2.5% binder content. It is therefore possible for the paper supplier to produce strongly or weakly bonded ceramic-fiber papers. There is, of course, no reason to add a higher binder content if the functional requirements of the paper do not require it.

Next to binder content, the strength of ceramic paper is influenced to a considerable degree by the fiber length or fiber-length distribution. With increasing fiber length, at constant formation and density, the paper will show improved strength properties or maintain the tion. With increasing fiber length, at constant formation and density, strength increases. The Mead process (51) of producing a dense bonded ceramic paper, then burning and sintering it, is proof of this fact (see Table 7.17).

Table 7.18 describes the physical properties of experimental ceramic-fiber papers bonded with silicone (1) and Teflon (54) resins.

Numerous inorganic binders have been investigated for bonding synthetic-fiber papers. Almost any metal hydroxide, such as colloidal silica, colloidal Mg-silicate, or colloidal bentonite, can be used to strengthen inorganic synthetic fibers. However, a major disadvantage of excessive bonding with nonflexible binder materials is that the paper becomes embrittled and difficult to handle.

TABLE 7.17

Properties of Binder-Free Fiberfrax® Ceramic-Fiber Paper

Fiberfrax Grades

	970 AH	970 FH	970 JH
Basis weight (24 × 36–500), lb.	94	154	308
Thickness, mils[1]	20	40	80
Approximate, ft.^{2}/lb.	32	20	10
Approximate, lb./ft.^{2}	0.031	0.050	0.1
Tensile, gm./in.	300+	600+	1000+

[1] Determined by Schopper paper thickness gage at 8 p.s.i. comparison.
Above Fiberfrax grades are manufactured by Hurlbut Paper Co.

Colloidal silica has proved to be suitable for the manufacture of ceramic-fiber papers (57). One recommended colloidal silica carries the trade name Ludox, by Du Pont. Ludox has the following approximate composition:

SiO_2—29–31%
Na_2O—0.09–0.11%
Na_2SO_4—0.02%
pH—9–10
Viscosity at 25°C.—25–50 c.p.s.

Ceramic-fiber paper, binder free or containing organic binders, can be impregnated repeatedly with inorganic colloidal binder solutions such as Ludox, bentonite, calcium silicates, and aluminum phosphates, and the inorganic binder content can be raised as high as 83% (83% silica binder + 17% fibers) or four times as much binder as fibers, as reported by Arledter in Table 7.18 (58). Callinan proposed the integral sizing of ceramic-fiber paper with bentonite. Table 7.19 lists the properties of a ceramic-fiber-bentonite paper of 20% bentonite content (54).

Arledter (51) was able to improve the strength of a 100% inorganic-fiber paper by adding combinations of inorganic and organic binders, followed by burning and sintering at an appropriate temperature (e.g., 2000°F.) for the required time, and by leading the paper through a heat-treating oven in a continuous operation. He also added small amounts of fine fibers or fillers of a somewhat lower melting, softening, or sintering point as the main fiber portion to bond the paper.

TABLE 7.18
Properties of Ceramic-Fiber Paper Repeatedly Impregnated with Colloidal Silica (Ludox) (58)

Impregnations	Penetration Solution-Time (sec.)	Basis Weight (24 × 36—500)	Thickness (mils)	Density (gm./l.)	% Silica Binder Solids in Paper	Tensile Strength (gm./in.)	Observations	Dielectric Strength (volts)	(volts/mil.)
0 (none)	—	44	12	0.24	0	1000	soft & flexible	1100	90
1	Instant	83.5	13	0.44	47.5	3600	Brittle	—	—
2	1.5	102	14	0.48	57	3600	Brittle	1600	115
3	3-4	125.5	14	0.58	65	8000	Brittle	—	—
4	15	152	14	0.71	71.5	—		2000	145
7	40	240	14	1.12	83.0	(8000)	Very brittle	2700	190

The properties of a combination bonded paper, with and without heat treatment, are listed in Table 7.20.

TABLE 7.19

Physical Properties of Ceramic-Fiber Bentonite-Clay Paper (54)

Characteristics

Ceramic fiber, %	80
Bentonite clay, %	20
Thickness, in.	0.0102
Density, gm./cm.^{3}	0.298
Basis weight (25 $\times$ 40–500), lb.	38.6
Tensile strength, gm./in.	832
Wet tensile (50% moisture), gm./in.	1320
Mullen burst, p.s.i.	1
Elmendorf tear no.	6
Porosity (Gurley), sec.	1.2
Air resistance, mm. water/mil.	4.6

TABLE 7.20

Properties of Fiberfrax® Ceramic-Fiber Paper, Bonded with Colloidal Silica
(Ludox)

Paper Grade	970 C	970 CL	970 CH[1]	970 CHL[1]
Silica binder in paper, %	0	36.6	0	40
Organic binder, %	7	4.5	0	0
Basis weight (24 $\times$ 36–500), lb.	65.5	102	65.5	96
Thickness, mils	12	12	12	12
Tensile, gm./in.	3900	5700	700	3650
Mullen	7	10	1	2

[1] H refers to heat treatment.

Ceramic-fiber papers on the market possess no greater than the functional strength required for their use, but their strength can be increased if necessary. Table 7.21 lists the stress-strain properties of bonded, unbonded, and wetted unbonded ceramic-fiber papers. It is specifically noteworthy (column 3) that at 400% moisture content ceramic-fiber paper shows a toughness and handling strength two to three times that of the dry unbonded paper.

TABLE 7.21
Stress-Strain Properties of Fiberfrax® Ceramic Fiber Paper
(dry and wet)

Paper Grade	970 F	970 FH	970 FH Wetted
Basis weight (24 × 36–500), lb.	170	170	170 (dry weight)
Binder content, %	2.7	—	—
Tensile, gm./in.	1026	335	423
Elongation, %	2.03	1.3–1.5	3.25
Breaking tenacity, gm./lb./in.	6.04	2.0	2.50
Toughness at maximum tensile, (work-to-break)	6.06	1.28	4.00
Toughness total (work-to-break)	10.14	2.85	7.01
Moisture content, %	0.3	0.3	400

A new 100% inorganic binder of the nature of synthetic-mica platelets of the general formula $X\ Mg_2SiO_{10}F_2$ (59) (where X is Li or Na) yields a ceramic-fiber paper of good handling strength combined with softness at room temperature. This paper embrittles above 100°C., but the embrittlement is reversible and the paper regains its flexibility under room conditions and reabsorption of moisture.

APPLICATIONS FOR CERAMIC-FIBER PAPER

The uses of a ceramic-fiber paper are determined by its physical and chemical functional characteristics and by its price limitations in areas in which it encounters competition with mineral wools, glass fibers, asbestos, and other materials. Following are the advantageous properties of ceramic-fiber paper which make it unique in a broad range of applications.

HIGH TEMPERATURE RESISTANCE

The new ceramic fibers extend the useful range of papers from 2300 to 4000°F. or higher, far beyond the continuous temperature limits of mineral wools, glass, and asbestos (about 1000°F.).

PHYSICAL PROPERTIES AT HIGH TEMPERATURES

The engineer can select ceramic-fiber paper with very high *strength and flexibility* retained up to its use temperature. Instantaneous changes in temperature (thermal shock) throughout the operating range of the ceramic paper do not affect its properties. It is reported that *electrical insulation* values are high at very high temperatures for some high-purity refractory fibers. *Vibration damping* is achieved at all temperatures. The *filtration effect* is not affected by the temperature. *Heat-insulating* properties are outstanding up to the temperature-use limit. The *acoustical insulation* remains good at high temperature (see Figure 7.21).

RESISTANCE TO WETTING BY MOLTEN NONFERROUS METALS

Molten metals, such as aluminum, magnesium, and some brasses and bronzes, do not penetrate or stick to the paper.

HIGH CHEMICAL AND CORROSION RESISTANCE

Some fibers, such as aluminum silicates and quartz, show excellent corrosion resistance to many strong acids, whereas others (e.g., Tipersul) are poor in this respect. The corrosion resistance to strong alkali is still limited in some of the available ceramic-fiber papers (aluminum silicates) but good for others. Potassium titanate, for instance, is stable in boiling alkali in concentrations up to 30% by weight. For most ceramic-fiber papers there is no outgassing in service that might attack or affect metals or other materials in contact.

PROPERTIES ENHANCED BY PAPER STRUCTURE

Paper can be made in random or aligned fiber distribution with exceptional uniformity and varying density and void volume. It can be saturated uniformly throughout with organic or inorganic materials to any desired extent between 0.1 to 83%. This paper form is useful in reduction of weight and allows elimination of operations and ease of manufacture.

The suggested and actual end uses of ceramic-fiber papers are manyfold, all of which cannot be covered in this chapter. Many applications remain in exploratory stages and have not been disclosed. Some of the more important uses are described in the following pages.

Heat Insulation. Ceramic-fiber papers are a new class of high-temperature insulating materials, light in weight, yet adequately strong. With very low thermal conductivity (see Figure 7.16), such ceramic fibers or paper made therefrom will withstand continuous use

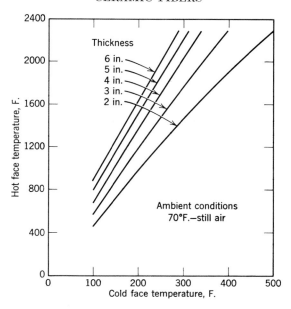

Figure 7.16. Insulation efficiency of bulk ceramic fibers.

at temperatures up to 2300°F. for a number of available materials
and up to 4000°F. or more for newer fiber types. However, no
ceramic-paper material has yet been developed that would continuously resist internal-combustion temperatures of 4000 to 7000°F.

TABLE 7.22
Thermal Conductivity of Various Construction Materials (60)

Materials	Thermal Conductivity Btu/hr./ft.^{2}/°F./in.
Reinforced plastics	0.75–1.25
Titanium	100–140
Stainless steel	100–170
Aluminum	840–1560

Table 7.22 lists for comparison the thermal conductivity of various
construction materials. In Figure 7.16 (60) the thermal conductivity
of various materials made of ceramic fibers, including paper grade
970 JH, are compared for mean temperatures, the average of hot-
and cold-phased temperatures. The superior performance of the
paper structure becomes more pronounced at higher temperatures.

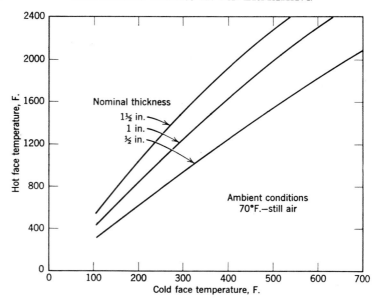

Figure 7.17. Insulation efficiency of ceramic blankets.

The insulation efficiency of Carborundum bulk ceramic fibers, ceramic blankets, ceramic blocks, and ceramic papers can be compared in Figures 7.17 to 7.19 (61). The new ceramic fibers and papers are clearly superior, in this respect, to first-quality fire-clay brick and other materials. Table 7.23 compares thicknesses of insulating forms to attain comparable performance (61).

TABLE 7.23

Comparative Thicknesses of Ceramic-Fiber Forms for
Equivalent Insulator (61)[1]

Product Form	Approximate Density (lb./ft.³)	Approximate Insulation Thickness (in.)
Paper	$9\frac{1}{2}$	1
Blanket	6	$1\frac{1}{2}$
Block	14	$1\frac{1}{2}$
Bulk	6	2
Fire-clay brick	136	11

[1] Hot face temperature,—2000°F.
  Cold face temperature,—420°F.

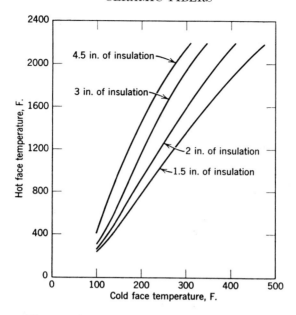

Figure 7.18. Insulation efficiency of ceramic block.

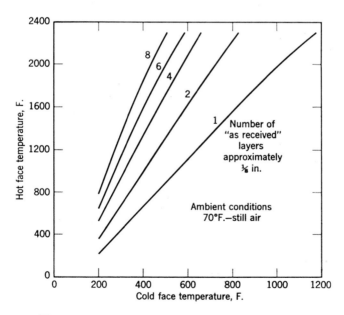

Figure 7.19. Insulation efficiency of ceramic papers.

The development of ceramic-fiber papers has made possible a new concept in the design of combustion chambers in oil-fired domestic furnaces. The use of thin, lightweight ceramic-fiber paper, supported by a mild steel shell, effectively eliminates massive and costly stainless-steel chambers lined with brittle refractory materials. The excellent insulating efficiency of ceramic-fiber paper helps to provide faster and more uniform heat for the homeowner.

In industry large induction furnace linings are made of ceramic-fiber paper rather than quartz in order to save on maintenance labor and replacements. Such linings are formed by saturating the paper with inorganic binder and winding it into a tube. Glass furnace forehearths utilize ceramic-paper gaskets between the orifice block and feeder bowl to provide a resilient, noncontaminating seal, easily installed, removed, and cleaned. Platinum bushings were replaced with ceramic paper to eliminate frequent replacement due to varying pouring quantities and occasional "freeze-up" with glass accumulation.

Uses of ceramic-fiber paper as gaskets between alloy or refractory assemblies, such as furnaces or hot-gas ducts, takes advantage of the paper resiliency, retained even on continued exposure at high temperatures. Cemented to metals, it also provides low-heat-capacity refractory facings to give protection from heat and corrosion.

Ceramic-fiber materials are available in a wide variety of prefabricated forms, such as tubes, papers, and laminates, each providing maximum effectiveness for specific applications. Ceramic fibers are specified for critical applications in the missile- and space-development program. On the project Mercury space capsules ceramic paper serves as insulation in tow areas: as a cut-out washer, it insulates the windows from the frames; and it is used under a glass cover for the antenna faring section of the capsule above the parachute compartment. Several layers of ceramic-fiber papers are sandwiched between the high-temperature outer glass cover and the inner glass-fiber structural shell.

Babcock and Wilcox Co. state that unique applications for its Kaowool include gas-turbine and gas-turbine muffler insulation. Johns-Manville Corp. cites an insulation use of its Cerefelt fiber in which 100-ton ingots are maintained at 1700°F. during a half-mile trip between the pouring plant and the forging plant.

In most missile and rocket applications there is a twofold problem of resistance to the temperature and of heat insulation to prevent heat transfer which will harm or destroy the contents of the missile, including delicate instruments and human beings.

Ceramic-Fiber Filter Papers. Their extreme fiber fineness, range of diameters, random arrangement, and high chemical and temperature resistance make ceramic-fiber papers excellent filter materials for gases and liquids in applications beyond the limit of usefulness of glass fiber. Glass-fiber filter paper can be used up to 1000 to 1300°F., but ceramic filter papers can be cleaned easily by burning or baking at a temperature of 2300°F. or higher. Ceramic filters permit removal of particles from high-temperature gases in excess of 1000°F., for example, from exhaust gases in atomic-energy installations. These products help chemists to conduct chemical reactions at very high temperatures.

Table 7.24 compares the chemical resistance of glass- and ceramic-fiber paper (62). Although the listed aluminum silicate-fiber paper

TABLE 7.24
Chemical Resistance of Ceramic Fibers and Glass Fibers (62)

Weight Loss After Leaching (%)	100% Ceramic-Fiber Paper	100% Glass Fiber Paper (med. chemical resistance)
24 hr. in boiling water	0.08	0.57
1 hr. in n-HCl at 96°C.	6.14	20.62
1 hr. in n-HCl at 20°C.	0.34	—
1 hr. in conc. HCl at 20°C.	0.28	—
1 hr. in H_2SO_4 (31.5° Bé) 96°C.	5.4	17.5–30
24 hr. in N-KOH at 20°C.	0.4	—
1 hr. in 5n-KOH at 90°C.	16–25	55–72

shows good acid resistance, the resistance to hot concentrated alkali remains poor. However, it is reported that filters made of fibrous potassium titanate (Tipersul, Du Pont) are stable in boiling alkali in concentrations up to 30% by weight. The Tipersul structures are not recommended for concentrated acids. Fused silica yarn is inert to all acids except hydrofluoric and hot phosphoric, but it dissolves in strong alkali.

All ceramic-fiber papers (Fiberfrax, etc.) show high, medium, or low porosity (Tipersul), good resistance to compression, and are inert to dilute acids, alkali (see Table 7.24), salt solutions, and organic solvents. Many liquids or gases can now be filtered in corrosive atmosphere and at elevated temperatures with the help of the new ceramic-fiber filter papers. Predicted applications include filtering molten metals, hot oils, tars, superheated air, and gases.

The air-filter properties of aluminum silicate-fiber paper are listed in Tables 7.25 and 7.26. The filter characteristics for liquid filtration of these filters in comparison with glass and cellulosic filters are reported in Tables 7.27 and 7.28.

Air-filter papers made of experimental ceramic fibers of an average fiber diameter of 1.25 μ have been produced; their filter properties are reported in Table 7.29. Tipersul fiber mats were also evaluated

TABLE 7.25
Air Filter Properties of Ceramic-Fiber Papers (56)
(3% rubber binder)

Paper Grades[1]	970 A	970 F	970 J	970 J $\times$ 2	935 B
Fibers used	#7 Fiberfrax	#7	#7	#7	Submicron glass
Basis weight					
(24 $\times$ 36–500), lb.	95	171	320	640	36
Thickness, mils	11.7	68	86	170	10
% DOP penetration at 85 l./min./100 cm.² (28 f.p.m.)	21	7	0.98	0.05	0.05
Air resistance mm. H₂O at 85 l./min./ 100 cm.² (28 f.p.m.)	27	46	78	127	100

[1] Manufactured by Hurlbut Paper Co.

TABLE 7.26
Air Filter Properties of Fiberfrax® Ceramic-Fiber Paper (56)
(100% inorganic)

Grades	970 AH	970 FH	970 JH
Basis weight (24 $\times$ 36–500), lb.	94	190	355
Thickness, mils	20	50	86
% DOP penetration 0.29 μ particles 100 cm.²			
28 f.p.m.	18	4	0.74
10 f.p.m.	13	2	0.25
5 f.p.m.	8	1	0.15
Resistance mm. H₂O 100 cm.²			
28 f.p.m.	25	49	78
10 f.p.m.	9	17	28
5 f.p.m.	4.5	9	14

TABLE 7.27
Industrial Filter Paper Properties of Fiberfrax®
Ceramic Fiber Paper (63)

		Ceramic Papers 970 F	Glass-Fiber Paper 934 A	Industrial Cellulosic- Filter Paper
Weight of paper, gm./m.^{2}		240	72	132
Thickness, mils		40	10	10
Retention Under Suction				
Cold Precipitate	Vacuum in Hg.			
Ca-Oxalate	1	—	100	—
Lead sulfate	27	100	100	—
	10	100	100	100
	1	100	100	100
Ferric hydroxide	27	100	100	100
	10	100	100	100
	1	100	100	100
Filter speed in 1000 ml. water under suction				
	1 in Hg.	150	295	540
	10 in Hg.	48	65	128
	27 in Hg.	8	13	32
		3	6	16

by the author and found to possess slower filter speed but showed good retentivity.

Experiments by First and Graham (64), MSA, and others have shown that heat-resistant fiber papers can be adapted to large-scale cleaning of hot gases.

Replaceable filter cartridges capable of treating 5000 ft.^{3}/min. of gas at a resistance of 5 mm. Hg. have been fabricated from ceramic-fiber filter paper mounted in a ceramic-fiber frame. These filters can resist continuous high temperatures and severe heat shock without physical damage or reduction in filter performance. A high-efficiency filter, which uses pleated ceramic-fiber paper capable of handling 1000 ft.^{3}/min. of gas with an initial air-flow resistance of 5 mm. Hg, has a 24 × 24 in. face area and is 11½ in. deep.

Papers, blankets, and bats of varying thicknesses and packing densities and of fibers of varying diameter may be formed to yield

TABLE 7.28

Filter Characteristics of Ceramic, Glass, and Cellulose
Filter Papers (62)

Paper Grade	100 % Ceramic Fiber Paper 970 FH	100 % Ceramic Fiber Paper X 970 CH Exp.	100 % Glass Fiber Paper 934 AH	100 % Cellulosic Analytical Filter Paper for Fine Precipitates
Basis weight (24 $\times$ 36–500), lb.	172	83	42	52
Thickness, mils	40	16.5	10	6
Cone retention Ca-oxalate				
cold precipitated	100	100	100	100
$BaSO_4$ hot precipitated, %	100	100	100	94
Ca-oxalate (cold) precipitate retention under vacuum, %				
1 in Hg.	49	59	99.8	19
10 in Hg.	24.4	29.5	69.8	16.6
Rapidity or filter speed, sec.				
Cone rapidity, sec.	4	13	19	190
Filter pressure, 30 in. H_2O, sec.				
to filter 1000 ml.	22	27	60	820
Burst wet strength 10 cm.^{2} rupture, in. H_2O (Schopper method)	22	14	14	10

TABLE 7.29

Air-Filter Properties of Experimental Ceramic-Fiber Papers
Compared with a Glass-Fiber Ultra Filter (56)

Paper Grades	X 970 C-2	X 970 C-1	X 970 C	935 B
Fiber used	Fiberfrax #10	Fiberfrax #10	Fiberfrax #10	Submicron Glass
Basis weight (24 $\times$ 36–500), lb.	141	110	70.5	36
Thickness, mils	32	22.6	16	10
% DOP penetration at 85 1/min./100 cm.^{2} (28 f.p.m.)	0.04	0.1	2	0.05
Air resistance mm. H_2O at 85 1/min./100 cm.^{2} (28 f.p.m.)	119	86	61	100

filters of a wide range of capabilities, with optimum filter performance
for specific design conditions.

Studies have further indicated that deep beds of Fiberfrax ceramic
fibers can be utilized to form high-temperature filters for particles
above 1 μ in diameter (see Table 7.30). For example, a graded fiber
filter composed of a 5-in. deep layer of 20-μ fibers and a 1-in. layer of

TABLE 7.30
Properties of Deep Bed Filters (64)

Air-flow capacity, c.f.m.	500 to 20,000
Superficial face velocity, f.p.m.	up to 400
Pressure drop (clean), in., w.g.	1 to 3
Efficiency, 2-μ particles, %	up to 99%
Temperature °F.	up to 1500

4-μ fibers was shown to have an efficiency of 99% for particles of 2 μ at temperatures above 1400°F. with dust loading of approximately 10 grains/1000 ft.³ of gas.

Ceramic-fiber paper pleated to provide more surface area has also found use in filter units for high-temperature gases. Canadian Patent 559,023 (65) describes a special filter design. Mine Safety Appliances Co. has also developed ceramic frames of high-temperature resistance for high-temperature filters.

First et al. (64) proposes to utilize ceramic filter paper in gas-cooled nuclear-power reactors that would provide a high-temperature heat source for chemical processing; for example, the gasification of coal or the production of acetylene from natural gas. One big problem in such a system would be the continuous removal of solids from the hot gases, for if the uranium-bearing fuel rods became coated with dirt the heat-exchange capacity of the system would be reduced and it is possible that the rods would become overheated and melt or rupture. An answer to this problem is the filtration of hot reactor gases with ceramic- or metal-fiber filters.

The chemical and petroleum industry uses ceramic filters for specific applications; for example, to recover platinum rhodium catalysts used in the production of HNO_3 from ammonia.

Electrical Applications. The use of ceramic-fiber papers for electrical applications is still limited. However, such papers are reportedly employed between ceramic plates of thermoelectric generators, in the semiconductor field, and in the form of braided coverings for high-temperature wire, cable, and electric insulators in circuit breakers. It is also reported that insulation values are high "at all temperatures" for some high-purity ceramic fibers.

Typical physical and electrical properties of ceramic-fiber paper, bonded with silicone, synthetic latex, and without binder, can be seen in Table 7.31. Callinan et al. (54) reported the results listed in Table 7.32 for Teflon-bonded ceramic-fiber paper (Fiberfrax). Table 7.33 gives typical properties of quartz versus E-glass.

TABLE 7.31
Typical Electrical Properties of Ceramic-Fiber Paper (1)

Paper Type	Exp. 1299	970 FH	970 F
Binder	Silicone	None	Synthetic rubber
%	22		3
Basis weight (24 $\times$ 36–500), lb.	76	170	170
Thickness, mils	12	40	40
Tensile strength, gm./in.	1900–3000	600	1600
Volume resistivity, ohm $\times$ cm.	$>10^{14}$	$>10^{14}$	$>10^{14}$
Dielectric constant, 10 kc.	1.26	1.08	1.12
Dielectric loss factor, 10 kc.	$\sim$0.0002	$\sim$0.0002	$\sim$0.0002

TABLE 7.32
Electrical Properties of Teflon-Bonded Ceramic-Fiber Paper (54)

Paper Sample	A	B
Ceramic fibers, %	42	57
Bentonite, %	—	15
Teflon, %	58	28
Moisture absorbency, 24 hr. immersion	0	0
Thickness, mils	4.5	—
Basis weight (24 $\times$ 36–500), lb.	34	117
Tensile strength, gm./in.	600 (6000)[1]	11,000
Dielectric constant, 1000 Hg. cycles	1.78	2.7
Loss factor	0.003	0.04
Power factor	0.23	1.5

[1] Mead Corp. Central Research made a similar paper, which, after sintering at 700°F., showed tensile strength of 6000 gm./in.

TABLE 7.33
Electrical Properties of Quartz versus E-Glass
(1 Mc at 20°C.)

	Clear Fused Silica	Typical E-Glass
Dielectric constant	3.78	6.3
Power factor	0.0009	0.023
Loss factor	0.0009	0.023

The electrical properties of Tipersul (density 65 lb./ft.[3]) at higher temperatures is reported by Du Pont (53) in Table 7.34. The vol-

TABLE 7.34
Electrical Properties of Tipersul (53)
(Density 65 lb./ft.[3])

Temperature (°F.)	Dielectric Constant (100 kc./sec.)	Dissipation Factor	Resistivity (ohm × cm.)
77	3.5	0.06	3.3×10^{15}
392	3.5	0.06	3.2×10^{9}
572	3.7	0.09	3.4×10^{6}

ume resistivity of quartz and glass and Tipersul-fiber materials as a function of temperature is reported in Table 7.35 (56). Although

TABLE 7.35
Volume Resistivity (ohm × cm.) as a Function of Temperature
of Fiber Materials (56)

Temperature (°F.)	Quartz Glass[1]	German 7-μ Quartz Containing No Alkali[1]	Pyrex "E"[1]	Tipersul (53) Pads (18 lb./ft.[3])
212	10^{14}	2×10^{13}	10^{13}	
392	3×10^{13}	2.7×10^{13}	—	3.2×10^{9}
572	5×10^{11}	2.4×10^{11}	3×10^{11}	8×10^{8}
752	10^{10}	—	10^{10}	9×10^{7}
932	10^{9}	5×10^{8}	10^{9}	3×10^{7}

[1] Mead Corp. Data.

no high-temperature measurements for ceramic-fiber pads (aluminum silicates, etc.) could be located, it can be speculated that the listed results for quartz glass may hold true for other ceramic fibers or can be surpassed by high-purity ceramic fibers.

The dielectric properties of silicone laminates measured at 9 kMc./sec. can be seen in Table 7.36 (66).

Ceramic fibers, reinforced with Teflon, are used as antenna windows in IRBM and ICBM missiles because they meet the key requirements for extremely high and environmental temperature conditions: first, uniform dielectric constant and uniform dielectric losses; second,

TABLE 7.36
Dielectric Properties of Silicone Laminates (66)
(measured at 9 kMc./sec.)

Reinforcement

Test Temperature	Silica Fiber		High Silica Glass		E-Glass	
	Dielectric Constant	Loss Tangent	Dielectric Constant	Loss Tangent	Dielectric Constant	Loss Tangent
24°C. (75°F.)	3.21	0.0026	3.43	0.0250	4.35	0.0060
60°C. (140°F.)	3.22	0.0025	3.47	0.0230	—	—
100°C. (212°F.)	3.22	0.0026	3.49	0.0200	—	—
149°C. (300°F.)	3.21	0.0027	3.43	0.0140	—	—
204°C. (400°F.)	3.21	0.0028	3.33	0.0073	—	—
260°C. (500°F.)	3.21	0.0025	3.28	0.0046	4.31	0.0060
24°C. (75°F.)	3.21	0.0026	3.41	0.0210	—	—

structural integrity, especially freedom from development of surface irregularities that distort signals.

The development of four new theoretically possible electric-power-generating systems operating at very high temperatures hinges on the development of new heat-resistant materials. It can be speculated that high-temperature and corrosion-resistant inorganic (metal)- and ceramic-fiber papers might find a place in these developments for the following temperature requirements:

1. Fuel cells, an electrochemical device which converts free energy directly to electric energy, will require 1800°F.

2. Thermoelectric power generators, based on the principle that the flow of heat through a metal segment can produce a voltage difference between its hot and cold ends, require 2000°F.

3. Thermoionic generators, producing electric power by using electrons emitted into a vacuum by a material when it is heated, will operate at 3500 to 4500°F.

4. The magneto hydrodynamic generator process consists of heating a gas to a temperature of about 5000°F., which ionizes it by stripping off electrons from the atoms. The hot gas is then passed between the poles of a magnet to separate the ionized particles of the gas on the electrodes, which, in effect, become the terminals of a generator. Heat requirements: 5000°F.+

Ceramic-Fiber-Paper Reinforced Plastic Laminates. The growing variety of laminates permits more precise selection of materials with the desired combination of properties. The future of industrial plastic laminates will be shaped, therefore, by better balancing of combinations of physical and electrial properties of absorbent paper and resin characteristics. The ceramic-fiber papers have their place in meeting the challenge of the space age.

There is evidence that advantageous applications can be made wherever any one or more of the following properties are required: high strength-to-weight ratio, thermal and mechanical shock resistance, low thermal conductivity, retention of high percentage of strength for prolonged times at high temperatures, short-term high-heat resistance, abrasion resistance, lowest ablation rates, erosion resistance, resistance to deformation at high temperatures, and chemical inertness. The improved properties of ceramic-, quartz-, and graphite-reinforced laminates have already been demonstrated in such products as air-frame structural parts, rocket nozzle liners, and heat shield for re-entry nose cones.

Fused-silica- or ceramic-fiber reinforced plastics could have a bright future in the high-temperature field. Table 7.37 compares the mean mechanical properties of silicone laminates reinforced with quartz and high-silica fibers at different temperatures (67).

It is speculated (68) that the eventual development of high-temperature resins of usefulness at temperatures in excess of 1000°F. may lead to the replacement of aluminum, steel, titanium, etc., for outer skins on missiles and airplanes mainly because of the possibilities of reduction of weight and costs.

Metal-Working Applications. Ceramic-fiber papers or webs find applications in the insulation of metals in vacuum annealing. They are used as gasket materials in vacuum casting of alloy-steel ingots, hot tops for metal-ingot molds, and liners for ladles, troughs, spouts, and molds in nonferrous metal processing. Molten-metal distributor pan linings, high-temperature steel turbine covers, and insulation of ducts and pressure vessels are other applications that permit use of lower cost steel structures.

Pouring troughs are lined with ceramic paper to prevent the leakage of molten aluminum and contamination by iron or other impurities. The paper also protects the trough refractory against thermal shock failure and minimizes temperature drop in transporting the molten metal to other processing stations. Ladles, spouts, and molds are also lined with ceramic paper for protection against heat and metal build-ups.

TABLE 7.37

Comparison of Mean Mechanical Properties (67)
(specimens were held for 30 minutes at temperature
before testing at room temperature)

	Phenyl Silane[1]		Silicone[2]	
	Quartz	High Silica	Quartz	High Silica
Flexural strength, 10^3 p.s.i.[3]				
24°C. (75°F.)	43.2	27.2	34.0	24.1
260°C. (500°F.)	37.0	25.0	18.5	13.1
316°C. (600°F.)	37.4	19.6	15.8	10.9
371°C. (700°F.)	34.5	15.0	13.3	5.4
Flexural modulus of elasticity, 10^6 p.s.i.[3]				
24°C. (75°F.)	3.47	2.50	2.60	1.97
260°C. (500°F.)	3.05	2.46	2.27	1.57
316°C. (600°F.)	3.37	2.35	2.18	1.51
371°C. (700°F.)	2.77	—	2.00	1.10
Compressive strength, 10^3 p.s.i.[4]				
24°C. (75°F.)	46.6	16.0	22.5	22.1
260°C. (500°F.)	32.7	11.4	9.4	7.8
316°C. (600°F.)	28.2	9.2	9.2	6.4
371°C. (700°F.)	10.9	7.7	5.8	4.9
Tensile strength, 10^3 p.s.i.[5]				
24°C. (75°F.)	26.5	18.9	20.5	13.9
260°C. (500°F.)	24.1	15.2	17.8	11.2
316°C. (600°F.)	14.3	16.0	17.2	9.5
371°C. (700°F.)	16.6	9.4	7.8	9.1

[1] CTL, Inc. 37-9X resin; [2] Dow-Corning Corp. DC-2106 resin; [3] D790: 1-in. span. 0.025 in./min. loading rate; [4] ARTC 11-1 test method; [5] ASTM D638 test method.

Sheets of ceramic paper are placed between the silicon carbide bricks in melting furnaces to prevent leakage. Plugs for the furnace tap holes, which are generally inserted manually, are wrapped in ceramic paper. The paper conforms to the shape of the tap hole and provides a nonfreezing seal that is easily removed without contaminating the molten metal. Piping systems for molten aluminum have been developed from ceramic-fiber paper tubes that have the advantage of being well insulated and free from build-ups in elbows or joints.

Use of ceramic-fiber paper has made possible many technical advances in the brazing process. Immunity to thermal shock, excellent insulating characteristics, ability to conform to contours, and resiliency and chemical stability, all qualities demonstrated by ceramic papers, have led to the reduction of rejects and to improved quality in the brazing process. Ceramic-fiber paper is accelerating the honeycomb brazing cycle. It helps to distribute heat uniformly throughout the work from both top and bottom and to distribute the pressure uniformly over the skin sheet being brazed. An 80-mil ceramic-fiber paper has been substituted for the 1-in. thick top graphite structure, estimated to be about equal in heat-balance characterisics.

Ceramic fiber can be used for reinforcing metals. According to General Electric Co., Metallurgy and Research Department, single-crystal fibers in a metal matrix substantially increase the high-temperature strength of the metal.

Miscellaneous Uses. Fiberfrax ceramic tubes made of ceramic paper are lightweight, high-temperature-resisting (2300°F.) structures. The material offers low thermal conductivity and high resistance to thermal shock. Table **7.38** lists properties of the new structures and

TABLE 7.38

Properties of Ceramic Fiberfrax Tubes Made of Ceramic-
Fiber Paper (52)

Properties	Types		
	T 30	T 30 R	QC 10
Approximate density, lb./ft.^{3}	35	47	25
Modulus of rupture, p.s.i.	221	458	130
Linear shrinkage, %			
24-hr. soak at 1500°F.	0	0.2	0
24-hr. soak at 1800°F.	3.1	4.9	—
24-hr. soak at 2000°F.	4.2	5.7	—
24-hr. soak at 2300°F.	5.3	6.5	4.2
Thermal shock resistance	Good	Good	Excellent
Thermal conductivity Btu./hr.-ft.^{2}-°F./in.			
mean temperature			
600°F.	0.6	0.6	0.52
1000°F.	0.8	0.80	0.73
1400°F.	1.04	1.04	0.95
1800°F.	1.34	1.34	1.22
2000°F.	1.49	1.49	1.36

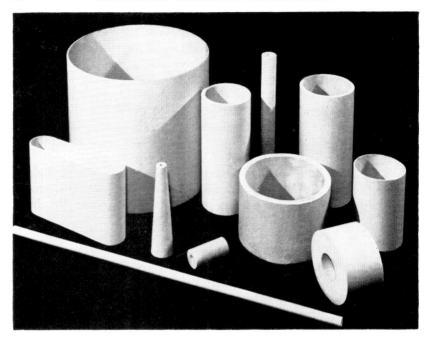

Figure 7.20. Fiberfrax ceramic-fiber tubes are lightweight, high-temperature-re-sisting (2300°F.) structures. The materials offer low thermal conductivity and high resistance to thermal shock.

Figure 7.20 shows the manifold shapes produced for many applications. These tubes are used to convey flat glass from the annealing furnace, and spools of ceramic fiber are used to convey glass bottles.

Ceramic-fiber blankets and papers for vibration damping need not show reduced strength nor increased rigidity on heating. When employed in sound and vibration damping in missiles, rockets, and jet engines, ceramic-fiber papers remain effective at very high temperatures (see Figure 7.21) (69).

Teflon-reinforced ceramic fibers are used for backup rings in the hydraulic system of developmental jet aircraft. No changes were reported for trial runs exceeding 50,000 cycles at 500°F. in tests of hydraulic fluid.

Ceramic fibers, like glass fibers, can be metallized to provide conductive or reflective surfaces. Glass-fiber rovings are metal-coated to make them electrically conductive in cores of automobile ignition wires to suppress signals generated by high frequency. Similar applications requiring high temperatures can be visualized. In addition to electrical shielding, ceramic fibers can be metal-coated to increase strength, impart chemical resistance, and develop energy in batteries, to supply catalytic action, and to provide means of resistance heating and heat dissipation at very high temperatures.

The highly resistant ceramic and quartz fibers can be coated with nearly any metal and matted into structural parts. Owens-Corning (71, 72) and others (73) hold patents on processes for vapor deposition of nickel, iron, molybdenum, and zirconium. Other methods include drawing ceramic fibers through molten metal at an orifice (74). Bjorksten Research Laboratories have developed a continuous process of simultaneously drawing and coating fused silica filaments with aluminum and other metals. The Sherrit Gordon Co. has also developed a method by which ceramic fibers are coated with large amounts of nickel (75). Fibers carrying as much as 83% were tested by the authors.

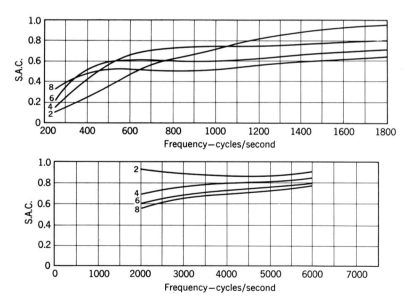

Figure 7.21. Sound adsorption coefficient (S.A.C.) versus frequency for B & W Kaowool blanket. One-inch thickness at density indicated by numbers on curves (69).

Other specific applications are as follows:

1. Facings to protect structural metal in furnaces, processing vessels, incinerators, etc., from heat and corrosion.

2. Linings for low dew-point hydrogen atmosphere furnaces, where ceramic fibers, unlike other insulators, do not react with hydrogen to form water.

3. Packing in steam generators.
4. Steam valve headers.
5. Annealing furnaces.
6. Ceramic kilns.
7. Wrap for steam tubes.
8. In rollers of hearth furnaces.
9. In necks of slag hoppers.
10. Oven linings.
11. Superheated seals.
12. Steel-tube wrapping for induction stress relief.
13. High temperature fans.
14. Heat exchangers.
15. Nuclear heater vessels.
16. Panels in brazing furnaces.
17. Infrared reflectors.
18. Gas infrared heaters.
19. Dry lubricant.
20. Special fuses.
21. Protection of globar units in assay furnaces.
22. Blow pipe insulation in blast furnaces.
23. Gaskets on electrodes.
24. Liners for high-frequency induction furnaces.

This review clearly indicates the great potentialities of refractory fibers and papers and their usefulness in modern industry.

OUTLOOK

The horizons for ceramic refractory fibers and papers are widening in industrial and space applications. A fourfold increase in demand is forecast by 1965 (70).

The fiber developer claims that he can convert almost any oxide to fibers, although interest has been primarily in materials with high heat resistance and maximum strength. Fibers today include alumina, alumina-silica combinations, zirconia, berylia, thoria, iron oxides, silica, chromium, and potassium titanate. Tomorrow's fibers and ceramic-paper structures will cover temperatures up to 5000 and 6000°F. and only the future can tell how far chemists, fiber producers, and papermakers will be able to extend this range to the upper limits in properties. The years between 1950 and 1970 should become identified with the period of development of paperlike materials of temperature resistance reaching the boundaries of physical possibility.

ACKNOWLEDGMENT

We sincerely appreciate the assistance provided by many friends and associates in supplying data, photomicrographs, and written material for this chapter. Mr. E. L. Scott produced most of the photomicrographs, Dr. D. C. McIntosh provided data on fiber strength, and Dr. E. B. Brookbank, Jr. assisted with grammatical corrections and constructive criticism.

We appreciate the cooperation of our friends at The Carborundum Co., Du Pont, Johns-Manville, Babcock and Wilcox, Hitco, The Boeing Co., and others in supplying technical data. We also appreciate the willingness of various authors and publishers listed in the references to allow the use of previously published tables and figures.

Our special thanks go to Dr. J. C. Redd, General Manager of Research, and to The Mead Corporation for the time required to prepare this chapter and for permission to publish.

REFERENCES

1. H. F. Arledter, "New Developments in the Manufacture of Synthetic Fiber Paper for Electrical Applications" presented at the Electrochemical Society Meeting in New York, April 15, 1953.
2. H. F. Arledter, "Filter Paper with High Acid and Alkali Resistance," presented at the Conference on Analytical Chemistry and Applied Spectroscopy, Pittsburgh, March 1, 1954.
3. "Structural Ceramic Fibers of Virtually Any Oxide," *Mater. Design Eng.*, 52, No. 1, 5 (July, 1960). (Source: Horizons, Inc., Cleveland 4, Ohio).
4. J. C. McMullen, U. S. Patent 2,557,834 (1951) and J. C. McMullen, U. S. Patent 2,686,821 (1954). (Assigned to Carborundum Co.)
5. British Patent 638,876 (1950) and J. Zobel, U. S. Patent 2,674,559 (1954). (Assigned to Babcock and Wilcox Co.)
6. W. P. Hahn, U. S. Patent 2,699,397 (1955). (Assigned to Johns-Manville Corp.)
7. W. P. Hahn and S. Steil, British Patent 728,354 (1955), S. Steil and I. Barnett, Canadian Patent 539,961 (1957); A. J. Brunow and S. Steil, Canadian Patent 539,962 (1957). (Assigned to Johns-Manville Corp.)
8. T. R. Haglund, British Patent 595,654 (1947). (Assigned to Landis & Gyr, S.A.)
9. H. C. Smith and C. L. Newport, Canadian Patent 455,781 (1949).
10. British Patent 507,951 (1939). (Assigned to W. C. Heraeus Company.)
11. J. C. Hill, German Patent 1,108,388 (1961). (Assigned to Engelhard Industry.)

12. "Fiberbfrax Production: Carborundum's Versatile Ceramic Fiber," *Ceram. Age,* (February 1962).
13. J. C. McMullen, U. S. Patent 2,873,197 (1959). (Assigned to Carborundum Company.)
14. W. A. Lambertson, D. B. Aiken, and E. H. Girard, "Continuous Filament Ceramic Fibers," WADC Tech. Rept. 60–244, 1960. (U.S.A.F. Contact No. AF 33-616-6246, with Carborundum Co.)
15. A. Silverman and L. Parker, U. S. Patent 2,736,141 (1956). A. Silverman, U. S. Patent 2,822,579 (1958) and U. S. Patent 2,838,882 (1958).
16. D. Labino, U. S. Patent 2,843,461 (1958). (Assigned to L.O.F. Glass Fibers Co.)
17. M. E. Nordberg, U. S. Patent 2,461,841 (1949). (Assigned to Corning Glass Works.)
18. *U. S. Gov. Res. Rept.,* 34, No. 4, (1960).
19. WADC Tech. Report 59–155, U. S. Department of Commerce (September 1959).
20. C. Z. Carroll-Porczynski, *Advanced Materials,* p. 118, 1962. ASTEX Publishing Company, Ltd., Guildford, England.
21. Mechanism of Growth and Physical Properties of Refractory Oxide Fibers, Rept., PB 171,520, U. S. Department of Commerce, (April 1960).
22. U.S.A.F. Contract No. AF 33 (616) 7264.
23. C. Z. Carroll-Porczynski, *Advanced Materials,* p. 121 (see ref. No. 20); also WADC Tech. Rept. 59–155 (September 1959).
24. PB 171,939; AD 243,205, U. S. Department of Commerce (August 1960).
25. British Patent 171,520 (1921). (Assigned to Radio Communications, Ltd., and Norman Lea.)
26. S. S. Brenner, "The Growth of Whiskers by the Reduction of Metal Salts," Acta Met., 4, 62 (January 1956).
27. G. W. Sears, A. Gatti, and R. L. Fulman, "Elastic Properties of Iron Whiskers," *Acta Met.,* 2, 727 (1954)
28. E. R. Johnsons and J. A. Amick, "Formation of Single Crystal Silicon Fibres," *J. Appl. Phys.,* 25, 1204 (1954).
29. J. M. Margottet, "Reproduction des sulfure, selenivre at tellulure d'argent cristallisés at de l'argent filiforme," C. R. Acad. Sci., Paris, 85, 1142 (1877).
30. C. Herring and J. K. Galt, "Elastic and Plastic Properties of Very Small Metal Specimens," *Phys. Rev.,* 85, 1060 (1952).
31. G. W. Sears, "A mechanism of Whisker Growth." *Acta Met.,* 3, 361 (1955).
32. G. A. Hoffmann, *New Scientist,* No. 216, 405 (January, 1961).
33. M. L. Williams, G. Gerard, and G. A. Hofmann, 9th International Astronautical Congress, Stockholm, 1960, Paper No. 18.
34. British Patent 861,802 (1961). (Assigned to E. I. duPont de Nemours, & Co., Inc.)
35. K. L. Berry, U. S. Patent 2,980,510. (Assigned to E. I. duPont de Nemours, & Co.)
36. P. Mergault and G. Branch, C. R. Acad. Sci., Paris, 238, 914 (1954).
37. K. L. Berry and H. S. Young, *J. Inorg. Nucl. Chem.,* 14, 231, (1960).
38. British Patent 758,312 (1956) and W. J. Cherry, British Patent 746,417 (1956). (Assigned to Carborundum Co.)
39. R. C. Meaders, U. S. Patent 2,704,603 (1955). (Assigned to Carborundum Co.)
40. R. C. Meaders, *Ceramic Abstracts,* 111-C (June 1955).

41. E. R. Powell, U. S. Patent 2,968,069 (1961). (Assigned to Johns-Manville Co.)
42. P. S. Haglund, *Steel,* 74–75 (January 16, 1961).
43. A. V. Levy, H. Leggett, and S. R. Locke, American Rocket Society.
44. *Advanced Materials Technology,* Vol. 3, No. 2, 126, (June, 1960) (Carborundum Co.).
45. *Materials in Design Engineering, Rept.* 144–145, June 1960. (Battelle Memorial Inst.)
46. H. I. Thompson Co., Bull. No. 21.
47. C. O. Hulse, "Formation and Strength of Magnesia Whiskers," *J. Am. Ceram. Soc.,* **44,** No. 11, 572 (1961).
48. Johns-Manville Technical Data Sheet.
49. D. C. McIntosh, Mead Corporation, Central Research Laboratories.
50. H. F. Arledter, U. S. Patent 2,971,877 (1961). (Assigned to Hurlbut Paper Co., Mead Corporation, and H. F. Arledter. U. S. Patent 2,721,139 (1955). (Assigned to Hurlbut Paper Co.)
51. H. F. Arledter, U. S. Patent 2,706,156 (1955). (Assigned to Hurlbut Paper Co., Mead Corp.)
52. Carborundum Co., Technical Data (1960).
53. H. C. Gulledge, "Fibrous Potassium Titanate," *Ind. Eng. Chem.,* **52,** 117 (February 1960), and E. I. duPont de Nemours Co., Inc., "Tipersul" Information Bull. No. 3 (June 1960).
54. T. D. Callinan and R. L. Lucas, Naval Research Laboratory Rept. "The Manufacture and Properties of Paper Made from Ceramic Fibers," Paper Trade J., **135,** No. 8, 24–28 (August 22, 1952).
55. G. I. Keim and William Thompsen.
56. Mead Corp. Central Research Laboratories (previously unpublished work).
57. British Patent 871,577 (1961). (Assigned to Carborundum Co.)
58. H. F. Arledter, Hurlbut Research, Rept. No. 355 (November 14, 1952) (unpublished).
59. Minnesota Mining and Manufacturing Co., data on "Burnil" brand microplates.
60. SPE J., 951 (August 1960); data by Carborundum Co.
61. R. C. Straka, Jr., "Product Forms of Alumina-Silica Ceramic Fibers," *Am. Ceram. Soc. Bull.,* **40,** No. 8 (August 15, 1961).
62. H. F. Arledter, "Inorganic Analytical Filter Paper," *TAPPI,* **38,** No. 12, 764–768 (December 1955).
63. H. F. Arledter, "New Developments in Industrial Filter Paper," presented at the American Chemical Society Meeting in New York City, September 13, 1954.
64. M. W. First and J. B. Graham, "Ceramic Filters for High Temperature Gas Filtration," *Ind. Eng. Chem.,* **50,** No. 6, 63A–64A (June 1958).
65. R. A. Bub and E. M. Becker, Canadian Patent 559,023 (1958). (Assigned to Mine Safety Appliances Co.)
66. *Advanced Materials,* p. 34 (quoted from *Mater. Design Eng.,* **52,** No. 5, 11 (1960). H. I. Thompson Fiber Glass Corp. Refrasil.
67. *Advanced Materials,* p. 34 (quoted from *Mater. Design Eng.* **52,** No. 5, 11 (1960).
68. R. M. Krupka and D. E. Taylor, *Corrosion,* **16,** No. 8, 91 (August 1960).
69. The Babcock and Wilcox Co., Information Bull. (1962).
70. *Steel,* 74–75 (January 16, 1961).

71. J. S. Nachtman, U. S. Patent 2,699,415 (1955). (Assigned to Owens-Corning Fiberglass Corp.)
72. H. B. Whitehurst and W. H. Otto, U. S. Patent 2,928,716 (1960). (Assigned to Owens-Corning Fiberglas Corp.)
73. J. S. Nachtman and J. Bjorksten, U. S. Patent 2,953,472 (1960).
74. C. B. Budd, and D. E. Weaver, U. S. Patent 2,934,458 (1960). (Assigned to B. F. Goodrich Co.)
75. B. Meddings, W. Kunda, and V. N. Mackin, "The Preparation of Nickel-Coated Powders," *Powder Met.*, 775–798 (1961), Interscience. New York.

8

THE POLYOLEFINS

VICTOR L. ERLICH

Vice-President in charge of Research and Development

CHARLES HOUSTON TEAGUE

Manager Fiber Research & Development

Reeves Brothers, Inc.

New York, New York

HISTORICAL BACKGROUND

POLYETHYLENE

The polyolefin story started in the laboratories of Imperial Chemical Industries in England around 1933, and one of the first descriptions of the forthcoming industrial polymerization process for ethylene can be found in a British patent of that company of 1936.   Polyethylene became commercially available in England in 1939 (1).   In the United States the patent was granted in 1939 (2), and Du Pont and Bakelite, a division of Union Carbide, became the sole licensees. During the war years the production of these companies was devoted exclusively to war requirements, primarily for high-frequency cables in radar equipment and for insulation of submarine telephone cables. At the end of the war civilian markets had to be created.   Applications were found for cable and wire insulation, films, tubing, and molded products.   Within a few years these applications not only absorbed the then existing production capacity of approximately 100 million lb. per year, but made steady increases necessary.

By the middle 1940's nylon opened the fiber field to the synthetic-polymer industry and was followed at that time by vinyl and vinylidene polymers, Saran in particular.   The new techniques of high-temperature melt extrusion to filaments had to be developed, and it took a decade of experimental work before these fully man-made synthetic fibers could be presented to the textile market.

It seemed inviting to offer polyethylene for similar purposes because it could easily be extruded into filamentary shapes.   By cold

245

drawing them they could be oriented to give filaments of a certain degree of strength but not, however, of a tenacity sufficient for fine fibers. Chemical inertness, water, spot and mildew resistance, flexibility, and resilience seemed to be interesting enough to consider certain applications in the form of heavy filaments, pigment-dyed in bright shades, and woven to patterned automobile-seat-cover fabrics. This started around 1946. Although the venture was commercially unsuccessful, it did not discourage the pioneers in this field, National Plastics Products Company and Reeves Brothers in the United States and Courtaulds, Ltd., in England, to continue research work which was primarily aimed at overcoming difficulties such as insufficient sunlight resistance and dimensional stability; this proved to be useful for the unexpected developments that ensued.

Polyethylene, as produced under high pressure at temperatures above 100°C. with peroxyde catalysts as polymerization activators, did not yield the straight-line molecular chain characteristics of a paraffin or polymethylene but had side branches of different lengths attached at random to the basic carbon chain.

By 1954 other methods of polymerizing ethylene emerged from the laboratories of Professor Karl Ziegler in Germany and of Phillips Petroleum, later Phillips Chemical Co., in the United States. This new concept of polymerization used aluminum alkyls and then more generally organo-metal compounds as reaction catalysts and permitted operation at considerably lower pressure and at temperatures below 100°C. It yields a polymer of a preponderantly straight or linear molecular chain and of higher molecular weight. This polymer has a greater density, 0.95 for the Ziegler type and 0.96 for the Phillips type against 0.92 for the old one, and is, therefore, designated also as *high-density polyethylene.* It has a higher degree of crystallinity, greater stiffness, and melting points ranging from 130 to 138°C. against only 110 to 120°C. for the old type material.

These polyethylenes became commercially available in 1956 and 1957. The Ziegler type was first manufactured by Farbwerke Hoechst in Germany and by Hercules Powder and Koppers, followed by Dow, Du Pont, Union Carbide and others, in the United States. Phillips Chemical produced their polymer and licensed Celanese, Grace, and Union Carbide in this country and several others overseas.

These were polymers that could be extruded into filaments and fine fibers of high tenacity approaching that of nylon. New fields of application were opened for monofilaments of comparatively heavy diameter in industrial fields to compete with Saran which was already established. The added properties of high strength and greater resistance to flat abrasion were important primarily in the rope and furniture-fabric fields. Adverse factors, however, were the so-called cold flow or creep characteristics which cause permanent elongation under heavy stresses. This was particularly pronounced for the highest density almost straight-line Phillips polymer which has less than 2.5 side branches on a 1000 carbon chain against at least 10 times as many for the high-pressure polyethylene. The Ziegler type with four to five such chains and intermediate modified Phillips types performed considerably better.

Low resilience and the still quite low melting point remained other limitations. Some attempts to produce fine filament yarns did not, therefore, meet with real commercial success.

POLYPROPYLENE

Almost simultaneously another breakthrough of fundamental importance for a broad section of the polymer field originated in Milan, Italy, where Professor Giulio Natta demonstrated that certain basically Ziegler-type catalysts could be used to polymerize unsaturated monomers, mono-olefins (other than ethylene), and di-olefins to polymers of specifically controlled molecular structure. These polymers have the paraffinic carbon backbone of polyethylene with methyl or higher carbon-hydrogen groups which are located in order as side branches in the same or in regularly alternating positions. Such molecular structures were termed by Natta isotactic and syndiotactic, respectively, and more generally stereospecific. They differ in the physical properties from their relatives of irregular or atactic molecular structure; this is pronounced with regard to crystallinity and the melting points which are considerably higher for the new polymers, as illustrated in Figures 8.1, 8.2, and 8.3 and Table 8.1 (3.4).

Fibers produced from *isotactic polypropylene* had the high tenacity of linear polyethylene coupled with excellent resilience characteristics, high flat and flex abrasion, better creep performance, and the higher melting points of 165 to 176°C. What created an explosive interest was the fact that low-cost components of natural or cracking gases could give a comparatively low-cost polymer as a basis for textile fibers; it was expected, indeed, that polypropylene would be priced on the same low level as polyethylene.

The basic patents were applied for by Natta in 1954 and by Ziegler and subsequently in other countries jointly by Montecatini and Ziegler (5). They covered the method and the composition of matter including the end products, film, and fibers especially. These patents, issued in most European and overseas countries, created a dominant position for Montecatini, the Italian chemical concern,

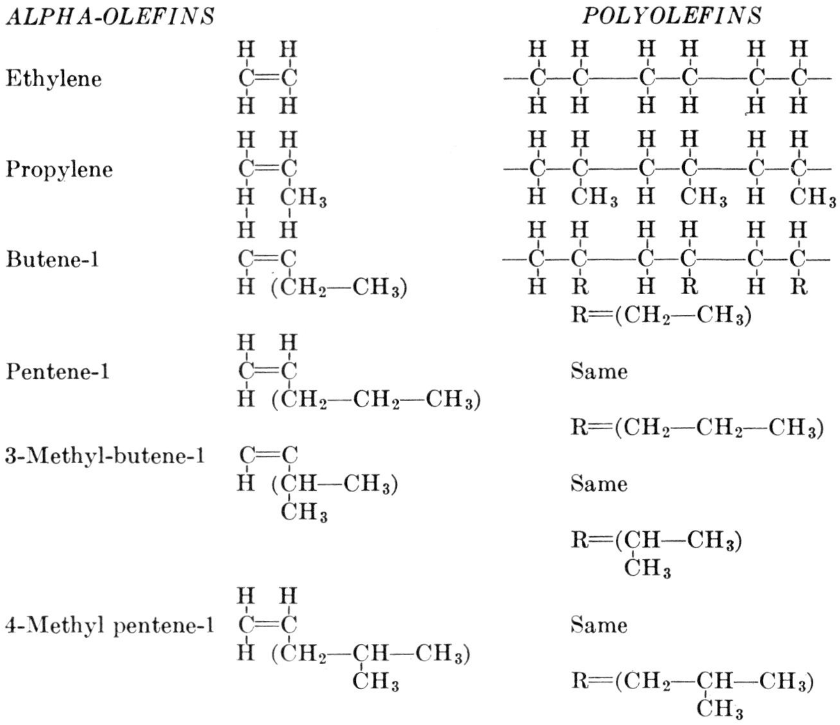

ALPHA-OLEFINS   *POLYOLEFINS*

Ethylene

$$\begin{array}{cc} H & H \\ C{=}C \\ H & H \end{array} \qquad \begin{array}{cccccc} H & H & H & H & H & H \\ -C-C & -C-C & -C-C- \\ H & H & H & H & H & H \end{array}$$

Propylene

$$\begin{array}{cc} H & H \\ C{=}C \\ H & CH_3 \end{array} \qquad \begin{array}{cccccc} H & H & H & H & H & H \\ -C-C & -C-C & -C-C- \\ H & CH_3 & H & CH_3 & H & CH_3 \end{array}$$

Butene-1

$$\begin{array}{cc} H & H \\ C{=}C \\ H & (CH_2{-}CH_3) \end{array} \qquad \begin{array}{cccccc} H & H & H & H & H & H \\ -C-C & -C-C & -C-C- \\ H & R & H & R & H & R \end{array}$$
$$R{=}(CH_2{-}CH_3)$$

Pentene-1

$$\begin{array}{cc} H & H \\ C{=}C \\ H & (CH_2{-}CH_2{-}CH_3) \end{array} \qquad \text{Same}$$
$$R{=}(CH_2{-}CH_2{-}CH_3)$$

3-Methyl-butene-1

$$\begin{array}{cc} & C{=}C \\ & H \quad (CH{-}CH_3) \\ & \qquad CH_3 \end{array} \qquad \text{Same}$$
$$R{=}(CH{-}CH_3)$$
$$\qquad CH_3$$

4-Methyl pentene-1

$$\begin{array}{cc} H & H \\ C{=}C \\ H & (CH_2{-}CH{-}CH_3) \\ & \qquad CH_3 \end{array} \qquad \text{Same}$$
$$R{=}(CH_2{-}CH{-}CH_3)$$
$$\qquad CH_3$$

Figure 8.1

not only to grant licenses for the polymer process but also and independently to produce the fiber. The situation was quite different in the United States in which several of the big polymer producers, such as Du Pont, Eastman, Hercules, Shell, Standard Oil of Indiana, and Avisun, are claiming their own processes. To date a number of process patents have been granted to polymer producers in the United States but in November 1963, two composition of matter patents were issued to Montecatini; at this writing it is to early to predict how they will influence the over-all patent situation.

Commercial quantities of polypropylene became available between 1957 and 1959, first from Montecatini in Italy and from Hercules Powder in the United States. In 1962 eight manufacturers in the United States had the polymer production on stream.* In England

* Polypropylene polymer manufacturers in the United States 1962/63: Avisun, Dow Chemical, Eastman, Firestone, Hercules, Humble Oil-Esso, Novamont-Montecatini, Shell Chemical. Monsanto, Phillips-National Distillers, and Standard Oil of California have announced similar projects.

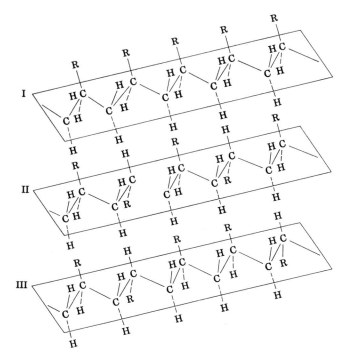

Figure 8.2. Steric configurations of polyolefins.

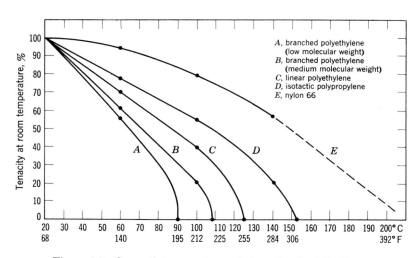

Figure 8.3. Strength-temperature relation of polyolefin fibers.

TABLE 8.1

Comparison of Structure and Melting Ranges

Polymer	Specific Gravity Range	Melting Range (°C.)	(°F.)
Polyethylene branched types	0.91–0.93	107–121	225–250
Polyethylene linear types	0.95–0.97	130–138	265–280
Polypropylene isotactic	0.87–0.94	165–176	330–348
Polybutene-1 isotactic	0.91	125–128	258–262
Polypentene-1 isotactic	0.87	75–80	165–175
Poly-3-methyl butene-1 isotactic	0.90	245, 300	470, 570
Poly-4-methyl pentene-1 isotactic	0.83	235, 241	455, 466
Poly-styrene atactic (conventional)	1.04–1.05	99–110	210–230
Poly-styrene isotactic	1.10	240	464
Poly-o-methyl styrene atactic	—	180–185	356–365
Poly-o-methyl styrene isotactic	—	Above 360	680

Imperial Chemicals Industries (ICI) and the Shell group started production in England (Shell also in Holland). Other producers in North and South America, Australia, and strongly in Japan have announced similar projects. The planned production capacity in the United States in 1963 approached half a billion pounds of polymer and about as much overseas. Such world capacity equals that now existing for linear polyethylene and is close to one fourth of the total capacity for the polyethylenes.

The commercial development of the fiber was much slower. Limited quantities of fiber were offered between 1960 and 1961 in the form of multifilament yarn and staple, first in Italy and then in North America by Beaunit, Canadian Celanese, Hercules Powder, and Reeves Brothers and in England by ICI. More producers are planning to enter this fiber field in the United States and overseas, particularly in Japan.*

Additional development work was necessary in the processing of the fiber to give it the properties expected from the laboratory and subsequently to adjust it to the requirements of individual end-use applications.

* Besides the concerns mentioned the following are planning to produce fine polypropylene fibers: In the *United States*, G. F. Chemicals, J. P. Stevens-National Plastics Products (Enjay), U. S. Rubber, and possibly Montecatini and Avisun. In *Japan*, Mitsubishi Rayon, Toyo Rayon, Shin Nippon Chisso Hiryo, Asabi Chemical, Nitto and Daiwa, and Danubia Petrochemie in Austria. In *South America*, Forti Argentini. In *Australia*, Synthetic Yarns Pty, Ltd. *In Europe*, the positions are not clarified except for Montecatini and I.C.I.

In the form of heavy *monofilaments* polyethylene had established its market for ropes, heavy furniture fabrics, and filter cloth. It was not too difficult to introduce polypropylene monofilaments for similar purposes because of better performance, especially in resilience, and new uses were added, for instance, in the bristle field in which stiffness and resilience were important.

Subsequently *multifilament yarns* of low individual deniers were made available for industrial applications, such as in ropes, fishnets, and laundry bags, and for textiles, especially in the carpet field. High strength, low weight, and chemical inertness are assets in favor of polypropylene, which in this category is competing primarily with nylon.

In the form of *staple and spun yarn,* woven or nonwoven, such end products as furniture, upholstery and automobile carpets, blankets, interlining, and filtrations were open. Potentially, much broader uses for the polypropylene fiber as such, and more so in blends, particularly with the natural fibers, were offered in the textile-apparel market.

Here some drawbacks had been attributed to this fiber. The melting point is lower than that of nylon, the acrylics, and the polyesters, and this created concern in regard to ironing. It is true that a 100% polypropylene fabric must be ironed carefully at a low temperature setting; in blends, however, preferably when the olefin content is lower than 50%, not more than the usual care commonly practiced for many synthetic fabrics is necessary.

Another adverse factor of these fibers, as produced from the initially available polymers, was a lack of resistance to sunlight, but greater purity of the polymer and progress made in stabilization techniques led to favorable comparison of polypropylene fibers with regular nylon. In addition, continuous improvements were forthcoming as a result of close cooperation between polymer and fiber producers.

A more important handicap, however, seemed to relate to dyeing. The advantage of the chemical inertness of the resin and its water-repellent characteristics turns against dye acceptance under normal conditions. This was a condition that repeated itself for more or less all previously known synthetics; acetate and the acrylics were thought to be undyeable in the beginning. The problem was solved in different ways and degrees by polymer-fiber producers and dye-stuff manufacturers, and of course, improvements are steadily made.

These staple fibers can be processed to yarn and fabrics on conventional types of textile machinery by spinning, weaving, or knitting. They can be piled, napped, and texturized or bulked.

HIGHER POLYOLEFINS

As far as the higher polyolefins are concerned, potential interest exists with regard to isotactic poly-methyl-butene and polymethyl-pentene (see Table 8.1) as possible fiber polymers in view of their considerably higher melting points.   Some pilot-plant work has been and is being done in the United States and in Europe.   Polymerization techniques are similar to those used for polypropylene, but conclusive results cannot yet be drawn from the standpoint of fiber properties nor from that of comparative economy.

COST POSITION

Whatever the end products are, the cost and price considerations are a determining factor in applications in which the olefin fiber has to compete with others, natural and synthetic.   The economics are basically in favor of polypropylene fibers produced from the simplest raw materials and subsequently basically from the least expensive polymers of the lowest density, which means a yield of fiber yardage per pound that is greater than for all presently available synthetics; this represents a cost advantage even for equal price per pound of polymer.

At present the polypropylene polymers are more expensive than the polyethylenes, with the low-density material cheaper than that of high-density.   But we are still in the introductory period, and the price trend is downward for the polyolefins as well as for other man-made synthetics, but in the competitive play and counterplay a margin should remain to place the olefin fiber on the lower cost level when the market has settled to permanent conditions.

At that time the early prediction may also come true that the polypropylene fibers could compete in price even with cotton.   This is a point of consideration for all fields of application, and, therefore, also if and when the olefin fibers find their place in papermaking.

POLYETHYLENE AND POLYPROPYLENE POLYMERS: PROPERTIES

CHEMICAL

Polyethylene and polypropylene, as members of the paraffinic hydrocarbon group, have in common a great degree of inertness to chemicals.   For instance, they are resistant to saline solutions,

strong alkalis, concentrated hydrochloric and 80% sulfuric acids up
to the boiling point of water and higher. They are also insoluble
at room temperature in most solvents but will swell in chlorinated
solvents and some aromatics and become soluble in these solvents at
elevated temperatures, say at 70 to 80°C. Mineral and vegetable
oils also are absorbed slowly and cause swelling which increases with
rising temperatures. There are, however, differences in the degree of
the reactivities between these polymers; low-density branched polyethylene is in some instances, but not in all, more resistant than
high-density linear, and, in turn, high crystalline polypropylene is
more resistant than low crystalline and in general more than the
polyethylenes. Table **8.2** lists some examples to illustrate these
positions comparatively.

TABLE 8.2

Change in Tensile Strength of Polypropylene and Polyethylene
on Long Immersion in Selected Liquids (6)
(four months or more)

| | Polyethylene | | Polypropylene | |
| | | | (% crystallinity) | |
Liquid	Low Density	Linear	63	56
Water	1.8	0	−1.1	−8.6
Isopropyl alcohol	1.1	−7.1	−7.1	−11.3
Primol D	−8.1	−78.0	−10.1	−20.0
Silicone oil	−1.5	−11.0	13.8	−7.1
Methylethylketone	−5.2	−42.7	0	−6.0
10% sodium hydroxide	−1.6	−14.0	3.2	−4.5
10% common salt	2.6	−6.5	0	−9.1
10% acetic acid	−8.1	9.8	13.2	−4.7
Dioctyl phthalate	−6.5	−2.3	5.9	−3.6
Linseed oil	−5.6	−60.5	1.1	−3.4
Corn oil	0	−50.5	16.0	−19.8
Methanol	2.2	2.5	2.3	−7.2
Igepal[1]	−100	−100	9.8	−1.8

[1] A surface-active agent used as detergent.

Oxygen uptake at elevated temperatures or under ultraviolet irradiation is of great practical importance. It causes a gradual break-
down of the molecular chains and is therefore a determining factor
of the stability of polyolefins to heat on one hand and to sunlight on

the other; linear polyethylene is considerably more resistant than either the branched type polyethylene or polypropylene. This becomes particularly evident in melt extrusion and in the use of the polymers in fiber form because of the ratio of surface to cross section which is so much greater here than for all other shapes. Stabilizing compounds are antioxidants to which ultraviolet absorbers may be added to combine heat and ultraviolet stability. Numerous compounds have been evaluated for their efficiency, but relatively few specific molecular groups have been found to be effective. The work done in this respect on the polyethylenes was only partly applicable to polypropylene, which requires different stabilizing systems in order to render its fibers fit for outdoor exposure. Finally, rot and mildew do not attack the polyolefins.

PHYSICAL

Much more dramatic, however, is the variance in the physical characteristics of the different polyolefins.

Table 8.1 lists the respective melting points. The softening points without load are not more than 10 to 15°C. below, the respective melt temperatures. Other properties, such as breaking or tensile strength, shear and impact strength, abrasion resistance, and stiffness, are inherent to the polymer, but they can also be controlled to a lesser or greater degree by the conditions of processing the polymer. This control is very pronounced during extrusion to films and fibers. Crystallinity is a factor in its influence on the physical properties, as is discussed later; Table 8.3 indicates, for instance, a correlation of the degree of crystallinity and the stiffness of the polyethylenes and of polypropylene (4).

More specific indications of these and other physical characteristics, such as thermal conductivity and dielectric performance, are found in the industrial literature of the individual polymer producers.

Because polypropylene is at present the most important polyolefin in the broad field of fibers, this polymer is discussed in more detail.

Its properties are dependent first on the formulation and preparation of the catalysts used and second on the conditions under which the polymerization is carried out and the formed polymer is aftertreated. Thus a gamut from the amorphous fluid type to the completely crystalline and isotactic form can be obtained, but the present commercial polymers have a preferred degree of crystallinity of around 65%. Further modification of polypropylene can also be obtained by copolymerizing it, for instance, with polyethylene. A wide choice of polymers therefore is or can be made available.

TABLE 8.3
Correlations of Crystallinity and Density for
Polyethylenes and Polypropylene
(room temperature)

Polymer	Density, (gm./cm.^{3})	Crystallinity Degree, (%)	Stiffness Modulus, (p.s.i.)
Polyethylenes			
Branched			
Amorph	(0.84)	0	0
Low density	0.92	60/65	25/30,000
Medium density	0.935	75	60/65,000
Linear			
Phillips copolymer	0.945	81	83,000
Ziegler type	0.95	85	90/110,000
Phillips type	0.96	91	130/150,000
	(1.00)	(100)	
Polypropylene			
Isotactic			
Amorph (molten)	(0.85)	0	0
Medium	0.90	60/65	125/130,000
(commercial as used			
for fibers)	0.91	70/75	130/180,000
High crystalline	0.92	80/85	200/220,000
	(0.93/0.94)	(100)	

There are other major factors which can influence the polymer properties; namely, average molecular weight, molecular weight distribution, and steric purity or degree of stereoregularity. A practical measurement widely used in the industry is that of the melt index, which gives a measure of the flow of the polymer under a standard pressure and temperature through the standard extrusion orifice. Another test method is that of the so-called intrinsic viscosity, which is correlated and increases with the molecular weight. Average molecular weights of commercial fibergrade polypropylene are indicated as higher than 300,000, against 60,000 to 130,000 for high-density polyethylene and only 19,000 to 25,000 for low-density polyethylene. This means that the length of the molecular chain of isotactic polypropylene is more than twice that of the linear and more than 10 times that of the branched type polyethylene.

Breaking and shear strength as well as flexural stiffness increase with average molecular weight and steric purity. The abrasion resistance increases with steric purity and falls between that of linear polyethylene and nylon; the impact strength falls between that of linear polyethylene and polystyrene. Other influences of the basic polymer structure on the properties of the processed materials are illustrated in connection with those of the fibers.

Polyethylene has a tendency to crack when stresses are applied while the surface is in contact with certain fluid agents such as detergents. On the contrary, the resistance of polypropylene to such "environmental stress cracking" is excellent.

Another point of importance is that of low-temperature effect on the flexibility of the polymers. Isotactic polypropylene showed brittleness on a higher level than polyethylene, which is outstanding in this regard because it does not deteriorate even at —100°C. (—150°F.). For unoriented polypropylene, particularly of high isotacticity, such brittlepoint may indeed be around 0°C. or even higher, but orientation brings the brittleness temperatures down to —70°C. (—94°F.) or even lower. No problems arise, therefore, in the form of oriented films or fibers.

POLYOLEFIN FIBERS: PROPERTIES

The fibers are produced by melting the polymers and subsequently extruding them through adequately small orifices, quenching and cooling them in their filamentary state under conditions that differ for the different polyolefins. In this form the polymer is still in its state of random distribution of its molecular chains and can be of practical interest where the shape of the fiber is desired but where the specific characteristics of a fully processed fiber are not of importance.

These fibers, to be processed, have to be *oriented*, which means that the molecular chains have to be aligned along the fiber axis. When stresses are applied to the unoriented polymer, it first undergoes elastic, which means completely reversible, deformation up to the so-called yield point; further stressing causes an irreversible plastic deformation up to the point at which the now oriented polymer breaks.

These "stress-strain" relations are basic considerations for the production of the oriented fibers. The conditions of orientation determine the tensile strength which increases and the elongation which decreases with the stretch ratio. Another controlling factor is the temperature at which the fiber is extruded which for polyolefins is considerably higher, 100 to 120°C., than the actual melting point. Furthermore, after-treatment of the oriented fiber, primarily by heat setting at temperatures below the softening point, is influential for the performance of the fiber, such as in residual shrinkage, flexural strength, and elastic recovery.

The properties of the resulting fiber, however, remain largely controlled by those of the polymer, particularly by its average molecular weight and molecular weight distribution.

A *comparison of the polyethylenes and polypropylene* can be made in the form of their monofilaments which are single continuous fibers of comparatively heavy diameter in the range of 35 to 1000 denier. Table 8.4 summarizes characteristic physical properties of these commercial monofilaments.

TABLE 8.4

Comparison of Physical Properties of Commercial
Polyolefin Filaments

Polymer	Specific Gravity	Tenacity, (gm./denier)	Elonga- tion to Rupture (%)	Shrinkage, % of Original Length (at 212°F.)
Polyethylenes				
Branched, low molecular weight (19,000–20,000)	0.92	1.0/1.5	45/50	50/60
Branched, medium molecu- lar weight (23,000–25,000)	0.92	2.0/2.3	25/30	40/50
Modified branched	0.93	3.0/3.3	17/25	25/35
Modified linear	0.945	5.0/5.5	14/20	10/15
Straight linear	0.95	5.5/7.0	10/20	5/10
	0.96	6.5/8.0	10/20	5/10
Polypropylene, Isotactic	0.90/0.91	5.5/9.0	15/25	10/15

Yield strength and breaking strength decrease with increasing temperatures up to the softening point at which orientation disappears, and this occurs somewhat below the crystalline melting point. There- fore the melting point is usually less important than the softening point, at which basic changes in the mechanical properties become apparent. Figure 8.3 gives an approximate comparative illustration for such decreases in fiber strength in percentages of that at room temperature (4).

The *interrelations between molecular structure, conditions of ori- entation and processing, and the properties of the fine fibers of low denier* are discussed more specifically with regard to polypropylene.

Important fiber properties are determined by the degree and the type of *crystallinity* that is chiefly influenced by the polymer process, as has been shown above, but that can also be controlled to some extent in end-product processing. By varying the cooling rates high crystallinity with heavy agglomeration of crystalline regions can be produced in the final product, whereas fast cooling creates growth of small crystallites. This also influences the clarity of the product, as is practically important in the production of films. The degree of crystallinity increases with the ratio and the time of stretch. In general, maximum crystallinity for a given polymer type is obtained by the proper combination of orientation and heat processing during and after stretch. Stiffness and abrasion resistance increase with higher crystallinity which also influences stress relaxation and elastic recovery. The modulus of elasticity increases with the tenacity of the fiber in closely linear proportion.

Table 8.5 describes the *range of typical properties of multifilament yarns and staple* available at present.

TABLE 8.5
Range of Properties of Commercial Polypropylene Fibers

	Multifilaments	Staple
Breaking strength, p.s.i.	58,000–95,000	45,000–70,000
Tenacity dry and wet, gm./denier	5–9	4–6
Elongation to break, %	15–30	20–35
Elastic recovery on 5% elongation, %	88–98	88–95
Modulus of elasticity on 10% extension, gm./denier	20–90	20–40
Shrinkage %, boiling water, 20 min.	0–3	0–3
Moisture regain	Less than 0.03%	

Figure 8.4 reproduces a diagram that compares typical stress-strain curves of oriented staple fibers for polypropylene (Meraklon of Montecatini), polyamides, polyacrylics and polyesters (7).

Figure 8.5 gives stress-strain curves established by I.C.I. (8) on their high-tenacity multifilament yarn compared with nylon and polyester (Terylene of I.C.I.)

The importance of the so-called *cold-flow or creep* (Figure 8.6) under continuous load has already been mentioned in the introductory paragraph. Although polypropylene performs considerably better than linear polyethylene (4), the fiber still is not equal in this respect to nylon or the polyesters. Growth at room temperature for polypropylene fiber has been given at 2 to 5% in 16 hours with 1.5

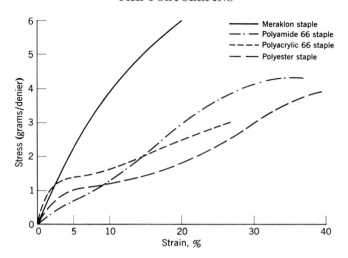

Figure 8.4.   Stress-strain curves.

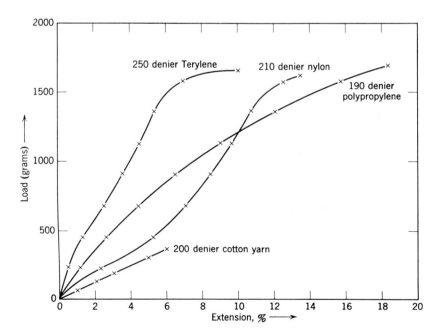

Figure 8.5   Load-extension curves.

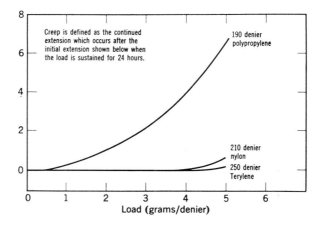

Figure 8.6.   Creep versus load.

gm./denier load; a comparative diagram is supplied in **Figure 8.7** (**8**).

An outstanding property of polypropylene fiber is its *zero moisture regain* and its consequent lack of effect on mechanical properties when wetted.

Shrinkage can be varied somewhat by the fiber producer. The fiber in higher deniers can be produced with shrinkages available from zero to 8% [1 hour at 100°C. (212°F.) water], whereas the range decreases to about zero to 3% for 1.5 denier fiber. At higher temperatures in air the fiber showing an initial 8% boiling-water

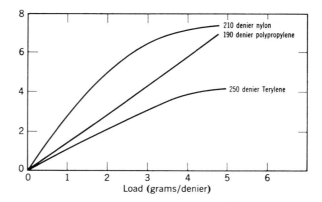

Figure 8.7.   Extension versus load.

shrinkage will shrink approximately 20% at 135°C. (275°F.) and 30% at 143°C. (290°F.) At 143°C., if the fiber is restrained and not allowed to shrink, the modulus will greatly increase.

Current fibers begin to stick in the 152 to 157°C. (305 to 315°F.) range, but blending with higher melting fibers is a means of decreasing the sticking tendency in practical applications.

It can be seen in Table 8.5 that some of the properties, for instance, those connected with *elasticity* and its recovery both on elongation in the fiber axis and on bending strain, vary over a rather wide range. Such performance of the fiber is dependent on the conditions of processing; the conditions are not definitely established at this writing but should lead to satisfactory performance where it is needed.

Highly characteristic of polypropylene is its outstanding *flexlife*. Resistance to repetitive bending of the fiber at a 175° angle in 200,-000 cycles has been reported (7), and a 30% addition of polypropylene fiber in a spun-yarn blend with cotton increased the life of the fabric tenfold under flex-abrasion (9). Such performance also favorably affects knot and loop strength which is only 5 to 15% below that of the straight fiber.

Finally, one remark regarding *flammability*. Although a hydrocarbon, and, as such, burnable, the polypropylene fiber is actually not ignitable. Exposed to a flame it shrinks, melts, and extinguishes itself to the effect that 100% polypropylene fabrics are better than required for Class 1 of the ASTM standard for generally accepted textile materials.

To summarize, Table 8.6 compares the high-tenacity polypropylene filament yarn of I.C.I. with other fibers used in a variety of competitive fields (10).

MANUFACTURE OF POLYOLEFIN FIBERS

MONOFILAMENTS

Monofilaments may be round, flat, or of special cross sections. When round, popular diameters range from a low of 0.003 in. to a high of 0.015 in., which corresponds to a range between 35 and 1000 denier. For special purposes, for instance, for polypropylene bristles, much heavier denier monofilaments are produced in a variety of cross sections.

The manufacture of these filaments is similar to that of other synthetic monofilaments such as polyvinyls, Saran, polystyrene, and nylon. A typical extrusion assemblage consists of a horizontal screw

TABLE 8.6
Some Comparative Mechanical Properties of High-Strength Yarns

Fiber	Specific Gravity	Moisture Uptake (%)	Yarn Tenacity (gm./denier)	Initial Modulus of Fiber Elasticity (gm./denier/unit strain)	Resistance to Abrasion	Melting Point (°C.)	Remarks
Steel	7.7	0	3.5	280	Good	~1450	} Minerals
Glass	2.56	0	6.0 to 7.0	307	Poor	~800	
Manila	1.48	8.0	around 4	250	Fair	140	} Cellulosics
Cotton	1.52	8.5	around 3.0	55	Fair	150	Decompose rather than melt
Flax	1.50	12.0	around 4.0	200	Fair	140	Tenacities very approximate
Rayon (Tenasco)	1.52	13.0	3.5 to 5.5	75–175	Fair	180–205	Regenerated cellulosic
Terylene	1.38	0.4	6.0 to 7.5	130	Very good	264	Polyester
Nylon	1.14	4.2	7.0 to 8.8	45	Excellent	264	Polyamide
High-density polythene	0.95	0	4.5 to 6.0	30	Good	135	} Polyolefins
Polypropylene	0.92	0	8.5 to 9.0	60–80	Good	165	

extruder with round or flat extrusion dies which supply the extruded material in the form of rods. These rods are quenched and subsequently drawn between pressure or godet rolls to orient them. Contrary to the branched type polyethylene, which can be oriented at room temperature, the more rigid linear polyethylene, as well as polypropylene, is hot drawn in a ratio of about 1 to 10, with hot water or steam or hot air. The oriented filaments are wound on spools or tubes and shipped to the fabricators.

To color monofilaments, selected inorganic or temperature-resistant organic pigments are added before extrusion. This work can be done by the so-called dry-blending technique, in which the pigments of lowest possible particle size are compounded directly with the polymer pellets or chips. Another method, often preferred to assure best dispersion, is that of first preparing pigment concentrates or master batches which are then blended with the polymer in the calculated proportions.

FINE FIBERS

The technique of producing fibers of small diameter in the ranges of 15 denier and below, differs from the conventional for monofilaments. Here vertical spinning systems are used. The polymer is melted in screw extruders or other melting systems and is metered to a multihole spinnerette. The fibers pass downward and are usually cooled by air and taken up at the bottom on high-speed bobbins. From this point processing differs for multifilament yarns on one hand for heavy tow or staple on the other. The equipment is basically similar to that used for other synthetic fibers such as polyesters and polyamids.

For *multifilament yarns* small bundles of filaments are processed on draw-twisting equipment, by which they are oriented under heat, twisted, and packaged on bobbins ready for shipment. The size of the individual filaments may be controlled to run from 15 down to 2 denier, generally produced in the range of 12 to 400 filaments per yarn.*

Multifil can be bulked or texturized by several methods. One involves a sawtooth crimp imparted by forcing the fiber to bend into a heated chamber. Another employs heat setting the fiber while it is being fluffed by an air or steam blast. Still another twists, heat sets, and detwists the fiber to leave a curly character. The fiber can also be bulked by running it over a knife blade to produce curl. These methods are widely covered in the patent literature.

* Fourteen-denier monofilament recently has been offered for women's hose.

For the production of *staple fiber* a number of filament bundles are combined in a tow of hundreds of thousands of filaments which are then drawn and subsequently crimped and cut to the desired staple length with fiber sizes down to 1.5 denier. Finishing agents at the different processing stages serve to counteract static problems and to provide lubrication.

Staple fiber is produced at several crimp levels. Heat relaxation at temperatures above 120°C. (250°F.) of the crimped polypropylene fibers tends to decrease stiffness, but to some extent it improves its recovery properties; for example, the crease angle of a woven fabric can be improved by proper heat setting.

Individual round fibers are usually produced, but it is possible to obtain the fibers in specially designed cross sections, for instance, for high-bulk fibers. Greater bulk in spun yarn can also be obtained by the method of mixing high- and low-shrinkage fibers and then post-shrinking the yarn to produce bulk by the differential shrinkage of the two fibers.

Much has been said about the *sunlight resistance* of polypropylene fibers. As with polyethylene before it, suitable stabilizers are being developed which will offer adequate protection. Several producers have already reported weather resistance intermediate between the nylons and the polyesters, and progress is expected as purer polymers become available and better stabilization systems are worked out. Excellent weather resistance is a property of stabilized polypropylene monofilament, which is produced with a much lower heat history than is practiced for fine filament fibers.

Heat and light stabilization are closely linked and appear to be related synergistically. Popular heat-stabilization systems combine a phenolic and organic sulfide, and ultraviolet light absorbers usually fall in the hydroxybenzophenone category; several newer stabilizers of different chemical types have shown promise, such as benzo-triazoles. Other heat and light stabilizer systems are based on nickel-thio-bis-phenol complexes. Proper stabilizers for general use should essentially be colorless and odorless, nonextractable by washing or dry cleaning, compatible with dyes and color pigments, and not cause staining by the oxides of nitrogen present in the atmosphere of areas in which gas and oil are used for heating.

Polypropylene has been offered in a number of *colors*, which are produced by adding finely dispersed pigments, as previously described for monofilaments. The use of melt-colored fibers is sometimes more economical to the user than dyeing; however, considerations of inventory costs and lack of flexibility offset this method in many applications.

Dyeability has been a major problem to fiber producers and users. Since polypropylene is a hydrocarbon and contains no polar or reactive functional groups, it has been a difficult problem to anchor the dyestuffs in the polymer properly in order to provide satisfactory end-use performance such as resistance to rub-off, laundering, and dry cleaning. Modifications of the fiber have been found to give the proper chemical characteristics to the fiber so that it not only accepts the dyestuffs, but also holds them. Different methods have been recommended to modify the polymer; for instance, by copolymerization with dye-receptive groups or by grafting such groups onto the fiber on activation by irradiation. Other procedures apply additives to the polymer to provide "lock-and-key" type mechanisms in which specific dyestuffs fit chemical "locks" within the fibers. Whatever methods are commercially acceptable, they must also meet the requirements of dry cleaning and adequate lightfastness and they must be economical.

END USES OF POLYOLEFIN FIBERS

As already mentioned, polyethylene, mainly in the high-strength linear types, and polypropylene have their end-use applications established in the form of continuous monofilaments of heavy deniers. The introduction of the fine fibers as continuous multifilament yarns and in the form of tow or staple or spun yarn is still in the state of market development. Polypropylene fiber as a newcomer is in a competitive position with the existing synthetics, and to a degree with the natural ones.

Properties and price are as always the factors in market acceptance. The favorable raw material position combined with low density gives polypropylene an economic advantage over the polyesters and polyamids, somewhat less in comparison with acrylics; polypropylene fiber is less expensive than wool but has not—at least as yet—come down in price to compete on this basis with cotton or rayon.

The properties have to meet the requirements imposed by the respective end uses. In any case, they must provide a definite advantage when the cost position is comparatively a less favorable one.

Inertness to water and chemicals in which the polyolefins excell over all other commercial fiber materials led to an early use as filter media, woven and nonwoven, for air and liquids, water, fuel, paints, etc. Water repellency imparts *quick-drying* qualities to the fibers and fabrics and improves drying in blends with other fibers. It also provides a *dimensional stability* that is often highly desirable under changing humidity conditions and cannot be provided by moisture-absorbant fibers such as cotton, rayon, and to a lesser degree, nylon, which have a tendency to swell or elongate. Fabrics used for certain coverings, for lamination and coating, and as nonjamming window channels are examples.

Because of moisture resistance physical properties are the same under dry and wet conditions; this is important when *high tenacity* paired with low *elongation, resilience, toughness* and *abrasion resistance* are essential. Therefore polypropylene multifilaments are making a strong bid in the categories of cordage, fishnets, seat belts, laundry bags, backing and woven filter fabrics, primarily in competition with nylon because polypropylene shows greater durability under the conditions of consumer application.

Additional properties are essential in other end uses; *good covering* and *good recovery from bending,* for instance, are needed for carpets and rugs. Here texturized multifilaments or bulked staple yarn are already used, solution dyed or dyeable. This is a field of tough competition, particularly with nylon. Blankets and upholstery fabrics are examples of other nonapparel textiles under development.

Industrial applications for dry mops, bristles, doll hair, and cable wraps are all based on similar properties required in varying degrees.

The resilience and recovery and good *thermal insulation* designate the needs of such items as interlinings, pillows, sleeping bags, and comforters, in which the fibers are used as battings or bonded mattings, in competition with the old goose down and more recently with synthetics, polyester especially.

Perhaps the potentially biggest market for polypropylene fiber may be that of the apparel fabrics. *Equal bulk at lower weight,* greater strength, and improved dimensional stability are attractive considerations. Polypropylene fibers lend themselves exceedingly well to knitting because of excellent *flex-, loop-, and knot-strength* performance. Sweaters, underwear, swimsuits, and laces are or will be on the market. In woven goods the possibilities are almost unlimited.

Blend properties with natural fibers, such as wool and cotton, and with synthetics, such as rayon, may be preferred in many textile uses to combine the advantages of the component fibers and also to improve the performance. The low elongation of the polypropylene fiber is satisfactory in the spinning of blended yarns, particularly with cotton. For apparel fabrics such blends containing between 10 and not much more than 35% olefin are sufficient for many purposes and are preferred to avoid the difficulties that could arise in careless ironing.

Whether used as such or in blends with other fibers, the outstanding *flexlife* of the polypropylene fiber added to its other characteristics is in many ways the basis of the durability of the end product; such performance often becomes dramatic in wear and tear or after repeated laundering and dry cleaning.

For any of the mentioned or contemplated end uses the properties of the fiber have to be adequately adjusted to meet the specific requirements. This is true of all fibers and refers not only to the physical processing of the fiber itself but equally so to the different finishing agents applied to provide lubrication, antistatic action, or bonding when necessary (11).

Introduction of olefin fibers in papermaking is still in early development, but several firms are known to be working in this direction. Continuous filaments, woven or nonwoven, have been considered as reinforcing elements of paper sheets. The use of olefin fibers in the form of staple or in blends with other fibers, cellulosics, for example, will probably offer the broad application.

Some of the first known data on the experimental use of polyolefin fibers in papermaking which appear in Chapter 1 of this book is based on work performed in the research laboratories of American Viscose Corporation.

Experience with other synthetic fibers in this field is already available. Specific characteristics of the polypropylene fibers have been described above for a variety of end uses in order to give food for thought to their utilization for paper. The wide range of properties obtainable by various techniques in the manufacture of this fiber allows tailoring to specific needs. It would seem that cost, favorable bulk-to-weight ratio, high dry and wet strength with dimensional stability, and, last but not least, durability should be factors in the evaluation of the usefulness of the olefin fibers. It is too early at this writing, however, to predict more accurately the areas of particular interest for the paper manufacturers.

REFERENCES

1. Imperial Chemical Industries, Ltd, British Patent No. 471,590 (1936).
2. Fawcett, Gibson, and Perrin to I.C.I.; U. S. Patent No. 2,153,553 (1939) "Polymerization of Olefins." See also Perrin, Paton and Williams to I.C.I., U. S. Patent No. 2,210,774 (1940) "Fibers from Ethylene Polymers."

3. G. Natta, "Stereospecific Catalysts and Isotactic Polymers," *Mod. Plastics,* 169 ff. (December 1956). This is a résumé of the original papers of Natta and co-workers published during 1955 and 1956.

4. V. L. Erlich, Reeves Brothers, Inc., "Polyolefin Fibers in Textiles," *Mod. Textiles Mag.* (November 1958); and "Polyolefin Fibers and Polymer Structure," *Textile Res. J.,* **29,** 679–686 (September 1959).

5. Montecatini Societa Generale and Karl Ziegler, British Patents No. 810,023 (1959) and No. 828,791 (1960) with Italian priority of 1954.

6. T. O. J. Kresser, *Polypropylene,* Reinhold, New York, 1960.

7. E. Z. Cohen, Chemore Corporation (Montecatini), "Meraklon Polypropylene Fibers," *Am. Dyestuff Reptr.,* (August 6, 1962).

8. Imperial Chemical Industries, Ltd., Fibres Division, "Polypropylene for Fishnets: Preliminary Information on Multifilament Yarn," (April 1961).

9. G. S. Hooper, Hercules Powder Company, "Polypropylene Up-to-Date," *Textile Industries,* 59 ff. (August 1962).

10. A. B. Thompson, I.C.I., "Fibres from Polypropylene," *J. Roy. Inst., Chem.,* 293–300 (August 1961).

11. "Method of Bonding Fibrous Structures Made from Fibers or Filaments of Polyolefin Polymers," U. S. Patent 3,049,466 (1962) (V. L. Erlich, assigned to Reeves Brothers, Inc.)

RECOMMENDED ADDITIONAL READING

Cappuchio, V., et al., "Isotactic Polypropylene Fibers," *Chim. Ind. (Milan),* **44** (May 1962).

Erlich, V. L., "Polyethylene Fiber today," *Mod. Textiles Mag.* (May and June 1956).

Hill, R., *Fibers from Synthetic Polymers,* American Elsevier, New York, 1953.

Hooper, G. S., "Polypropylene Textile Fibers," *Textile Res. J.,* **32,** 529–539 (July 1962).

Natta, G., "Progresses in Five Years of Research in Stereospecific Polymerization," Annual Meeting of the Society of Plastics Engineers, New York, January 1959.

Press, J. J., *Man-Made Textile Encyclopedia,* Textile Book, New York, 1959.

Sittig, Marshall, *Polyolefin Resin Processes,* Gulf Publishing, 1961.

9

WEB FORMATION AND BONDING

R. A. A. HENTSCHEL

Product Development Manager
E. I. du Pont de Nemours & Co., Inc.
Wilmington, Delaware

WEB FORMATION

For many thousands of years the basic raw material of the paper industry has been cellulose. As so often happens, the natural characteristics of cellulose make it peculiarly adaptable to papermaking. Being hydrophylic, cellulose fibers wet out readily when they are suspended in water and form a uniform suspension of individual fibers. When this suspension is subjected to appropriate mechanical action, as in a beater, the cellulose fiber splits, and many fine fibrils are formed which for the most part remain attached to the main fiber stem. In addition, the fibrils become highly hydrated. When, during sheet formation, these hairy fibers are formed into a mat on the wire of the paper machine, they become mechanically entangled. Then in the final stages of water removal surface tension forces draw the fibrils into sufficiently intimate contact to permit strong hydrogen bonds to form between adjacent fiber surfaces. Thus the dried sheet develops a high degree of strength and integrity. In elementary terms, then, cellulose fibers work in papermaking because they have certain inherent properties:

1. Hydrophylicity, which permits them to be readily dispersed in water.

2. A fine structure which permits fibrillation.

3. Sufficient fiber length to form a highly entangled mat of considerable strength.

4. The ability to form hydrogen bonds between fibers as the web is dried out to provide strength in the sheet.

In recent years the textile industry has seen the birth, growth, and, in some cases, maturity of a whole family of new man-made fibers. These fibers have supplemented and broadened the range of characteristics formerly available in natural fibers and in many ways have revolutionized the textile industry. Even more recently there has been a growing interest in what these new fibers might have to offer to the paper industry in the development of new products and new markets. In a very general way, what properties do the man-made fibers offer? Such things as highly controllable and uniform length and diameter, high strength and toughness, in certain cases resistance to moisture, rot, and mildew, dimensional stability and resilience, and finally a variety of chemical types, all differing from one another in their particular balance of properties.

Broadly speaking, the man-made fibers can be divided into two classes: one made up of fibers based on natural polymers and the other of fibers based on completely synthetic polymers. The first class includes the older man-made fibers, such as rayon (regenerated cellulose), cellulose acetate, and casein; the second includes the newer polyamide (nylon), polyester, acrylic, and polyolefin (polypropylene) fibers. The first group is generally hydrophylic and the second, hydrophobic, although there are exceptions in both classes.

What happens, for example, if a polyester textile fiber is cut in short lengths and an attempt is made to process it as wood pulp would be on papermaking equipment. A whole series of problems would be discovered almost immediately. Polyesters, being highly hydrophobic, are difficult to disperse in water. If such a fiber dispersion is beaten, the fibers, instead of fibrillating, are simply cut to shorter and shorter lengths. If a sheet is formed on the wire from such a suspension, it is found to be weak and poorly formed. If, finally, the web is dried, as soon as the water is gone it reverts to a loose mass of unbonded fibers. Clearly, almost every step in the paper process demands some modification in the man-made fiber to permit it to be shaped into a useful product. Let us go back, then, and discuss each step in the process in detail.

The formation of a uniform, well-dispersed suspension of fibers requires that each fiber be well wetted-out and free of adherent air bubbles which would cause flotation. In hydrophylic fibers this is not much of a problem, but in hydrophobic fibers the case is quite different. Since these fibers do not wet readily, either a wetting agent in the water or some surface pretreatment of the fiber is necessary. Wetting agents in the water unfortunately do not work well. Since there is so much water in relation to fiber, rather large amounts of wetting agent are required to be effective. And since most wetting agents are also good foaming agents, when enough is present to wet-out the fiber satisfactorily, relatively low agitation will generally generate copious quantities of foam. The problems with foam in paper equipment are too well known to require much discussion. This has led to the development of surface treatments by the fiber producer to promote dispersion of the fibers in water. Today there is a broad range of fiber types available which have been so treated. Unfortunately, for the purposes of this book, the methods used are closely guarded "trade secrets" of the fiber producer, and not much can be said about them. However, this is no longer a problem for the paper producer, since essentially all types of man-made fibers are available in a readily dispersible form.

The next requirement for a man-made staple for use in paper equipment is freedom from crimp. All textile staples have crimp to permit them to be processed into yarns. In the paper process, in contrast, a crimped fiber is almost impossible to handle. The crimps provide "hooks" through which the fibers can attach themselves to one another during agitation of the slurry. This action leads to the rapid formation of knots and, in many cases, ropes of fiber and prevents the formation of a uniform web on the wire. Thus synthetic fibers for use on paper equipment must be in the form of straight "rods." A somewhat analogous problem can be presented by fiber bundles fused together in the cutting operation. All man-made fibers are manufactured as long, continuous bundles of filaments. To form short staple fibers, these continuous strands are mechanically cut to the required length. Since most kinds of man-made fibers are thermoplastic, if any heat is generated in cutting the fiber ends can fuse together to form a fiber bundle. Because the forces applied in dispersing fibers in water are relatively low, these fibers cannot be separated and appear in the sheet as "stars" or fiber bundles, depending on whether one or both ends of the fiber bundle are fused. Quality of cutting must be high to avoid this problem. These, then, are the basic requirements for a fiber to be handled in a water suspension: freedom from crimp and from fused ends and a treatment to permit rapid wetting-out with no tendency to form adherent air bubbles.

Let us consider next what the effects of fiber length and diameter are on the quality of the suspension. Fibers are inherently flexible, and the longer they are in relation to their diameter the more flexible they become. If a short fiber is dispersed in water and stirred, it will act very much like a stiff rod, with little or no tendency to entangle with its neighbors. But, as the fiber length is increased, the fibers become more flexible and ultimately begin to entangle with their neighbors. If a series of handsheets is examined, those made from the short fibers will have good formation, but as the length is increased and entangling sets in the sheet formation becomes poorer and ultimately unacceptable. To some extent, this degeneration of formation can be avoided by using high dilutions to keep the individual fibers well separated, but this, too, has its obvious practical limitations. It is well known in paper technology that long fibers are necessary for high property levels, and the same thing is true for synthetic fibers. What are the practical limits? Auspos and Winn (1) have shown that these limits are reached at a fiber length-to-diameter ratio of about 500. This ratio will vary somewhat with fiber modulus, being lower for lower modulus and vice versa. The effect of modulus is small, however, and is not of great practical significance.

The viscosity of the suspending water will also affect formation. It has been observed, for example, that it is somewhat easier to get good sheet formation in winter when the water temperatures are low than in summer. Thickeners, such as carboxymethyl cellulose, can also be used in the water to raise its viscosity and thus improve the behavior of long fibers in suspension, but these products again lead to other problems, not the least being cost. Thickeners can also lead to difficulties in the wet press, since the water does not drain so freely through the felts and therefore piles up in the nip of the press. This pile up can lead to disruption of the sheet at that point. From a practical standpoint water viscosity is not a useful variable, and the fibers must be engineered in such a way that they can be handled in normal paper-mill water.

A well-dispersed suspension of long synthetic fibers must be properly handled to remain in that condition. Because of their length the fibers can readily become entangled, and the liquid flows must be kept as streamlined as possible. Any twisting action transmitted to the fibers from vortices or waterfalls can twist the fibers in suspension into knots or, in the extreme case, even into long ropes. This action can be minimized by keeping the suspended fibers well separated, so that high dilutions in the range of 0.05 to 0.10% favor good sheet formation. It has been observed recently that fiber entanglement can also be minimized by going in the other direction and using relatively high consistencies, in the order of 0.5% or higher, in preparing the initial stock. It is handled at this consistency up to the headbox, where it is diluted down to 0.05% or less to achieve good formation. This suggests that there is a fairly critical range of fiber separation in the suspension, encountered at consistencies between something under 0.5 and about 0.10% which favors entanglement and which should be avoided whenever possible. The use of screens should also be avoided in the handling of synthetic fibers. The action of the fibers on the screen in itself promotes entangling, so that any gains from the removal of knots of fibers are more than offset by the formation of new ones.

Synthetic-fiber stocks are free draining. Thus, in spite of the fact that high dilutions are used, the web is formed rapidly on the wire, and there is little opportunity to improve formation during the drainage. Shake is ineffective for this reason and is not used with wholly synthetic webs. Wet ends must be arranged in such a way that large amounts of water can be removed in a very short time without formation of waves or turbulence.

Subsequent drying of the webs, particularly with the hydrophobic synthetics, is also rapid. Most synthetic fibers, however, shrink more than pulp fibers, which leads to greater web shrinkage during the drying process. This must be allowed for in the handling of the web, or the sheet will actually rupture because of shrinkage forces.

BONDING

The basic difference between conventional papers and those made from man-made fibers is in the mechanisms of bonding. Man-made fibers, in general, cannot be made to bond together as a result of subjecting the fibers to mechanical action in water, as in the usual cellulosic raw materials of papermaking. Thus some external means of bringing about bonding must be used. An adhesive must be introduced into the system by some route. For simplicity of discussion, bonding systems may be divided into two general classes: (1) Those called "self-bonded" systems in which the binder is derived from the fiber itself. (2) Those called "externally bonded" systems in which an external binder is added to the fiber web.

SELF-BONDED SYSTEMS

The simplest adhesive system is one that uses the polymer of the fiber itself. Synthetic fibers, almost without exception, are spun from soluble thermoplastic polymers. Thus, if a web of fibers is wet by a solvent, under properly controlled conditions a small amount of the fiber surface can be swelled or dissolved. Fiber surfaces in contact with one another will be bonded as the solvent is subsequently removed and the dissolved polymer is reprecipitated. A variety of solvents or swelling agents can be used in this way. The action of most solvents, however, is difficult to control so that the fiber surfaces will dissolve without destroying the fiber at the same time. One approach that is more easily controlled depends on the fact that certain salts dissolved in water at rather high concentrations are either solvents or swelling agents for many synthetic polymers. These are called "hydrotropic salts." Examples are such compounds as calcium bromide and calcium thiocyanate (2). In more dilute solutions these salts are no longer solvents. Thus, if a web of synthetic fiber is wet-out by a dilute solution of a hydrotropic salt, it is initially unaffected. However, as the water is evaporated away, the salt concentration of the remaining water gradually rises until it becomes high enough to bring the solution into the solvent range. The water remaining in the web during evaporation tends to collect at the fiber crossovers by capillary action. Thus, if the initial salt concentration is properly adjusted, the solvent action can be confined to the fiber crossover points and the fibers will be bonded to themselves as the water is completely removed and reprecipitation of the polymer occurs. Subsequent washing of the bonded web with water will then remove the remaining salt. This system, although having the merit of simplicity, also has several drawbacks which are quite serious. First, most hydrotropic salts, unfortunately, are quite corrosive to metals and will attack various parts of the paper machine. Second, in the unoriented state the polymers from which most fibers are spun are relatively brittle. Salt-bonded webs therefore are not so strong as those bonded by some other means. Third, this system involves handling very weak webs on the machine in the stages before the bonds are established so that some supplementary way of increasing the strength of the web while it is still on the wire is necessary. As a result, this system has not achieved any commercial importance.

Another theoretically interesting route to bonding is by introducing chemically reactive groups into the polymer chain from which the fiber is formed. With most of the common fiber-forming polymers, this is difficult to do. One exception is found in the cellulosic fiber RD-101 of American Viscose (3). This fiber is a multicellular thin-walled product, and sheets formed from it are self-bonding. Its properties are described in greater detail in Chapter 1 of this book.

Finally, self-bonding can in certain cases be brought about by developing a highly fibrillated morphology in the synthetic fiber. Such a fiber will, when formed into a web, entangle with its neighbors sufficiently to give a sheet of appreciable strength. Most synthetic fibers cannot be fibrillated. There are, however, exceptions among the acrylic fibers based on acrylonitrile, which have been disclosed in the patent literature (4,5). The lateral bonding between poly-acrylonitrile molecules is relatively weak. When a polyacrylonitrile fiber is highly oriented and then beaten, it will split into a highly fibrillated structure because of this weak lateral bonding. This same behavior is observed in polyacrylonitrile fibers which are wet-spun under certain conditions. It is also possible to cause fibrillation in some fibers by blending small amounts of incompatible materials into the fiber-forming polymer before spinning (6). Extrusion of the polymer through the spinneret holes to form fiber results in these inclusions being drawn out into elongated microfibrils within the filament. They then become planes of weakness, and the fiber splits when it is beaten to produce a fibrillated filament.

Webs of fibrillated fibers can be made fairly easily on the paper machine, since the interlacing of the fibrils gives the waterleaf a certain degree of cohesion. However, the beating process also produces rather short fibers to the detriment of final sheet strength. The bonding of the fibers is largely the result of the mechanical interlacing. As a consequence of these two factors, only moderate dry-sheet strengths are achieved, but they can be improved to some extent by the subsequent addition of external binders.

EXTERNALLY BONDED SYSTEMS

In the great majority of the work that has been done with synthetic-fiber webs on the paper machine, a separate bonding agent is added to tie the fibers together. These bonding agents can be divided into two classes: (1) aqueous polymer dispersions and (2) fibrous polymers. Such systems are readily controlled. The amount and type of bonding agent in relation to fiber is readily changed and adjusted, and the desirable polymer properties to give maximum fiber strength on the one hand and maximum bonding on the other can be freely chosen. Consequently the webs can be engineered to give the most desirable characteristics for any particular end use.

Aqueous polymer dispersions can be obtained in both vinyl and condensation polymers. By far the commonest, however, are the vinyls. Polymers in this class are the polyacrylates, polyvinyl acetates, polybutadiene, polyacrylonitrile copolymers, polyvinyl chloride, and polyvinyl chloride copolymers. Such polymer dispersions are available in a wide range of composition and include formulations ranging from soft and rubbery materials to those that are stiff and hard. Condensation polymers, on the other hand, are difficult to obtain as dispersions and are available only in a much more restricted range of compositions and properties. Examples are certain polyamides (nylons) and the melamine and urea-formaldehyde resins.

In the bonding of wholly synthetic webs dispersion binders can be applied by precipitation on the fibers before the web is formed, analogous to "beater addition" in cellulose paper, or by saturation after web formation. "Beater addition," unfortunately, is rather inefficient, for the dispersed polymers are generally not substantive on the synthetic fibers. Saturation of such webs also has its problems, since the webs are weak before bonding. Small amounts of dispersion can be sprayed on the web while it is still on the wire. This will give the web enough strength to be handled through drying and subsequent saturation, but the process is not easy to run successfully. Small amounts of cellulose in the form of wood pulp can be added to the furnish to increase the strength of the web, when this is not objectionable in the finished sheet. Generally, maximum properties are reached when the binder content is around 40% of the sheet weight with dispersion bonding agents.

Binders can also be added to the web in the form of low-melting fibers. The melting point of the binder-fiber must be low enough so that the properties of the strength-fiber in the web are not affected. "Vinyon" HH fibers (7) have been used in this way. Such fibers, again, contribute little or nothing to the strength of the wet or dry web before they are fused, and some carrier such as cellulose or a beater-additive resin must be used to process the sheet through the paper machine.

In order to ease the problems of paper-machine operation with synthetic fibers, a synthetic-polymer binder with the morphology and characteristics of wood pulp has been sought. One such product, a fibrid patented by Du Pont (8),* has approximately the morphology of wood pulp and contributes sufficient strength to the waterleaf and the dried sheet to permit them to be handled readily on paper machines. Subsequent melting of the fibrid completes the bonding process. The production process allows a wide variety of polymers to be made into fibrids and closely matches the characteristics of the binder to the fiber in the web. In this way the maximum strength can be achieved with binder contents of around 25%. A somewhat similar product has been offered by Union Carbide under the name

* Fibrids have been experimentally produced by Du Pont, but have not been commercialized.

"fibrous binder." All fibrous binders must be melted to bring about the final bonding of the fibers and to develop maximum sheet properties. This melting can be done either in the absence of pressure or in a hot calender. Webs bonded without pressure are of low density and are soft and easily draped. Calendering, on the other hand, gives a dense, stiff, and "papery" sheet with a higher level of strength than fusing in the absence of pressure.

So far we have discussed the formation and bonding of webs of synthetic fibers alone or with only minor additions of wood pulp. Another class of structures consists of blends of synthetic fibers with wood pulp, in which the cellulose is a major structural component. In these structures the synthetic fiber makes up about 20 to 50% of the web and wood pulp, the remainder. These webs are essentially cellulosic, reinforced with the synthetic fiber. Because of the high pulp content, they are treated much like conventional papers on the paper machine but with modifications in the stock handling to accommodate the long synthetic fibers.

Since there is relatively little inherent bonding between the synthetic and pulp fibers, a binder is added to tie the two together and to permit the synthetic fiber to make its proper contributions to the sheet properties. The binder is added by saturation of the web with a polymer dispersion. A binder content between 20 and 50% of the sheet weight is commonly used. For maximum properties the binder must tie the pulp and synthetic fibers together effectively. Thus its composition is dictated to some extent by the specific combination of synthetic fiber and pulp. Sheet properties are also greatly influenced by the characteristics of the binder, in that soft, rubbery binders produce softer, more easily draped sheet structures and harder, stiffer binders produce more rigid sheets. Saturated sheets can also be water-resistant. Papers of saturated pulp–synthetic-fiber blend do not develop the high levels of properties achievable in completely synthetic sheets. On the other hand, they are relatively inexpensive because of the high content of pulp. For this reason they are finding uses in areas in which ordinary papers lack the required properties and synthetic sheets are too expensive.

EQUIPMENT FOR HANDLING SYNTHETIC FIBERS

There are many ways in which synthetic fibers can be handled in papermaking equipment. Success depends to a greater extent on an understanding of the factors that influence the behavior of these long fibers when they are suspended in water than on the specific pieces of hardware and their arrangement. This section therefore attempts only to describe some approaches that have been successful rather than to set rules that must be rigidly followed. It discusses first the handling of synthetic fibers alone; second, the handling of mixtures of fibers and pulp.

INITIAL DISPERSION OF FIBER

A synthetic-staple fiber properly prepared for use in papermaking equipment will disperse readily in water with only gentle agitation. The simplest equipment for preparing fiber slurries is a tank provided with a lightning mixer mounted to one side. The stirring action should avoid development of a violent vortex, which can lead to rope formation. Fibers added to the top of a stirred tank at fiber consistencies of around 0.10 to 0.05% will be completely dispersed by the time they reach the bottom. Water and fiber can be continuously metered to the top and drawn off at the bottom for feeding to the headbox. If the fibers tend to stick together, a hydropulper can be used to put more work into the system, but it is seldom necessary. Hollander beaters, with the roll lifted off the bedplate, can also be used but are less desirable. Storage time of the slurry should be held to a minimum, since prolonged agitation can result in deterioration of quality by gradual entangling and knotting of the fiber.

STOCK TRANSFER

Synthetic-fiber slurries are best handled in open impeller nonclogging pumps. Closed impeller pumps will tend to clog with long-fibered stocks. Fiber stock should not be passed through Jordans, disc mills, or similar refining equipment, since they will at best produce poorer sheet formation and at worst reduce fiber length and consequently sheet properties. Screens should also be bypassed or removed from the system, since they too will degrade the formation of the sheet.

BINDER PREPARATION

When a highly fibrillated binder or carrier is used, such as fibrids or wood pulp, it can be separately dispersed and mixed with the fiber dispersion just before the headbox, by using a metering system to blend the two streams in the proper proportions. A stock preparation system of this kind is illustrated schematically in Figure 9.1. Early in the development of techniques for handling synthetic fibers it was

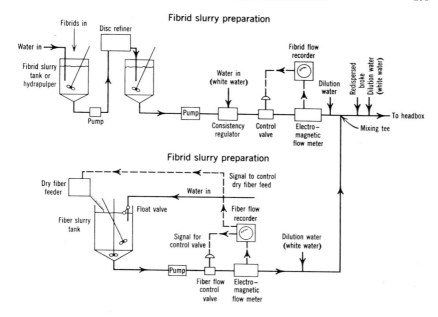

Figure 9.1. Continuous stock preparation system.

observed that mixing of fibers with fibrous binders, especially when the fiber was the major component, in these dilute suspensions led to rapid entanglement and knotting and a highly adverse effect on sheet formation. This also led to the use of separate systems for dispersion of the fiber and binder, with blending as short a time before sheet formation as possible. More recently it has been found that mixing of fibers and fibrous binders is possible if much higher stock consistencies are used. If these stocks are prepared at about 0.5% consistency and then passed through a high-speed pump, such as the Tri-Clover running at 1750 r.p.m., excellent fiber dispersion is obtained. Further mixing is possible if the stock is again diluted to about 0.05% and passed through a high-speed open impeller pump such as the Ingersoll-Rand running at 3450 r.p.m. The stock from this pump is then diluted to the desired headbox consistency and fed directly to the headbox. Such a system is shown schematically in Figure 9.2. This method of stock preparation is obviously much simpler and much nearer to conventional paper practice than the separate fiber- and binder-stock preparation scheme.

The other extreme in stocks containing synthetic fiber is in wood-

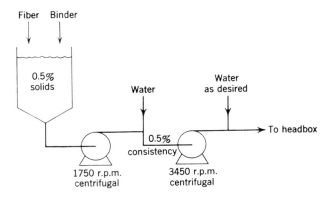

Figure 9.2

pulp blends in which the synthetic is generally present to the extent of 15 to 50%; the remainder is pulp. These stocks can be prepared by beating the pulp in the conventional way to the required freeness in a Hollander. The roll is then raised and the synthetic fiber added to the beater and mixed in with the raised roll. In the subsequent handling of the stock Jordans and screens should again be bypassed. Alternatively, the fiber can be added at the stock chest and mixed at that point if sufficient agitation is available.

PAPER-MACHINE WET END

Synthetic-fiber stocks require high dilutions at the headbox to obtain good formation. The handling of the large amount of water required leads to difficulties with conventional flat-wire headbox arrangements. Although this equipment can be used with skillful machine handling, the formation obtained is at best not ideal. A more favorable arrangement is the inclined wire shown in Figure 9.3. Since these stocks are extremely free draining, the formation zone is short. Stock consistencies of 0.05 to 0.02% have been found desirable at the headbox. Fine wires, such as a 70 × 210 cigarette wire, are desirable to minimize losses through the wire. Another type of wet end that can be used to good advantage with synthetic-fiber stocks is represented by the Rotoformer* shown schematically in Figure 9.4.

Pulp blends, with a high pulp content, are much nearer to conventional papers in handling. Good sheet formation can be achieved

* Manufactured by Sandy Hill Brass & Iron Works.

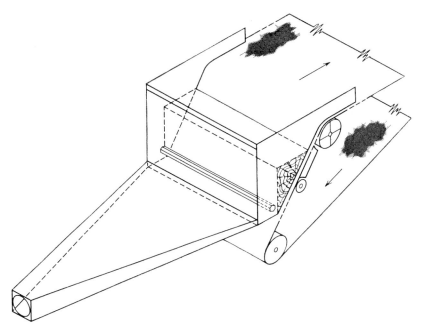

Figure 9.3. Inclined wire headbox.

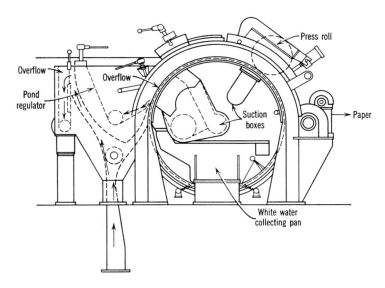

Figure 9.4. Typical elevation of Rotoformer.

with a flat wire or the Rotoformer. The inclined wire, with its relatively short forming zone is not so adaptable to this type of stock.

WET PRESS

Wet pressing presents a few problems with synthetic webs and with pulp blends. Fiber picking may be encountered and can be corrected by Teflon tetrafluoroethylene polymer coatings on the press roll.

DRYERS

Most synthetic fibers will shrink on drying. This shrinkage must be allowed to take place as the sheet passes over the dryer cans or the sheet may rupture in spots and even break down. Dryers that are split into several sections with individual speed controls are advantageous. Synthetic-fiber webs dry quickly, and most paper dryers will have excess capacity. If sticking is encountered, lowering the temperature of the first dryer cans will generally correct the condition. Silicone-resin roll coatings can also be used to minimize this problem.

REFERENCES

1. L. A. Auspos and E. B. Winn, "Structure Property Relationships in Textryls." *TAPPI,* **45,** No. 9, 741–744 (September 1962).
2. J. K. Hubbard, F. H. Koontz, J. R. McCartney, and R. A. A. Hentschel, "Physical Properties of Papers Made from Synthetic Fibers, *TAPPI,* **38,** 257–261 (May 1955).
3. American Viscose Corp., Tech. Service Bull. S12 "Fiber RD 101," 1960.
4. U. S. Patent 2,810,646, W. M. Wooding and N. T. Woodbury, American Cyanamid Co. U. S. Patent 3,047,455, R. R. Holmes and N. T. Anderson, Monsanto Chemical Co. U. S. Patent 3,047,456, P. A. Ucci and N. T. Anderson, Monsanto Chemical Co.
5. H. F. Arledter, "New Developments in the Manufacture of Synthetic Fiber Paper," *TAPPI,* **42,** 177A–181A (February 1959).
6. British Patent 836,328, Miller and Merriam, Union Carbide Co. British Patent 781,512, E. I. du Pont de Nemours & Co., Inc.
7. American Viscose Co., Tech. Service Bull. S23 "Vinyon HH in the Manufacture of Paper," 1960.
8. U. S. Patent 2,999,788, P. W. Morgan, E. I. du Pont de Nemours & Co., Inc.

10

STRUCTURE-PROPERTY RELATIONSHIPS

R. A. A. HENTSCHEL

Product Development Manager
E. I. du Pont de Nemours & Co., Inc.
Wilmington, Delaware

In its simplest terms any synthetic-fiber sheet is made up of a random array of fibers held together by an adhesive binder. The properties of this sheet structure are a composite of the properties of the two components and are governed by the weakest link. If the sheet is ruptured, failure can occur either by deficiency of the binder or of the fiber, depending on which is the weaker. This chapter considers the factors influencing this behavior. An understanding of these factors will often permit achievement of desired properties or realization of the limitations with a minimum of empirical research.

Since both fibers and binders are generally synthetic polymers, a brief review of the structural features that govern their properties seems in order. More detailed treatment of structure-property relationships in polymers can be found in the literature (1,2) but would be out of place in a book such as this.

Synthetic polymers are long-chain molecules built up by joining large numbers of smaller molecules. There are two basic chemical mechanisms by which essentially all long-chain molecules are formed. The first involves reaction of a double bond and is called "addition polymerization." The key feature of this reaction is that no by-products are produced. The molecules are literally "added" one to the other. The simplest polymer starts with ethylene:

$$H_2C{=}CH_2$$

Under the proper conditions, the double bond can rearrange, linking together a long series of these base molecules to form "linear" polyethylene:

$$-\overset{\displaystyle \overset{H}{|}}{\underset{\displaystyle \underset{H}{|}}{C}}-\overset{\displaystyle \overset{H}{|}}{\underset{\displaystyle \underset{H}{|}}{C}}- \quad - \quad HC-\left[\overset{\displaystyle \overset{H}{|}}{\underset{\displaystyle \underset{H}{|}}{C}}-\overset{\displaystyle \overset{H}{|}}{\underset{\displaystyle \underset{H}{|}}{C}}\right]_n -\overset{\displaystyle \overset{H}{|}}{\underset{\displaystyle \underset{H}{|}}{CH}}$$

Such chains are characteristically several hundred thousand repeat units long in a typical high polymer. Many variants of this basic reaction are possible. One arises through branching of the chain:

$$\begin{array}{c} C-C-\underset{\displaystyle |}{C}-C-C \cdots C^* \\ C-C-C \cdots C \end{array}$$

Aggregations of these branched molecules obviously cannot nest together as uniformly as the linear, and the resulting polymer will have lower density, crystallinity, and strength.

Other molecules containing double bonds can also be polymerized by the same mechanism. Acrylonitrile or vinyl cyanide is the base molecule or "monomer" for a common fiber-forming polymer of this type and is the basis for the "acrylic" fibers:

$$C{=}C-CN$$

This polymerizes to

$$C-\underset{\displaystyle \underset{CN}{|}}{C}-C-\overset{\displaystyle \overset{CN}{|}}{C} \cdots C-\underset{\displaystyle \underset{CN}{|}}{C}$$

Two or more kinds of molecules can be polymerized together to produce a "copolymer." The two different molecules will alternate in a random fashion along the polymer chain in the ratio of the monomer units present. An example is the copolymer of vinyl chloride and vinyl acetate, the base polymer from which Vinyon fibers are made:

$$-C-\underset{\displaystyle \underset{Cl}{|}}{C}- \quad \text{and} \quad -C-\underset{\displaystyle \underset{O}{\underset{\displaystyle |}{\underset{C{=}O}{\underset{\displaystyle |}{C}}}}}{C}-$$

Vinyl chloride   Vinyl acetate

* For simplicity, the hydrogen atoms are omitted in this and subsequent formulas.

Since the second component molecule in a copolymer reduces the regularity of the structure, copolymers are generally softer, more rubbery, and lower melting than the corresponding homopolymers.

The second basic polymerization mechanism is a chemical reaction between two or more double-ended or "bifunctional" monomer units. In this polymerization the reactive group at the end of one monomer unit reacts with a group at the end of the other, with the elimination of a by-product such as water. Since the reaction can take place at both ends of the bifunctional molecules, the monomer units link themselves into long chains under the proper conditions of reaction. Polymers formed in this way are called "condensation" polymers. Many chemical reactions can provide the basis for such polymerization. Two that are used in the manufacture of well-known fibers are the reaction of an amine with an acid, the basic reaction for the preparation of the nylons, and the reaction of an acid with a glycol, the basic reaction for the polyesters.

66 Nylon.

$$H_2N—C—C—C—C—C—C—NH_2 +$$
Hexamethylene diamine

$$HOOC—C—C—C—C—COOH \rightarrow$$
Adipic acid

$$\left(\begin{array}{c} —N—C—C—C—C—C—N—C—C—C—C—C—C— \\ \;\;\;| \qquad\qquad\qquad\qquad | \;\;| \qquad\qquad\qquad\quad | \\ \;\;H \qquad\qquad\qquad\qquad H \;\;O \qquad\qquad\qquad O \end{array} \right)_n$$

Polyhexamethylene adipamide

$$+ H_2O$$

Polyethylene Terephthalate Polyester.

$$HOOC—\langle \bigcirc \rangle—COOH + HOC—COH \rightarrow$$
Terephthalic acid   Ethylene glycol

$$\left(\begin{array}{c} —C—\langle \bigcirc \rangle—C—O—C—C—O— \\ \;\;| \qquad\qquad\qquad | \\ \;\;O \qquad\qquad\qquad O \end{array} \right)_n + H_2O$$

Polyethylene terephthalate

The polymer chains in condensation polymers are characteristically in the order of 10,000 to 15,000 monomer units long.

Large groups of these long-chain polymer molecules are held together by binding forces between the molecular chains. These forces are frequently hydrogen bonds, which are relatively strong, and are the bonding forces in polymers such as polyethylene, the nylons, and the polyesters. Other binding forces such as polar bonds, are found, for example, between the CN groups in polyacrylonitrile:

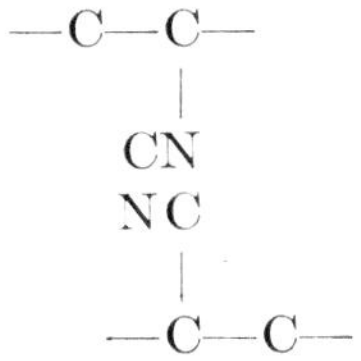

Long-chain molecules in a mass of polymer can assume several arrangements. One is a completely random interlaced array that produces an "amorphous" polymer, as in Figure 10.1. Such an array has an ill-defined melting range, low physical properties, and a more rubbery behavior.

These molecules can also be more or less parallelized, as in the "oriented" structure sketched in Figure 10.2. This array still has an ill-defined melting point, but it also has considerably higher strength because of the stretched-out arrangement of the molecules.

Finally, there is the most highly ordered form in which the molecules are placed in a precise lattice arrangement in relation to one another to give the "crystalline" polymer shown in Figure 10.3. This array has a sharp melting point, high strength, and is relatively stiff.

A block of polymer is seldom if ever found completely in any one of these arrays. Since it is formed in the polymerization reaction, a

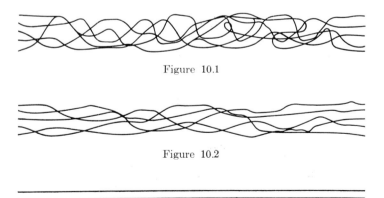

Figure 10.1

Figure 10.2

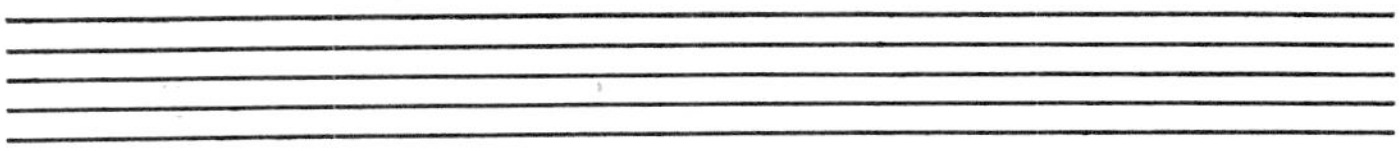

Figure 10.3

Figure 10.4

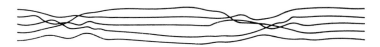

Figure 10.5

high polymer is frequently a mixture of amorphous and crystalline areas (Figure 10.4). The "degree of crystallization" is a term used to express the relative proportion of crystalline to amorphous regions. Polymers with a high degree of crystallization will approach the characteristics of the "crystalline" polymer and vice versa.

Oriented polymers are obtained only by stretching the solid polymer or by freezing in the flow orientation, which takes place when molten polymer or polymer solutions are extruded at high velocities through small holes. Such stretching, which can elongate the polymer thread six- or eightfold or more, straightens out the randomly intertangled molecules of the amorphous region of the polymer. See Figure 10.5. In this state the polymer will have the highest practically attainable strength.

Fibers are formed from polymers by extruding a melt or solution of high viscosity through small holes to form long filaments. In most cases these extruded filaments are then stretched, or "oriented," to give the highest possible strength. This oriented fiber form of polymer is generally the strongest of all the states in which polymers are used. Thus in a synthetic-fiber sheet made up of fibers held together by an adhesive binder of another polymer the fiber is in general the strongest component in the structure.

Since synthetic-fiber sheets are always made up of a fiber and a binder, let us consider the state of the binder component. In Chapter 2 it was pointed out that there are three ways in which a synthetic fiber web can be bonded:

1. By partial solution at the surface of the fibers of the web and subsequent reprecipitation.
2. By coalescense of a dispersed polymer.
3. By melting a binder component.

In all these cases the binder component is an unoriented polymer and is inherently weaker than the fiber component. Opposing this, however, is the fact that the binder is present as a thin film between the strong fibers. If the adhesive bond is strong and the film of the binder is tough and sufficiently elastic to permit it to deform and accommodate itself to the deformation strains without brittle failure, rupture of the web can be made to take place in the fiber rather than in the binder. Thus the binder characteristics leading to high sheet strength are as follows:

1. A good adhesive bond with the fiber. This is generally favored by chemical similarity between the binder and the fiber, although it is not a strict requirement.

2. Toughness and deformability. This is favored by the more rubbery polymer states: amorphousness and copolymerization.

3. The ability to form thin films between the surfaces being joined. This is favored by fluidity in the system as the bond is being formed.

Recapitulating, then, a bonded web of fibers can rupture either by failure of the fiber or failure of the binder, depending on which is the weaker. Because of the effects of orientation, the fiber form for any given polymer is inherently stronger than the binder form, and the highest attainable sheet strength is achieved when the failure is in the fiber rather than in the binder.

With this groundwork, we can now turn to a more detailed examination of the structure-property relationships in a bonded web of fibers. This section discusses the effect of varying the structural parameters in the sheet in a general sense, without reference to specific fibers, since it has been found that there are general behavioral patterns that hold for all systems. These relationships have been most extensively studied in the textryl system using Du Pont's fibrid binder system (3,4).*

The first and most obvious variable to be studied is the effect of binder content on sheet strength. Figure 10.6 shows the relationships between binder content and tensile strength, elongation and tear strength.

Characteristically, all of these properties at first increase with increasing binder content, reach a maximum at around 20 to 30% binder, and then fall off again. Two details should be noticed. First, the maxima in tensile and burst strengths are reached at some-

* Fibrids have been experimentally produced by Du Pont, but have not been commercialized.

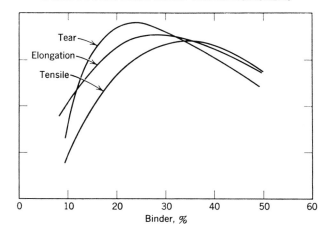

Figure 10.6. Physical properties versus binder content.

what higher binder content than the maximum in tear. Second, the maximum in tensile strength is reached at about 25 to 30% binder content. These are the relationships characteristic of good binder systems. As the binders become less efficient, their content at which the maxima are reached rises and the maximum level of strength attained becomes less. As shown later, the absolute strength properties reached depend on the physical properties of the fiber being used.

The reasons for the shape of these curves can be hypothesized: as the binder content is increased initially, more and more of the fibers are bonded into the web network, thus increasing the strength. Ultimately, all fibers in the web make their individual contributions to the strength of the aggregate, and any further increase in binder content then only reduces the amount of the strongest component, leading to a decrease in over-all strength of the sheet.

The next variable in the system is the length and diameter* of the fibers in the web. Figures 10.7 and 10.8 show how the tensile and tear strengths change as fiber dimensions change. Inspection of these curves shows that as the fiber length increases the tensile rupture properties again increase, reach a maximum, and then decrease. Tear strength, on the other hand, continues to increase with length within the range of lengths investigated. It will also be noted that the length at which the maximum in tensile properties is reached increases

* Diameter is expressed here as "denier." Denier, a textile unit, is the weight in grams of 9000 m. of fiber. Thus denier is strictly a measure of cross-sectional area and is directly proportional to the diameter squared.

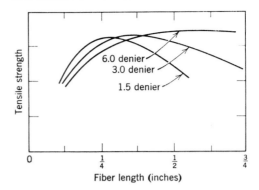

Figure 10.7. Tensile strength versus fiber length and diameter.

as the diameter of the fiber increases; the absolute level of maximum strength, however, is essentially constant for a given fiber type.

The initial strength increase can again be explained in terms of the fiber being more effectively bonded into the web as the length increases. The shorter the fiber, the greater the chance that it will not be bonded at or near both ends and the greater the chance that it will not, therefore, make its maximum individual contribution to the strength of the web. The reason for the subsequent decrease in tensile properties, however, is to be found in the flexibility of these long fibers. Inspection of the sheets used in this study shows that the formation is excellent up to the point at which maximum strength is reached but that it then begins to deteriorate. The fibers become so long in relation to their diameter that they begin to tangle and knot

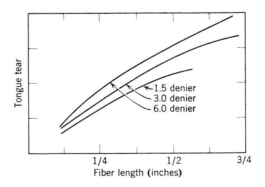

Figure 10.8. Tear versus fiber length and diameter.

with one another to the detriment of good formation. Auspos and Winn (4) have shown that the strength maximum is reached at a length-to-diameter ratio of about 500:1. They have also shown that this ratio will vary somewhat, but not greatly, with fiber stiffness (modulus). The stiffer the fiber, the higher the l/d ratio can be. It has also been found, by using what are today commercially impractical techniques such as dispersing the fibers in foam, that if good formation is obtained with the longer fibers the tensile properties will rise to the same maximum but will no longer decrease; rather they will remain constant as the length increases further.

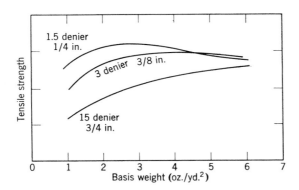

Figure 10.9.   Tensile strength versus basis weight.

The tensile properties of a web are determined by the cooperative behavior of a web of fibers. Tear properties, on the other hand, depend on the sequential transverse failure of individual fibers or bundles of fibers. Thus tear properties are not so dependent on good web formation. Rather they depend on the fibers being sufficiently well anchored into the structure to permit transverse failure to occur before the fibers are pulled loose. It has been found that tear strength reaches a maximum level at fiber lengths between 1 and 1.5 in. and remains essentially constant beyond that length.

The final sheet variable studied is basis weight. The effect of basis weight on sheet properties is shown in Figures 10.9 and 10.10. In these graphs the properties are given in units of strength per unit basis weight. Thus, if basis weight has no effect on properties, these graphs would become horizontal straight lines. Inspection shows that as basis weight is reduced properties remain essentially constant down to a certain level, then begin to fall off. This fall-off appears to occur when there are no longer enough fibers in the sheet to form a complete network. Auspos and Winn (4) have shown that this critical basis weight is reached when the sheet basis weight in grams per square inch is about 7 to 10 times the fiber diameter in centimeters.

The preceding relationships have been discussed without quantitative references to sheet strength. The absolute levels of sheet strength have been shown to depend on the properties of the fibers from which they are made (3). Maximum sheet tensile strength

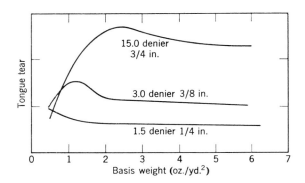

Figure 10.10.   Tear versus basis weight.

has been related in a properly bonded system to fiber tenacity as shown in Figure 10.11.

Expressed mathematically,
sheet tensile strength in lb./in./oz./yd.^{2} = 3.7 × fiber tenacity in gm./denier

This is the maximum strength that has been observed experimentally with the best binder systems. Poorer binders, at any level of fiber tenacity, will produce lower maximum strength values. If the same units are used for both sheet and fiber tenacities, the proportionality constant is 0.22. Similarly, sheet elongation at break has been experimentally related to fiber elongation at break, as shown in Figure 10.12.   The form of this relation is

sheet break elongation, % = 0.6 × fiber break elongation, %

Intuitively, one would expect tensile strengths and elongations of fiber and sheet to be linearly related. Sheet tear strength, on the

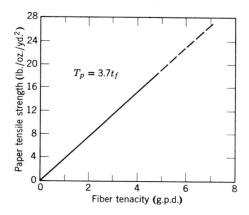

Figure 10.11. Paper tensile strength versus fiber tenacity.

other hand, has no obvious counterpart in fiber properties. Empirically, the fiber property that seems to correlate most closely with sheet tear strength is work-to-break. This relationship is shown in Figure 10.13. The following expression has been found to hold quite closely:

sheet tongue tear strength in lb./oz./yd.^{2} =
$0.6 \times$ fiber work-to-break in grams

If the foregoing three relationships are used, the maximum properties obtainable with any given fiber can be calculated quite closely

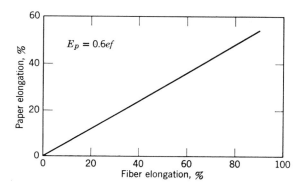

Figure 10.12. Paper break elongation versus fiber break elongation.

for a sheet made up of only one fiber type and dimensions and an effective binder system. Sheets can also be made up of mixtures of fibers. These mixtures can include different fiber dimensions with a given type of fiber or fibers of different types and properties. Again by using fibrid binders with synthetic fibers several interesting relationships have been shown.

Consider first blends of fibers of different size and shape but identical physical and chemical properties. Figure 10.14 shows tensile strength, elongation, and tear strength for a series of papers made up of a blend of 1.5-denier $\frac{1}{4}$ in. fiber with 15-denier $\frac{3}{4}$ in. nylon fiber, both of the same chemical makeup and physical properties. The properties of the blends fall on straight lines between the properties

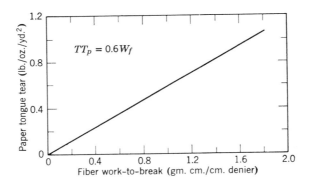

Figure 10.13.   Paper tear versus fiber toughness.

of the homogeneous sheets. Thus, when only dimensional differences exist between the blend fibers, paper properties will vary in a straight-line fashion with composition between the properties of the homogeneous sheets.

The next degree of complication is illustrated by fibers that differ in both chemical makeup and in tenacity but have the same initial modulus (stiffness) and similar elongations. Here a binder must be chosen to bond both fiber species equally well. Figure 10.15 is an example. Again the tensile strength, tear, and elongation vary linearly with composition between the properties of the two homogeneous sheets.

Finally, consider the case in which the fibers are closely related chemically, have the same tenacity, but differ markedly in initial modulus, as illustrated by Figure 10.16. Now a pronounced minimum is found in the tensile-strength curve, even though the prop-

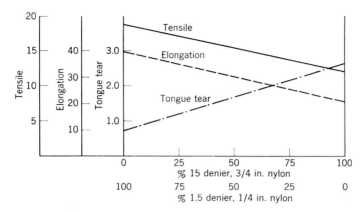

Figure 10.14. Paper properties of fiber blends; blends of fiber dimensions.

erties of the homogeneous sheets are identical. Here the stiffer fiber is the first to take up the load as the paper is stressed and is also the first to rupture, leaving the lower modulus fiber to take over later in the final stages of failure. Thus the averaged tenacity of the paper is lower, since fewer fibers are supporting the load at any one time. The paper elongations also show a minimum in the blends. The tear strengths of the blends, however, are still linearly related to the tear strengths of the homogeneous sheets. Thus, when the two fibers in a blend paper differ markedly in modulus, minima in the paper tensile and elongation curves can be expected. Tear

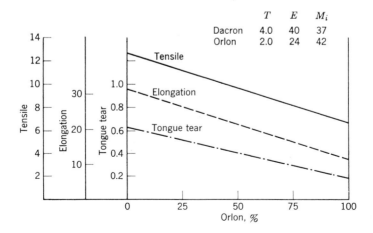

Figure 10.15. Paper properties of fiber blends; blends of fiber tenacities.

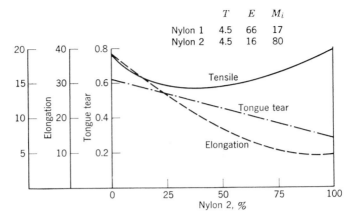

Figure 10.16. Paper properties of fiber blends; blends of fiber moduli.

strengths, on the other hand, tend to be related linearly to the properties of the homogeneous sheets, regardless of differences in fiber properties. This may come about from the fact that in tear the failure process is marked by the successive failures of individual filaments or relatively small groups of filaments. This would lead to an averaging process as opposed to tensile or elongation behavior, in which relatively large groups of fibers react simultaneously to the load.

We can now summarize a few rules for the way in which the properties of papers made from blends of fibers are related to the properties of the homogeneous sheets.

1. Linear relationships exist for tensile strength and elongation when (a) blend fibers differ only in dimensions (i.e., length and diameter), (b) blend fibers are similar in modulus and do not differ in elongation by more than about 2:1.

2. Minima are found in the tensile strength and elongation curves when the moduli of the two fibers are markedly different.

3. Tear strengths are linearly related regardless of differences in fiber properties.

4. Maxima in property-composition curves have never been found and are not to be expected. Thus the properties of a blend sheet will never exceed highest homogeneous sheet property.

To illustrate the use of these rules, a series of two and three component blends of nylon fibers of various lengths and diameters were made. Since the blend properties are all linearly related, they were calculated by relationships of the form

$$\text{property}_{\text{blend}} = \frac{(\% \text{ A}) \text{ prop}_A + (\% \text{ B}) \text{ prop}_B + (\% \text{ C}) \text{ prop}_C}{100}$$

The homogeneous sheet properties (from handsheet data) on which these calculations were based are shown in Table 10.1. In Table 10.2, the calculated properties of the blends are compared to the

TABLE 10.1
Nylon Papers—Handsheets
$(20\%$ binder, 101 fibrid, #2 oz./yd.$^2)$

Fiber Content	Tensile Strength (lb./in./oz./yd.^{2})	E (%)	Elmendorf Tear (lb./oz./yd.^{2})
1.5 denier $\frac{1}{4}$ in.	15.3	40	0.47
3.0 denier $\frac{3}{8}$ in.	12.8	34	0.80
6.0 denier $\frac{5}{8}$ in. (high tenacity)	16.0	22	1.20
15.0 denier $\frac{3}{4}$ in.	9.5	26	1.77

TABLE 10.2
Nylon Papers—Machine Made
$(20\%$ binder 101, #2 oz./yd.$^2)$

Fiber Content					Tensile Strength (lb./in./oz./yd.^{2})	R (%)	Elmendorf Tear (lb./oz./yd.^{2})
(%, 1.5 denier, $\frac{1}{4}$ in.)	(%, 3 denier, $\frac{3}{8}$ in.)	(%, 6 denier, $\frac{5}{8}$ in.)	(%, 15.0 denier, $\frac{3}{4}$ in.)				
—	95	5	—	M*	12.5	32	0.97
				C	13.0	33	0.82
50	—	—	50	M	11.8	30	1.34
				C	12.4	33	1.12
—	—	50	50	M	11.2	22	1.35
				C	12.8	24	1.49
47.5	47.5	5	—	M	13.9	36	0.92
				C	14.1	36	0.69
33.3	33.3	—	33.3	M	12.6	35	0.98
				C	12.5	33	1.01
25	50	—	25	M	12.6	36	0.95
				C	12.6	34	0.96

* M = measured
  C = calculated

measured properties using machine-made papers for the measurements. It may be seen that the agreement is good throughout.

A particular case of growing commercial importance is found in blends of fibers of differing modulus: wood pulp and synthetic fibers. In these structures, the binders are incorporated in the sheet by saturation with polymer dispersions. These sheets are complex not only because the properties of their fibers are different but the fibers also vary chemically. It therefore becomes difficult to find a binder that is equally effective in binding the wood pulp and the synthetic fiber into the structure. Such blends, in agreement with the principles already discussed, show improved tear strength, fold endurance, and, with the dimensionally stable synthetics, improved dimensional stability to variations in humidity. In general, they show, at best, equal and usually somewhat lower tensile strengths to sheets made of either fiber. Since tear strength is often of prime importance in these structures, the longest fibers that can be handled and still give good sheet formation are used. It is difficult, however, at the present state of the art to generalize about the properties of fiber blend sheets of this type. Each blend must be studied individually and, to a great extent, empirically. Such discussions are presented in Chapters 2, 3, and 4 of this book.

REFERENCES

1. W. R. Sorensen and T. W. Campbell, *Preparative Methods of Polymer Chemistry, Interscience,* New York, 1961.
2. Rowland Hill, Fibers from Synthetic Polymers, Elsevier, New York, 1953.
3. R. A. A. Hentschel, "Structure-Property Relationships in Synthetic Fiber Papers," *TAPPI,* **42**, 979–982 (December 1959).
4. L. A. Auspos and E. B. Winn, "Structure-Property Relations in Textryls," *TAPPI,* **45**, 741–744 (September 1962).

11

MARKETS FOR NONWOVEN MATERIALS

WILLIAM K. SAUNDERS

J. P. Stevens & Co., Inc.
New York, New York

The possible end uses for nonwovens have sparked the imagination of everyone during the last decade. Unfortunately, however, the romance and novelty of this new textile and paper concept have resulted in many greatly exaggerated predictions concerning the immediate future of this field. The inflated production estimates and growth predictions were extremely misleading and included many types of product that properly belonged in batting, padding, waste-fiber, or other market categories. These materials are very different from the resin-bonded, fiber-bonded, airlaid, waterlaid, and other types of nonwovens with which this chapter deals.

About 10 years ago several substantial markets were found for resin-bonded synthetic-fiber nonwovens, and these markets, together with the "Blue Sky" publicity given the field, encouraged a number of new companies, both in the textile and paper industries, to enter the area of nonwoven manufacturing. The known markets were saturated with a wide variety of materials, and both the new manufacturers and some of the older ones were forced to look about for new applications for their products. As a result, nonwovens were promoted for many uses for which they were not at all well suited. Materials that had been thoroughly evaluated for a particular end use were put on the market prematurely, and the result was many product failures and deficiencies. This history has caused numerous prospective customers to look askance at nonwovens in general.

It has now become obvious to most nonwoven manufacturers that this search for new markets for their products requires a great deal of time, patience, technical talent, marketing ability, special equipment, and, not the least, money.   Because of these requirements, several manufacturers in recent years have decided to discontinue their production of nonwovens.

This history is typical of many new industries.   When new products, such as metals, plastics, foams, fibers, electronic components or nonwovens, are introduced, they quickly find the most obvious markets, and a number of companies start producing the accepted products.   The obvious markets become saturated and new markets develop slowly and at great cost.   Some of the companies that go into making these new products are forced to drop out, and only those remain that are willing and able to do the expensive research required to develop new markets.

Nonwovens have gone through their first stage of development. The obvious markets have been exploited, and it is now going to require a great deal of concentrated effort to develop other uses for these unique and promising materials.

Any product must justify its existence on a cost/performance basis. Nonwovens are no exception.   In all of the market areas in which they have penetrated, nonwovens have done so only because they perform the functions required as well as, or better than, other materials, such as woven fabrics, films, and foils.   They must do so at a price that is acceptable to the market.   This cost/performance criterion must be kept constantly in mind.

To a great extent the markets for nonwoven materials depend on the type of machinery employed to produce them.   The variety of processes used for nonwovens is large indeed.   Although there is certain conventional machinery on the market that can be purchased to manufacture nonwovens, most manufacturers have developed processes of their own or combinations of processes to produce the materials that their markets require.   For purposes of simplification, we divide these processes into three basic groups:

1. textile process,
2. paper making or "wet" process,
3. miscellaneous.

In each of these categories several of the more important products and markets are discussed.

TEXTILE PROCESS

Nonwovens were first produced, and the majority of them still are, by organizations with backgrounds in which textiles predominate.

The reasons are fairly obvious. The textile companies deal with fibers of various descriptions, and it was natural for them to develop new and different methods for putting these textile fibers together.

Although fibers other than synthetics are widely used in the nonwoven industry, synthetic fibers are dominant in this area. The major synthetic fibers listed approximately in the order of their importance are

1. rayon and acetate,
2. nylon,
3. others.

Although there are many methods of putting these fibers together by the so-called textile or "dry" process, the nonwovens found in major markets are usually manufactured by saturating, print bonding, or spraying a randomized air-deposited web or a unidirectional fiber web produced on cards or garnetts.

Surprisingly, these possible nonwovens do not compete strenuously with one another, nor do their markets overlap particularly; therefore each type and its markets is discussed independently.

RANDOM WEB: SATURATED

These well-known materials have found many large markets in a wide variety of industries.

Interlinings. The largest and best known market is probably the garment interfacing and interlining field, in which these materials compete successfully with, and have often replaced, the woven fabrics, either plain or resin-finished, that were formerly used for this purpose.

The properties of nonwovens made from a random web are approximately omnidirectional. They can be cut and sewn in any direction and there are no threads to ravel. Being saturated with resin, resilience, nondiscoloration, and stretch can be built into the material. On a weight-for-weight basis these materials are usually bulkier than woven fabrics, and this is an advantage in many garment applications. These nonwovens are, of course, washable and dry-cleanable.

Shoe Industry. Another large market area for nonwovens of this description is the shoe industry. Here a number of applications have been found in plumper or doubler materials, box-toe materials, and innersoles. Here again the nonwovens can be easily cut and have the bulking properties and the resilience that make them uniquely suited to these applications.

Coated-Fabric Backing.   As a backing material for the coated-fabrics industry, the properties of softness, bulk, good tear resistance, and stretch have enabled manufacturers of these saturated random-web materials to find several substantial market areas in automotive and commercial upholstery.

Filtration.   Nonwovens of this type are also used in the wet-filtration field in areas such as milk filters.

Wiping Cloth.   Nonwoven materials are also found in the wiping-cloth field, and here the predominant fibers are both, cotton and synthetic.

For the major end uses mentioned, such as interlinings, shoe materials, and vinyl backing products, the textile process permits long fibers and crimped fibers to be used, thus giving the products the properties of tear strength, bulk, and stretch that would not be obtainable with short fibers.

Although virgin synthetic fiber is employed in the majority of these end uses, certain types of waste, such as nylon garnetts, are being extensively adapted.   Off-grade fibers not suitable for normal textile processing into woven fabric can also be utilized, since color, dyeability, and exact uniformity are not so important as they are in woven fabrics.

UNIDIRECTIONAL WEBS: PRINT-BONDED OR SATURATED

The production of these materials is mainly accomplished by means of cards or garnetts set up in tandem to produce webs ranging in weight from one half ounce to several ounces per square yard.   The web is then print-bonded or intermittently bonded by some other process.   These materials have greater strength in the machine direction than in the cross-machine direction because of the alignment of their fibers.   They are usually extremely soft and absorbent because much of the web remains unbonded.

Sanitary Napkins.   Because of their softness and absorbency, one of their major markets has been as a covering for sanitary napkins. This field alone consumes several million pounds of these materials.

Medical Items.   In the medical area products of this nature are used for bandages, pad coverings, and other items.

Towels and Wiping Cloths. Another large end use for unidirectional print-bonded materials, also utilizing the properties of softness and absorbency, is in wiping cloths and towels. For the last few years these nonwovens have been seen at golf courses and bowling alleys. They are also used as restaurant wiping cloths and are even packaged into table napkins for use in the home. The printing industry also uses a product of this type.

Filtration. Milk filters and oil filters are also made of this type material.

RANDOM WEB: SPRAY-BONDED

These synthetic-fibered nonwovens are relatively new, but because of their unique properties they have found substantial markets. The largest of these markets are as follows.

Automotive Industry. Random spray-bonded nonwovens are extensively used by the automotive industry as padding for door panels and seat inserts. These materials are lofty per unit of weight and have the softness and bulk required for this end use. The resin with which the webs have been sprayed is usually of a thermoplastic heat-bondable type, so that when the padding has been covered by a vinyl outer material it can be embossed with the wide variety of patterns extensively employed in today's automotive interiors. The major fibers included in spray-bonded webs for automotive requirements are acetate, rayon, and nylon, sometimes combined with a natural fiber such as wool or cotton.

Air Filtration. These spray-bonded materials are steadily gaining acceptance in the heating, air-conditioning, and automotive air-filtration field. Because of their random nature, they have excellent airflow and dust-holding characteristics. The fibers can be varied in denier to give progressive filtration effects, and the resin with which they are sprayed gives them the required rigidity, washability, and flame-retardant characteristics.

In this area fibers vary from acetate and viscose in the less expensive filters to the polyester, acrylic, and nylon fibers in the thicker, washable, higher dust-capacity types.

Abrasive Industry. Random-fiber spray-bonded webs have been introduced in a wide variety of new abrasive products. For this end use a web is formed, sprayed with a resin, and impregnated with abrasive particles. The resulting material is tough and resilient and, depending on its characteristics, is used for floor cleaning, wood and furniture finishing, metal finishing, and as scrubbing pads for pots and pans. The fibers normally selected are those with good abrasion characteristics such as nylon.

UNIDIRECTIONAL WEBS: SPRAY-BONDED

Garment Quilting. The largest market for materials in this category is as garment insulation for the quilting trade. The nonwovens are normally produced by garnetts in fiber weights ranging from 1.5 to 4 oz./yd.^{2} The fibers are then lightly spray-bonded on each side to hold them together and are shipped to the quilter who quilts them to outer or lining fabric.

The fibers used range from acetate to the polyesters, depending on the end-use requirements. Acetate materials are less expensive, but the polyesters give much better washability and insulation.

Electronic Quilting. Another market for these materials is the electronic quilting industry. Here the sprayed binder is a thermo-plastic that allows the electronic quilter to heat-seal the material between layers of vinyl or vinyl/cloth combinations. This spray-bonded material gives the appearance of bulk in such items as garment bags, automobile seat covers, and playpen pads.

In summary, the textile process is normally used for nonwovens when the product or end use requires the following characteristics: high tear resistance, permanent washability and dry-cleanability, bulk, drape-ability, stretch, resilience, and weights of more than 2 oz./yd.^{2}

From a utilization standpoint, the textile process can use almost any length crimp, or grade of fiber.

PAPERMAKING OR WET PROCESS

This family of materials is among the newest and the most interesting of the nonwovens. The volume produced today is small in comparison with those produced by the textile process, but it is finding ever-broadening markets.

The use of synthetic fibers in the wet process has permitted lightweight, smooth, uniform products to be engineered for a number of promising markets.

Nonwoven materials made by the wet process may be either 100% synthetic or combinations of synthetic fibers and conventional pulp furnishes. Resin finishes may be added either by on-machine or off-machine treatments. The end-use requirements dictate the furnish and finish necessary.

There are few markets that are particularly dominant, and a great deal of the work being done today is experimental, but many companies have high hopes for the future of these nonwoven materials.

There are, of course, a number of markets in which these wet-process materials are now being used in a commercial or semicommercial way. In the sections following these markets are discussed briefly and some of the reasons for the suitability of the synthetic-fibered wet-process nonwovens are given from a cost-and-performance standpoint.

Electrical Tapes. Materials made from the polyesters or acrylics have excellent electrical properties and are being used for tapes in that field. These tapes are usually highly calendered to thicknesses between 1 and 2 mils. For this end use a 100% synthetic-fibered sheet is required, and the bonding of the sheet takes place by calendering which fuses some of the lower melting fibers or fibrids in the furnish. This product has adequate tensile strength, tear resistance, and smoothness.

Medical Tapes. Medical tapes of synthetic-fibered wet-process nonwovens are made from polyester fibers which have the characteristic of nonadherence to wounds and can be made with the strength, smoothness, porosity, softness, and drape required for medical applications.

Coated-Fabric Backing. By using 100% synthetic fibers with a resin treatment, or by using nylon or rayon in a 20 to 25% portion of a pulp furnish, resin-treated, a material suitable as a base for coated fabrics can be made. These coated fabrics go into wall coverings or into automobile or commercial upholstery. The base material has good tear resistance, smoothness, and sewability and can be made heat-sealable as required. When used as a wall-cover backing, it accepts standard paste and can be easily removed from the wall when necessary.

Interlinings. The new Textryl materials developed by Du Pont are gaining acceptance as interlinings and interfacings in the garment industry. These lightweight, strong, soft, smooth, washable, and sewable products are uniquely suitable for collars and fronts of blouses, dresses, and shirts. They are particularly desirable in blend fabrics and lightweight wash-and-wear materials.

Filtration. Various wet filtration products, including medical masks, are being made from synthetic-fibered wet-process nonwovens, mainly for the chemical or oil-filtration industries. For this end use material can be produced with engineered porosity and chemical-resistant characteristics.

Impression Ribbons. Synthetic-fibered wet-process nonwovens are being considered for impression ribbons in office machines ranging from typewriters to computers. These materials may be manufactured as one-use ribbons or as a multiple-use type. For this purpose a smooth, thin, strong material with enough porosity to hold the ink is required.

Plastic Overlay Materials. In the fast-growing field of reinforced plastics lightweight nonwovens made from acrylic or polyester fibers are being adapted as overlay materials. As the outer layers of laminates, these materials show improved abrasion, chemical, and weather-resistant qualities. For certain end uses they may be printed with attractive designs which become an intrinsic part of the laminate.

Drapery Buckram. One of the larger end uses for a product made from a combination of wood pulp and nylon or rayon fibers is in the drapery buckram field. This material is saturated with resin either on the paper machine or after it has been removed and has the stiffness, tear resistance, sewability, washability, and dry-cleanability required. It can be slit into 3- to 4-in. widths without raveling, and because of its unique characteristics has replaced, to a great extent, the woven fabrics previously used.

Food Packaging. Tea-bag paper has been made for many years and is a wet-process synthetic-fibered nonwoven. There are other food packaging applications in which stronger, more durable materials are needed. With the new fibers, fibrids, and resins available today these wet-process nonwovens can be made to fit the product requirements.

Man-made fibers have become important to the paper industry because they offer the manufacturer an opportunity to develop new and profitable business in areas heretofore not suitable for conventional paper-machine products. Because of improved properties of strength, toughness, flex, chemical resistance, and moldability, paper manufacturers can compete in many areas with textiles and films. The speed with which the wet process operates is a great advantage from an economic standpoint. As manufacturing techniques improve and as new fibers and resins are made available, it is certain that these wet-process nonwovens will find larger markets.

OTHER NONWOVEN MANUFACTURING PROCESSES

Several other methods of manufacturing nonwovens are given below, and some of their characteristics and markets are mentioned briefly.

NEEDLE PUNCHED MATERIALS

In this process a web of fibers is bound together and often to an internal woven scrim by driving barbed needles in and out of the fiber batt and scrim, thus mechanically interlocking the fibers together. Depending on the extent of this needle punching, the material can have various qualities. It can be soft and strong enough for blankets, skirting materials, and other textilelike items, but the process is commonly used with fibers such as jute to produce rug-underlay materials and automobile padding products.

LAID SCRIM PRODUCTS

In this process filament or spun yarns are laid on one another and are bonded together by a resin adhesive rather than interlocked by weaving. Several types of machine are available that will make this product. The adhesively bonded scrim can then be used as a reinforcement for various tapes or building papers. It is also surfaced with cellulose wadding to make a soft, opaque, textilelike, sewable material that is being applied extensively in a variety of hospital products, clothing, and disposable-linen categories. A sanitary-napkin cover is being made from this type of scrim onto which cotton fiber has been blown to give it softness and absorbency.

SPUNBOND® PROCESS

This new nonwoven material, invented and produced by Du Pont, consists of various hot-melt resins that can be extruded into a sheet of synthetic fibers of excellent strength characteristics. The material is being experimentally used as an interfacing and as a base for various coated fabrics.

CLOTHING AND HOUSEHOLD FURNISHINGS FROM NONWOVENS

A great deal of discussion has been heard in the last few years about clothing and household furnishings made from nonwoven materials. There have been, and still are, on the market several items such as feltlike skirting materials made from needle-punched, resin-saturated, or felted nonwovens. Experimental garments have been made from wet-process synthetic-fibered nonwovens.

In the curtain market limited-use products printed in attractive patterns are being sold today. These items have a certain amount of washability and are satisfactory for cottages, camps, and kitchens.

However, to date, nonwovens have made little impact on the apparel and home-furnishings markets. It is the dream of every nonwoven manufacturer to produce a material that will have the required drape and hand and one that can be styled in the manner required to become an acceptable product for these end uses. This day will come, but it is still in the future and a great deal of work has to be done to produce such an item.

Disposable clothing has also been a favorite subject in the discussion of nonwoven materials. Some of the low-cost scrim-reinforced products in today's market have the required sewability, opacity, and design possibilities. They are being used for disposable clothing in selected areas such as lab coats, coveralls for industrial plants, graduation gowns, pillowcases, sheets, and hospital items.

They do not compete in price with the cost of laundering or with a laundry service mainly because of the expense of fabricating the garment. The cost of the material contained in each item of clothing is small, but by the time it is cut, sewn, and distributed it is no longer in the laundering-cost category. Because of the importance of this fabrication cost, a great deal of work is being done on high-speed cutting and fabrication by such means as gluing, heat-sealing, and molding.

MARKETING

The markets to which all of these nonwovens are sold dictate the type of distribution necessary. For end uses in which there are large industrial customers most manufacturers sell on a direct basis with their own sales forces. In other areas, however, in which the market consists of a large number of smaller users, distributors are employed. These distributors buy the products in quantity and sell it in smaller yardages to the end customer. At the present time most of the markets for nonwovens are in the textile area and the distribution pattern followed is primarily that of the textile industry.

Because of the unique nature of nonwoven materials, special sales-men are required. These sales people must have a broad knowledge of the technical aspects of the manufacturing process and are actually sales engineers. They must maintain a close relationship with their own and their customers' manufacturing, research, and development personnel.

Because of the wide range of fibers, binders, and processes available and the possibilities of combining these nonwoven materials with other fibrous and nonfibrous materials, the range of end products is a broad one. With the proper basic research, technical, and market development, the growth potential of this nonwoven market is an excellent one.

The companies that realize the benefits of this potential will be those that are prepared to engineer their products to fit specific end-use requirements. Trial-and-error experimentation both in the technical and marketing areas of nonwovens will not be enough in the coming years. The future will belong to the companies that are organized and able to do a systematic job of product and market research. For these companies the future in nonwovens looks very bright.

12

REVIEW OF EUROPEAN DEVELOPMENTS

D. McLEAN WYLLIE

Chief Chemist, T. B. Ford Ltd.
High Wycombe, England

It would appear inevitable that European work on synthetic fibers in paper making must largely follow American practice and await developments from that continent. The per capita consumption of paper in the United States is twice that of the average European country, and it is not to be expected that any specific demand for a paper having the particular properties conferred by the use of synthetic fibers would exist on the one side of the Atlantic and not on the other. Thus it is admitted at the outset that the most important development of all, that of commercial exploitation, is closely bound to, and indeed dependent on, the United States.

Nevertheless, there are some exclusive European papers, and one at least new and novel process apart from special modifications of those outlined in the preceding chapters, which have been patented in various countries. The knowledge that the large potential market has not yet been exploited leads to secrecy, and although many of the big paper groups are known to have put in a considerable amount of research and development effort they are not willing to publish their work until the products are fully established. In some cases the availability of established American products is suspect, perhaps because of a heavy home demand or the uncertainty of European interest or because a new raw-material plant is to be set up locally. Examples are the American Cyanamid Company's acrylic-fiber sheet, which was offered as such, the production of acrylic fiber by the Chemstrand Corporation and the commissioning of new plant in Northern Ireland, the development of a hollow staple viscose filament imported from the United States, but which could be produced in the

United Kingdom, and the nonappearance of fibrids and textryls to date on the European market.

There has been some confusion in terminology regarding the term nonwoven. For example, some of the early publications (1, 2, 3, 4) called unwoven products papers, which were formed by laying down webs in a dry textile process. The conventional term paper up until this time had always been applied to products made by the process of laying down a web from a water suspension of fibers on a paper-making machine. As shown in later publications (5, 6), the term nonwoven is being used more or less interchangeably for similar types of products made by either the wet process (paper machine) or the dry process (textile machine).

The general emphasis has been on fiber length; when conventional paper machines have to work with fibers of less than 10 mm., airlaid nonwovens can go up to 25 mm. and higher (7). Attempts at classification have been made (8, 9) to distinguish nonwovens from textiles, but differentiation from paper is not so clear. Some hybrid products, starting with a nonwoven base and being finished by paper-coating techniques, have been described. Claims for such products obviously include resistance to chemical attack by acids, alkalis, and solvents, with consequent resistance to soiling, mechanical strength, especially good fold properties and wear resistance, and, naturally, excellent printing characteristics.

German publications refer to Topnyl (10), Viledon (11), and a polyester-fiber paper from the Faserprodukte G.m.b.H., Frankfurt (12). These also claim dimensional stability. This property is a particular feature of synthetic-fiber papers and has received special attention in presenting most new products. A novel demonstration of printing properties on a coated synthetic paper was given by the Feldmühler Papier-und-Zellstoffwerke A.G. in reproducing a section of the Gutenberg bible (13).

Papertex from Snia Viscoa in Italy is a polyamide-based material having similar strength and resistance properties to those mentioned above but with the additional feature of being workable when hot (for embossing, etc.). It is made in weights of 60 to 220 g.s.m.: strength figures quoted are for 95 g.s.m. (Table 12.1). The dimensional stability is similar to that of normal paper (14, 15, 16).

The problems of cutting fibers to specific lengths for paper making, the nonfibrillation, poor fiber cohesion, and consequent difficulty of picking up the wet web have been dealt with elsewhere, together with the need for suitable bonding agents according to the particular fiber used. It is sufficient to mention that in the last decade there

TABLE 12.1

	Dry	Wet
Tensile	16.405 kg.	12.100 kg.
Tear	792 gm.	1600 gm.
Burst	11.1 kg./cm.^{2}	
Tensile after 20,000 double folds	12,800 kg.	

have been innumerable patents covering every aspect of solvent and salt bonding, resin and latex bonding, and bonding by fusion with thermoplastic fibers. Without, therefore, giving an exhaustive list of such modifications to known methods, one or two might be mentioned because of their simplicity.

A Dutch patent by Algemene Kunstzidje Unie N.V. describes the cutting of synthetic fibers carded and formed into a rope by extrusion through a funnel, where they are wrapped in strong kraft paper tape. This continuous cylinder is then fed to a rotary knife, by which it is sliced into discs, the thickness of which corresponds to the required fiber length. The cut fibers are collected in a water slurry, the kraft paper dispersing, and the stock is made up on the normal Fourdrinier machine (17).

Nonfibrillation and poor fiber cohesion are often overcome by having some cellulose fibers in the furnish, but dispersion of the synthetic fibers still presents a problem. This has been tackled according to a process of coating these fibers with gelatine, patented by Société Rhodiaceta. This can take place before or after cutting to the required length, and warming the fiber suspension can be an advantage. A minimum of 40% gelatine is retained. The cellulose fibers are beaten separately (18, 19).

As an example of a simple binder, chemically related to the synthetic fiber, Portals Ltd. (20) have a patent that may be quoted in which the methyl methoxy derivative of nylon is used with cellulose and nylon fiber. Longer fiber lengths may be more easily dispersed in an alcoholic solution of the binder, and subsequent insolubilization to organic solvents can be ensured by heating the paper to 160°C.

Undoubtedly, one of the most successful European papers comes from the Sihl Paper Mill, Zurich, Switzerland, under the name Syntosil (21, 22, 23). A wide range of weights from 80 to 200 g.s.m. in various colors and shades has been produced on a standard Fourdrinier machine. Fiber lengths are approximately those of normal sulfite pulp, and obviously the type of binder used is the reason for the extremely impressive list of properties that this paper possesses. The ratio of wet-to-dry strengths is extremely good and in some case above unity, for example, tear and dynamic tensile. Typical values are given in Table 12.2 (22).

TABLE 12.2

	Dry	Wet	Stretch
Breaking length	4462 mm.	2590 mm.	8.7%
Burst	2.76 kgm./cm.	2.25 kgm./cm.	
Tear	218.4 gm.	415.1 gm.	
Dynamic tensile	4.53 cm./kgm.	6.33 cm./kgm.	
Fold	64,405		

Dimensional stability is another much sought-after feature of paper. It has been suggested (24) that cellulosic paper can be treated with a dilute (1¼%) solution of zinc chloride. The paper is dried at an elevated temperature, that is, 1 minute at 190°C., with a 40% improvement. A further improvement to 60% is obtained by treating this paper with formaldehyde vapor. By far the best method is to add the synthetic fibers to the furnish, and polyesters have been shown to be most effective. Reference has also been made to the use of glass fibers in this connection (25); 5-μ fibers give good results.

An excellent review (26) of the use of glass fibers in paper making discusses this point and also deals with the general development of paper with a 100% glass furnish. Speciality papers, of high tear, tensile, and impact strength, low density, and high wet strength used for filtration and electrical components (capacitors, etc.) and for resin impregnation by virtue of a high resin absorbency, are mentioned.

The most important European contributions by R. Peteri of the Compagnie Saint Gobain is, however, not noted. R. Peteri deals (27) with papers having a high percentage of glass as well as those having a small percentage. He is concerned with fibers of 10 μ and larger in thickness, and therefore papers with 100% glass are not possible. Only very fine fibers, down to 50 mμ, have sufficient pliability and self-adhesion to make the manufacture of such papers possible, and, since these fibers are currently available, most recent work has been concerned with them. If binders are used to improve the strength, then some of the advantages of a 100% glass furnish, especially those with high temperature applications, are lost. Accepting this, it is shown that the addition, say, of 15% well-beaten kraft to 85% glass fibers 10 μ in diameter makes sheet formation and sub-sequent processing possible. If normal wet strengthening advantages of melamine are used, a still further increase in strength appears. An example is quoted of a furnish with the kraft beaten to 70°S.R. absorbing 600% of its own weight of a 40% melamine-solution. The cellulose fraction has also been replaced by asbestos fibers with some advantage but with loss of natural elasticity and stretch. The use of glass fibers is recommended with hardwood pulp and mechanical pulps or mixtures giving papers with an average or weak tear strength. With better furnishes the increase in strength properties does not justify the cost. Again, although fine glass fibers give even better results, the extra cost over 10 μ qualities is not justifiable. Normal Hollander beaters were found to be ideal for breaking up wads of glass waste, either from the extrusion or spinning stages.

Claims for a new process are described by S. A. Pusyrew of the Central Research Institute for Pulp and Paper, Leningrad, in many publications (e.g., 28, 29, 30). Based on work started as far back as 1931, modern synthetic fibers are airlaid onto a moving wire. The pretreatment depends on the fiber. For example, the use of cotton linters follows normal practice of boiling, washing and bleaching, centrifuging, and bulk drying. Synthetics are chopped to lengths which can measure as many as 45 mm. Fibers are fed to a double combing unit, the first section of which consists of the normal drum comb rotating at 1000 r.p.m. The fibers are removed by a brush and passed to a perforated condensing cylinder from which the batt is fed to a second comb. From this unit the fiber is passed vertically down a duct onto a moving wire, under which a vacuum box is placed. Several units of this type can be used to build up a thicker paper or boards. The web is passed through sizing baths, pressed, dried, and calendered in the normal way. In the references given interesting figures for strength properties of a variety of papers are quoted in terms of normal paper tests.

The appearance of synthetic fibers in papers has led to an interest in their properties and in means of identifying them, so that general articles have appeared on these subjects in the trade press (31, 32). For example, tables of solubilities give a good indication of the fibers concerned, but it is reported that although normal formic acid—zinc chloride solution—can be used with some papers formic acid—calcium chloride reagent—is preferred if chemical wood is present. One would expect the textile trade publications to be more comprehensive, and paper technologists have referred to articles in which textile fibers are identified (33, 34). In this connection, the Publication of the Textile Institute, Manchester, is particularly helpful (3).

Finally, mention can be made of a pioneer effort, albeit by a complete amateur working single-handed in a small college in the United Kingdom. Articles and even a book (36) describe this venture in refreshingly enthusiastic terms. John Mason's work captures the imagination, and the lay press may be forgiven for believing that nylon and terylene papers were with us some six years ago. In his own words,

. . . In went the mixture, the tap was turned and I had a lovely even glistening wet sheet of nylon waterleaf. When dry, the sheet looked like a layer of matted wool. A final process of pressing under heat and I had made my first sheet of nylon paper.

Tests proved the sheet had enormous strength and resistance to mould and strong chemicals. Here was the ideal imperishable material for documents and records and for paper currency, for packaging corrosive substances and who knows what else.

Who, indeed. Alas, Mr. Mason's mill is significantly called the "Twelve by Eight" Mill at Leicester, England. The units are inches.

REFERENCES*

1. F. Ohl, *Neue Verpackung,* **10** (9), 582, (1957).
2. K. Klein, *Fachorgan Texilveredlung,* **13** (2), 61 (1958).
3. R. A. Higham, *Proc. Tech. Sect. B.P.B.M.A.,* **39** (2), 323 (1958).
4. *Algem Pap.-Rundschau,* **705** (June 20, 1960).
5. R. S. Lenk, *Chem. Ind.* **165** (October 14, 1961).
6. P. W. Sherwood, *Papeterie,* **83** (11), 866 (1961); **83** (12), 964 (1961).
7. *Chem. Eng. News,* 118 (August 10, 1959).
8. H. Jorder, *Z. Ges. Textil-Ind.,* **63** (11), 914, (1961).
9. J. Woydich, *Textil-Praxis,* **17** (6), 571 (1962).
10. C. Scheitlin, Textil-Rundschau, **15** (12), 704 (1958).
11. C. Freudenberg, *Wochbl. Papierfabrick.,* **89** (3), 119 (1961).
12. *Algem. Pap.-Rundschau,* **946** (September 20, 1961); also C. Fruedenberg, *World's Pap. Tr. Rev.,* **156** (6), 542 (1961).
13. *World's Pap. Tr. Rev.,* **155** (7), 601 (1960); also *Papier,* **14** (2), 73 (1960).
14. *Indian Pulp & Paper,* **13** (10), 463 (1959).
15. *World's Pap. Tr. Rev.,* **156** (2), 146 (1961).
16. *Litho-Printer,* **3** (3), 142 (1960).
17. *Algem, Kuntzidje Unie N.V.,* B.P. 834,192.
18. Société Rhodiaceta, French Patent 1,153,589.
19. J. C. Chezaud, and H. M-C. Lachauesée, *Papier,* 13 9, (1959).
20. H. M. G. Williams, British Patents 820,785 and 820,786.
21. B. S. Marek, *Textile-Rundschau,* **13** (12), 721 (1958).

* ( ) refers to part number of volume.

22. *Algem. Pap.-Rundschau* (2), 62 (1961).
23. B. S. Marek, *Pulp Paper Mag. Can.,* **63** (C), t-111 (1962).
24. *World's Pap. Tr. Rev.,* **153** (17), 1492 (1960).
25. L. W. Warner, *Southern Pulp Paper Mfr.,* **62** (April 1959).
26. J. H. Martin, *Paper Technol.,* **1** (2), 153 (1960).
27. R. Peteri, *TAPPI,* **41** (5), 228A (1958).
28. S. A. Pusyrew, *Zellstoff Papier* (7), 201 (1957).
29. S. A. Pusyrew, *Pulp Paper Internal.,* **2** (6), 19 (1960).
30. S. A. Pusyrew and M. Dimitriev, *Pulp Paper Mag. Can.,* **61** (1), T3 (1960).
31. *World's Pap. Tr. Rev.,* **148** (21), 1729 (1957).
32. M. Faulhaber and A. Rosenberger, *Wochbl. Papierfabrik.,* **86** (13), 589 (1958).
33. F. Feigl, *Textile Res. J.,* **28** (10), 892 (1958).
34. P. A. Koch, *Textil-Rundschau.,* **14** (8), 438 (1959).
35. *Identification of Textile Materials,* Ed., C. E. M. Jones, 4th edition, 1958, rep. 1961, *Publ. Textile Inst.,* Manchester 3.
36. J. Mason, *Papermaking as an Artistic Craft with a Note on Nylon Paper,* Faber & Faber, London, 1959.

13

THE FUTURE OF SYNTHETIC
FIBERS IN PAPERMAKING

O. A. BATTISTA

Manager of Interdisciplinary Research
Central Research Department
FMC Corporation
Princeton, New Jersey

This book is a vote of confidence in the future of synthetic fibers in papermaking, representing as it does the first known book to be published on the subject. Our comments in this chapter about the prognosis for synthetic fibers in papermaking have been distilled from the contributions of our distinguished roster of chapter authors who have made the book possible, and we unhesitatingly extend this acknowledgment to them.

The versatility of the organic chemist in producing synthetic polymers in fiber form for a host of service requirements has already been capitalized on by the textile industry with great commercial success. Despite the relatively high cost of textile-grade synthetic fibers, they have managed to contribute, particularly in blends with natural fibers, outstanding physical properties which in terms of the service performed have overcome the seemingly insurmountable obstacle of cost. The mushrooming multibillion-dollar synthetic-fiber industry stands as proof that tailor making fibers to meet certain rigorous performance functions can offset an otherwise seemingly hopeless basic pricing picture.

Yet one needs only to review the dates of the literature cited in the chapters of this book to realize that it has been *only* in very recent times, essentially during the last decade or two, that the quantity of paper made from fibers other than those of natural cellulose has risen to significant levels when compared with the output of the industry as a whole. The paper industry, unlike the textile industry, has not yet reaped the benefits that are existent in the availability of the numerous species of commercial man-made fibers with their wealth of outstanding physical properties. The time now seems ripe for this harvest to be cultivated with vigor.

Throughout the centuries and almost to our present day man has been and continues to attempt to extract from natural fibers, wood-pulp fibers in particular, every conceivable possible advantage for papermaking. Cellulosic or vegetable fibers have always demonstrated unusual versatility for papermaking purposes. They have good swelling properties in water and they fibrillate easily on mechanical treatment and are readily transformed into excellent paper products because of their web-forming ability and the hydrogen bonding on drying they exhibit. The properties of cellulose-based papers, however, have certain limitations because they are dependent entirely on the chemical and physical properties of the component carbohydrate fibers. It would not seem unreasonable to say that a plateau has been reached in regard to what can be done with natural papermaking fibers to produce from them sheets of paper with substantial improvements in specific physical properties.

An apparent leveling off does seem to have been reached with natural fibers. There is, therefore, mounting justification for papermakers to be more receptive to the utilization of premium synthetic fibers, particularly in blends with natural fibers, to achieve further advantages in new paper products that have not been possible to make heretofore. One might offer the prediction that synthetic fibers are about to make aggressive inroads into the fields of papermaking, inroads that will parallel the extensive advancements that these same fibers have already made in the textile fields. In other words, the competition between products made by papermaking processes and conventional textile processes will surely become more intense during the years that lie immediately ahead.

For the first time in history the papermaker has at his disposal a vast array of new commercially available raw materials which he can transform at will into paper and paper products, new waterlaid synthetic-fiber webs that can be handled on existing capital equipment to give rise to a product with a performance behavior that will fit almost any predesired set of physical properties to serve particular end uses. Papers made from synthetic fibers, either 100% or in blends, are being made which possess the following properties:

1. High tensile strength, both wet and dry, and other physical properties.

2. Chemical resistance.

3. Dimensional stability in atmospheres of widely varying relative humidity.

4. Resistance to common mildew, moths, carpet beetles, and other biological agents.

5. Improved durability under outdoor exposure in adverse weather conditions, prolonged exposure to sunlight, etc.

6. Improved aging resistance at elevated temperatures.

7. Good printability.

8. Reduced flammability.

9. Greater variability in elasticity and toughness.

10. Fibers, such as those made from glass, silica, and ceramics, which can endure heat from 1000 to 2000°F. for long periods of time.

11. Papers possessing high electrical conductivity by the very nature of their chemical makeup or by blending with metal fibers.

12. Papers ideally suited to meet the unusual needs of our space age.

Although in the beginning synthetic fibers presented what appeared to be serious problems before they could be handled on conventional papermaking machinery, the development of numerous dispersing agents and techniques has reduced the severity of these problems substantially. As would be expected, the regenerated cellulose fibers are the easiest synthetic fibers to disperse. On the other hand, the more hydrophobic polyester, polyamide, polyethylene, and polyacrylonitrile fibers are not readily dispersible in water. They tend to flocculate and normally require the assistance of auxiliary dispersing agents. Furthermore, such fibers must as a rule be handled at very low pulp dilutions (e.g., of the order of 0.02 to 0.1%). Numerous dispersing agents or wetting agents are recommended in amounts of 0.1 to 5%, based on the weight of the fibers, and the patent literature in this area is already extensive. The success in overcoming the technical problems of dispersing the synthetic fibers has helped to increase their current commercialization. Furthermore, the cost differential which has been and will continue to be an obstacle in the utilization of synthetic fibers in papermaking is receiving a limited and perhaps only temporary respite from the increasing quantity of waste synthetic fibers that is becoming available from textile mills, waste synthetic fibers that can be rechanneled at a substantially lower cost per pound into papermaking outlets.

Most synthetic fibers can be used in papermaking either by themselves or in blends with natural fibers without a preliminary beating operation. The fiber is delivered to the papermaker already cut to the specified length (preferably $\frac{1}{4}$ to $\frac{1}{2}$ in.) and prepared to a prespecified diameter. In the preparation of furnishes for papermaking on conventional Fourdrinier machines, blends of synthetic fibers with regular papermaker stocks containing as much as 60% or more of the synthetic fiber are processable. For synthetic cellulosic fibers, such as the rayons, the practical limitations with respect to blending proportions are still broader. Some papers containing 50% Dacron and 50% natural cellulosic fiber have been made and subsequently coated with a plastic binder to give a product with a tear strength at least equal to that of a coated cotton sheeting.

The rayon papermaking fibers which are beginning to be utilized with greater frequency represent potentially, at least, the lowest cost man-made fibers available to the industry. Being cellulosic, they are particularly compatible with the natural fibers and present no unusual problems in handling on the various types of papermaking machinery. Their advantages stem from the fact that their denier, or diameter, and length, as well as their tensile strengths and extensibilities, can be altered to contribute significant improvements to such properties as tensile strength, tear, and burst. It is conceivable that the cost advantage of these cellulosic man-made fibers may permit them to reach larger markets more rapidly than more expensive synthetic fibers, which undoubtedly will receive wide and immediate acceptance for more highly specialized paper products in which their outstanding physical and chemical properties automatically give them significant advantages.

The properties of papers that can now be achieved with synthetic fibers, either by themselves or in combination with wood pulp, will undoubtedly permit the manufacture of new paper products that will be utilized for purposes considered to be completely unconventional on the basis of the normal uses for which we deem cellulosic paper satisfactory. A representative list of products made from synthetic-fiber papers includes the following: striped linens, lining materials, filter materials, webs for artificial leather, drape materials, backings for plastics, porous cloths, clinical linens, vacuum-cleaner bags, working clothes, tablecloths, handkerchiefs, napkins and other sanitary goods, military maps, documents, filing cards, improved overlay papers possessing better transparency and moisture resistance, improved printing papers, and wrapping papers for the electrical industry.

An assured future looms for synthetic organic and inorganic fibers. Synthetic fibers will grow in papermaking because they offer a new base on which a pyramid of superior paper and nonwoven products can be built on available papermaking equipment. Their rate of growth will be in direct proportion to their performance/price ratio; for many severe service applications they already have proved their mettle. Extrapolation of the market potential for nonwoven products in the presently established product applications for the United

States alone in the year 1965 leads to an expected consumption in excess of 200 million pounds. Current production of nonwoven fabrics in continental Europe is about one tenth of the United States production. However, it is widely agreed that if the synthetic fibers succeed in achieving price reductions, as well as overcoming some of the technical production problems of making synthetic-fiber papers by the wet papermaking process, these products could make deep inroads into the clothing and related regions of the textile industry and could readily reach an annual consumption of the order of 3 billion pounds.

Tomorrow, as well as today, when the papermaker will require specific properties that are beyond the reach of the inexpensive natural cellulosic fibers, he will most assuredly have to look to the newer synthetic fibers as the sources of raw materials that will provide the necessary stamina to solve his problems. It is the hope of all of us who have contributed to this book that in its pages the researchers as well as the planners who will move forward with this exciting industry will find the technical wherewithal to give them much solace, renewed encouragement, and many new ideas.

APPENDIX

GLOSSARY OF PAPERMAKING
AND RELATED TERMS

alum. The term commonly used in the paper industry for aluminum sulfate, $Al_2(SO_4)_3 \cdot 18H_2O$. Frequently called papermakers' alum.

basic size. The sheet size recognized by buyers and sellers as the one on which the basis weight is figured. Typical basic sizes are the following:

Type Paper	Sheet Size	Sheets/Ream
Writing, printing, bond, ledger	17×22	500
News, wrapping, tissue, waxing	24×36	500[1]
Bristol, tag	$24\frac{1}{2} \times 28\frac{1}{2}$	500
Book	25×38	500
TAPPI Standard	25×40	500

[1] The weight of white tissue is sometimes based on 480 sheets (20×30).

basis weight. The weight in pounds of a ream (either 480 or 500 sheets).

bast fibers. Flax, hemp, jute, and ramie are typical bast fibers.

beater. A machine consisting of a low open elongated tank or tub with a central partition or "midfeather" that creates a channel in its periphery to accommodate a heavy roll, usually fitted with metal bars and revolving against a bedplate. The papermaking stock in the form of a water slurry circulates around the channel and passes between the roll and bedplate. This action separates the material and frees the fibers for further processing.

323

beater additive. Broadly speaking, any nonfibrous material added to the papermaking stock in the beater. More specifically, a starch, gum, resin, or other chemical added to the stock in the beater for the purpose of supplementing the beater operation and enhancing the properties of the paper sheet. Beater additives are often called wet-end additives when mixed with the papermaking stock at some point other than the beater before sheet formation.

beating. The general term for the mechanical treatment given to papermaking materials suspended in water to mix and prepare them for forming on the paper machine into a paper or board of the desired character.

board. One of the two broad subdivisions of paper (general term), the other being paper (specific term). The distinction between board and paper is not sharp, but, generally speaking, board is heavier in basis weight, thicker, and more rigid than paper. All types of fibrous material 12 points (0.012 in.) or more in thickness are boards. Nearly all types less than 6 points in thickness are paper. Most types ranging from 6 to 12 points are paper.

bond paper. A grade of writing or printing paper originally used when strength, durability, and permanence are essential requirements. Must also have good printing, writing, and erasing qualities, cleanliness, formation, finish, color, and freedom from fuzz.

book paper. A general term used to define a class or group of papers having in common physical characteristics that in general are most suitable for the graphic arts, exclusive of news print.

box liners. Papers used for the inner surfaces of boxes containing food or meat or crates containing vegetables to keep products fresh by the retention of moisture and to protect from contamination.

breaking length. The length of a strip of paper, cut either in the machine or cross direction, which would break of its own weight when suspended vertically. It is a value calculated from the tensile strength and the basis weight of the sheet and is usually expressed in meters.

breast roll. The first large roll over which the Fourdrinier wire passes before the stock is run onto the paper machine. It is made of noncorrosive metal and is driven by the wire.

brightness. As commonly used in the paper industry, the reflectivity of a sheet of pulp or paper for blue light measured under standardized conditions on a particular instrument designed and calibrated specifically for the purpose. Strictly speaking, brightness is not a colorimetric quantity.

broke. Paper that has been discarded anywhere in the process of manufacture. Wet broke is paper taken off the wet press of a paper machine; dry broke is made when paper is spoiled in going over the driers or through the calenders, trimmed off in the rewinding of rolls, or trimmed from sheets being prepared for shipping. It is usually returned to the beater for reprocessing.

burst factor. A numerical value obtained by dividing the bursting strength in grams per square centimeter by the weight of the sheet in grams per square meter.

bursting strength. The pressure required to rupture a specimen when it is tested in a specified instrument under specified conditions. The Mullen tester is generally used.

calender. A set or "stack" of horizontal cast-iron rolls with chilled, hardened surfaces, resting one on the other in a vertical bank at the end of the paper machine. The paper is passed between all or part of these rolls to increase the smoothness and gloss of its surface.

caliper. The thickness of a sheet measured under specified conditions. It is usually expressed in thousandths of an inch (mils or points).

caustic soda. Sodium hydroxide (NaOH).

close formation. A well-closed sheet is one in which the formation is uniform or compact, free from a "wild" or porous appearance when viewed by transmitted light.

clothing. A term applied to paper-machine felts and Fourdrinier wires.

coated. A term applied to paper and paperboard, the surface of which has been treated with clay or some other pigment and adhesive mixture, or other suitable material, to improve the finish with respect to printing quality, color, smoothness, opacity, or other surface properties. The term is also applied to lacquered and varnished papers.

cockle. A spot in the paper sheet which has been warped or bulged from the general plane of the sheet by excessive shrinkage during drying.

cockle finish. A ripplelike finish caused by shrinkage during drying under little or no tension. It may be caused deliberately or inadvertently and is frequently desired, in varying degrees, in some grades of writing papers.

conditioning. Essentially the same as seasoning, except that in general usage it refers to the exposure of paper to accurately controlled and specified atmospheric conditions, so that its moisture content may reach a reproducible equilibrium. The properties of paper are measurably affected by its moisture content.

consistency. The percentage, by weight, of airdry (or ovendry) fibrous material in a stock suspension. It is also called density or concentration.

conversion. (1) A general term for processes or operations applied to paper or board after the normal papermaking operations, such as waxing, gumming, coating, printing, bag manufacture, and box and container manufacture. (2) The term is also applied to the transformation of halfstuff into paper.

cook. The operation of treating any raw material (rags, pulpwood, straw, etc.) with chemicals, usually at a high pressure and temperature, for the purpose of removing ligneous impurities and producing a pulp suitable for papermaking.

cord. A term used in the mensuration of pulpwood; the usual definition is a pile 8 ft. long, 4 ft. wide, and 4 ft. high, containing 128 ft.³

cotton linters. The short fibers adhering to cottonseed after the grinding operation. They are later removed and after processing are used to a limited extent as a fibrous raw material for some papers. The principal use, however, is as a raw material for the manufacture of cellulose derivatives.

couch roll. Usually a light metal roll around which the wet web-forming wire passes and above which there is frequently an upper felt or rubber-covered couch roll to apply pressure to the web and to assist in its transfer from the wire to the pickup felt.

creep. The dimensional change with time of a material under constant load, following the initial instantaneous elastic or rapid deformation. Creep at room temperature is sometimes called "cold flow."

curl. Curvature of the sheet. It may appear as a gross curl around some direction in the sheet (e.g., the machine direction) or as an uneven warping of the edges of the sheet. Curl is produced by one or more of the following factors: the moisture content of the atmosphere or of the sheet, the distribution of the moisture throughout the sheet, orientation of fibers throughout the sheet, or the internal stresses within the sheet.

cylinder machine.   A type of wet web-forming machine using one or more wire cylinders that rotate in vats containing the dilute stock suspension and on which the web is formed.   The webs are successively couched from the cylinder, one upon the other, to give the desired paper weight.

dandy.   A skeleton roll covered with wire cloth and supported above the Fourdrinier wire.   It rides on the wet web of paper of a Fourdrinier machine at a point near the first suction box for the purpose of marking the sheet with a design carried on the surface of the roll. The arrangement of the wires of the dandy determines the wove or laid effect of the sheet.   When letters, figures, or other devices are worked on the surface of the roll, a watermark is produced.   A roll carrying such figures or devices is known as a watermarking dandy.

deckle.   The arrangement in the side of the web-forming wire of the paper machine which keeps the dilute stock suspension from flowing over the edges of the wire.   It is usually a thick endless rubber belt which is carried along at the speed of the Fourdrinier wire belt.

denier.   The weight in grams of a 9000-m. length of fiber or strand of fibers.   Denier increases with the square of the fiber diameter.   Approximate diameters of rayon fiber are the following:

Denier	1.0	1.5	3.0	5.5
Diameter (microns)	10	12	17	23
Diameter (mils)	0.40	0.45	0.65	0.90

digester.   The pressure vessel in which rags, pulpwood, straw, or other papermaking material is heated with chemicals for the production of wood pulp.

doctor.   A thin plate or scraper of wood, metal, or other hard substance placed along the entire length of the roll or cylinder to keep it free from paper, pulp, size, etc., and thus maintain a smooth clean surface.

dry end.   The mill term for the drying section of the paper machine, which consists mainly of the driers, calenders, reels, and slitters.

emulsion. A suspension of droplets of a liquid dispersed in another liquid with which it is not miscible and stabilized by the addition of a compound known as the emulsifying agent.

felt. A woven textile belt for picking up, carrying, pressing, or drying the wet web following its formation on the wire of the papermaking machine. Felts are known by different names, depending on the specific function served.

felt side. That side of the paper web which has not been in contact with the wire during manufacture. It is the top side of the sheet.

fill. The maximum width of paper that can be made on a given paper machine.

filler. (1) A loading material, such as clay. (2) In paperboard, the inner ply or plies of a multiple-layer composition.

fines. Very short pulp fibers or fiber fragments. They are sometimes referred to as "flour" or "wood flour."

formation. A property that is determined by the degree of uniformity of distribution of the solid components of the sheet with special reference to the fibers. It is usually judged by the visual appearance of the sheet when viewed by transmitted light. This property is important not only because of its influence on the appearance of the sheet but because it influences the values and uniformity of values of nearly all other properties.

Fourdrinier. The most widely used type of papermaking machine. It consists of five main sections: the wet end containing the head box from which the stock flows onto the wire as a dilute suspension; an endless wire belt, on which the thin wet sheet is formed; the press section which picks up and presses excess water from the newly formed sheet and conveys it to the drier section; the drier section, consisting of one or more tiers of heated cylinders or revolving cans; and the calender section which is equipped with a roll device for pressing and rolling up the paper.

freeness. A measure of the rate with which water drains from a stock suspension through a wire mesh screen or a perforated plate. It is also known as slowness or wetness, according to the type of instrument used in its measurement and the method of reporting results.

free stock. A pulp suspension from which the water drains freely.

friction calender. Usually consists of three rolls: the bottom of chilled iron, the intermediate roll of cotton, and the top roll of chilled iron, bored so as to admit steam.   It has a burnishing action on the paper.

furnish.   The mixture of various materials that are blended in the stock suspension from which paper or board is made.   The chief constituents are the fibrous material (pulp), sizing materials, fillers, and dyes.

glassine paper.   A grease-resistant, smooth, semitransparent, dense paper made by supercalendering a medium-weight paper of highly beaten hydrated wood pulp.   When waxed it may be impervious to moisture vapor.   It is largely used as a protective wrapper for food-stuffs and chemicals.

halfstuff.   Pulp in condition to be charged into the beater.   After beating, it is called wholestuff or simply stuff.   The expression is normally used only in connection with rag-paper manufacture.

hard beating.   A term applied to pulp which must be given a long treatment in a beater or refiner to develop the required slowness or strength.

hardwood.   A term applied to trees with broad leaves, such as aspen, basswood, birch, gum, maple, oak, or tulip poplar.   The botanical term "angiosperm" (meaning seeds enclosed in an ovary) is a more consistent designation.   Hardwoods are designated as porous woods.

headbox.   A large box which receives the diluted furnish from the stock chest and keeps it sufficiently agitated to prevent flocculation of the fibers.   At the same time it steadies the flow to secure a uniform delivery of the furnish to the paper machine.   The height of the liquid in the headbox provides the hydrostatic head necessary to give the stock the requisite speed of flow onto the Fourdrinier wire.   A headbox is also a part of the equipment of a cylinder machine, in which it serves the same purpose.

Hollander.   The original name given to the beater.

hydration.   (1) In the physical sense, the condition of materials containing water of adsorption or imbibition.   (2) In papermaking, the chemical, mechanical, or the combined chemical and mechanical treatment of fibers, other than cooking and bleaching, before sheet formation; it relates especially to altered sheet characteristics, includ-ing density, strength, opacity, and formation.   (3) The characteris-tics resulting from the foregoing treatment.

Jordan. A machine for refining the papermaking pulp by cutting down the fibers to a more uniform short length than obtained from the beater. It consists of an adjustable conical rotating plug fitted into a stationary metal casing. The outer surface of the plug and inner surface of the casing are equipped with bar knives which grind or cut the fiber stock.

machine direction. The direction of paper parallel to its forward movement on the paper machine. This is also called "with the grain." The direction at right angles to it is called the cross direction.

Mullen. An expression used for bursting strength, so called from the name of the instrument used in the test.

point. (1) One thousandth of an inch. It is used in expressing the thickness of paper or board. (2) A term used for expressing certain values of paper properties (e.g., points per pound, pounds per point). (3) The printer also uses the point as a unit of measurement; it is, practically, one seventy-second of an inch (actually it is 0.013837 of an inch).

press. A pair of rolls between which the web of paper is carried on the felt for the removal of water by the application of pressure before the web enters the dry end of the paper machine.

ream. A number of sheets of paper, either 480 or 500 according to grade. For purposes of physical testing a ream is considered as 500 sheets, except for wrapping tissues, for which the ream is 480 sheets.

refining. A general term applied to several operations, all of which involve the mechanical treatment of pulp fibers in a water suspension to develop the papermaking properties of the fibers.

scuffing. The raising of the fibers on the surface of a paper or paperboard when one piece is rubbed against another or comes in contact with a rough surface. Paper and paperboard are more susceptible to scuffing when wet.

size. Any material used in sizing (q.v.). The common sizing agents are rosin, glue and gelatin, starch, latex, etc.

size press. The equipment used in the tub sizing of paper. It consists principally of a suitable container for the sizing material through which the sheet of paper is led and a pair of superimposed press rolls, one of which is usually rubber covered, to remove the excess sizing material from the surface of the previously immersed sheet. The container is filled with size solution that has been diluted to the proper density and heated to the correct temperature. The level is maintained by constant addition of size through a pipe.

sizing. Material added to the paper furnish or formed sheet to increase its stiffness, body, and resistance to liquids.

slice. That part of a Fourdrinier machine which regulates the flow of stock from the headbox onto the Fourdrinier wire in a sheet of water of even thickness or volume. The slice extends across the wire and forms that side of the headbox adjacent to the wire. It is usually adjustable in width within limits to the width of the sheet being made. Variations in the thickness of the sheet of liquid passing the slice are obtained by adjustment of the entire slice or of its bottom edge (the lip), which may be straight or curved.

slowness. The opposite of freeness.

soda. The word is used as a designation for soda pulp.

soda ash. A commercial anhydrous sodium carbonate.

softwood. The botanical term "gymnosperm" (meaning seeds not enclosed in an ovary) is a more consistent designation for the class of trees. Softwoods are designated as nonporous woods.

stock. (1) Pulp which has been beaten and refined, treated with sizing, color, filler, etc., and which after dilution is ready to be formed into a sheet of paper. (2) Wet pulp of any type at any stage in the manufacturing process. (3) Paper on inventory or in storage. (4) Paper or other material to be printed, especially the paper for a particular piece of work. (5) A term used to describe a paper suitable for the indicated use, such as coating raw stock, milk bottle stock, tag stock, and towel stock.

strike through. The penetration of the vehicle of a printing ink through the sheet so that it is apparent on the side opposite to that of application. The result is frequently a stain on the opposite side of the sheet.

suction box. A closed-trough device extending the width of the Fourdrinier with its perforated top pressing against the underside of the wire to suck water from the wet web as it passes over.

supercalender. A stack cold-roll calender consisting of alternate hard polished metal and soft rolls used apart from the papermaking machine to alter the appearance and properties of the paper.

surface coated.   A term applied to any paper or paperboard that has one or both sides coated with a pigment or other suitable material.

TAPPI.   Technical Association of the Pulp and Paper Industry.

tear factor.   The tearing strength in grams (per sheet) divided by the basis weight in grams per square meter.

tearing strength.   The force required to tear a specimen under standardized conditions in an instrument designed to simulate in a general way the tearing encountered under use conditions.   The edge of the specimen is cut before the actual tear.   It is commonly expressed in grams of force required to tear a single sheet.

tensile strength.   The force parallel to the plane of the specimen required to produce failure in a specimen of specified width and length under specified conditions of loading.   This definition must be distinguished from that which is commonly used in engineering practice to express the tensile strength in force per unit area.   In the paper industry it is expressed in kilograms per 15 mm. width or pounds per inch width.

thickness.   The thickness (in thousandths of an inch) of a single sheet of paper or paperboard when placed under a steady pressure of 7 to 9 p.s.i. between two circular and parallel plane surfaces, the smaller of which has an area of approximately 0.25 in.^{2} It is also called caliper.

top.   The correct term for the so-called felt side of machine-made paper.

transparency.   That property of a material which transmits light rays so that objects can be distinctly seen through the specimen. Transparency ratio is a measure of transparency as judged when a space separates the specimen and the object viewed through the specimen.   Thus transparency should be carefully distinguished from opacity; opacity is measured by the show-through of light and dark objects placed immediately behind the specimen.

trim.   (1) The widest sheet of paper, trimmed to remove deckle edges, that can be made on a given machine.   (2) To cut true to exact size by cutting away the edges of paper in the web or sheet.

tub size press.   A tub or vat arranged with rolls so that the paper is submerged as it passes through the sizing liquid.   The surplus size is removed from the paper by the rolls, one of which is usually made of rubber and the other of brass.   This press may be used for surface, top, or tub sizing.

two-sidedness.   The difference in shade or texture between the felt and wire sides of a sheet of paper.   The term is generally used in connection with dyed papers and thus refers to a difference in shade. Two-sidedness may also occur in a paper prepared from a mixed furnish, such as a mechanical pulp-sulfite, or with the use of fillers.

uncalendered.   A term applied to paper that is reeled directly from the drying cylinder without passing through the calenders.

vapor permeability.   That property of a sheet which allows the passage of a vapor.   This property must be measured under carefully specified conditions of total pressure, partial pressures of the vapor on the two sides of the sheet, temperature, and relative humidity. Because of the fact that paper has specific affinity for such vapors as water vapor, vapor permeability should not be confused with air permeability or porosity.

virgin stock.   Pulp that has not previously been used in the paper-making process.   It is to be distinguished from secondary stock.

watermark.   A term applied to a distinctive mark or design produced by the raised pattern of the dandy roll on the wet sheet before going to the couch rolls.   It includes a laid mark.   The design may also be produced by a depressed pattern in the dandy roll; the result is a shaded watermark.   In this case there is more fiber at the point of the mark than in the balance of the sheet, as contrasted to a regular watermark in which the design is thinner than the rest of the sheet; this is also called a shade-craft watermark.

web.   The (endless) sheet of paper coming from the paper machine in its full width or from a roll of paper in any converting operation. The term is most commonly used in connection with the sheet at any stage in the papermaking process before drying.

wet broke.   The undried waste stock taken off the paper machine at the presses or before entering the driers.

wet-strength paper.   A paper with extraordinary resistance to rupture or disintegration when saturated with water.   This property is produced by chemical treatment of the paper or of the fibers from which it is made.   Wet strength is to be distinguished from water repellency or the resistance of a paper to wetting when exposed to water.   Wet strength is most evident and most significant when it occurs in absorbent papers. Normally a paper loses most of its strength when truly wetted with water. A paper that retains more than 15% of its dry strength when completely wetted with water may properly be called a wet-strength paper.

wet tensile strength. The tensile strength of a specimen of paper after it has been wetted with water under specified conditions. The wet strength may be of a more or less temporary nature, as in paper towels and tissues, or of a more permanent nature, as in vegetable parchment and bag and sack papers.

white water. A general term for all waters of a paper mill which have been separated from the stock or pulp suspension, either on the paper machine or accessory equipment, such as thickeners, washers, and savealls, and also from pulp grinders. It usually carries a certain amount of fiber and may contain varying amounts of fillers, dyestuffs, etc.

wild. An irregular formation of the fibers that produces a mottled appearance in the look-through of the sheet, opposite to close. It has a number of causes, such as partial clotting or lumping of the fibers and high freeness or excessive suction at the first suction box. It is particularly noticeable in long-fibered papers, such as kraft, although it is possible to imitate a wild formation with short-fibered stuff by manipulation of the sheet-forming equipment. It is also termed cloudy.

Yankee machine. A large revolving-drum dryer used in place of or in conjunction with dry cans in the paper production line. It is usually equipped with a dryer felt to hold the wet pulp sheet in close contact with its metal surface. The side of the dried sheet in contact with the drum surface has a glazed finish.

INDEX

335